D1030023

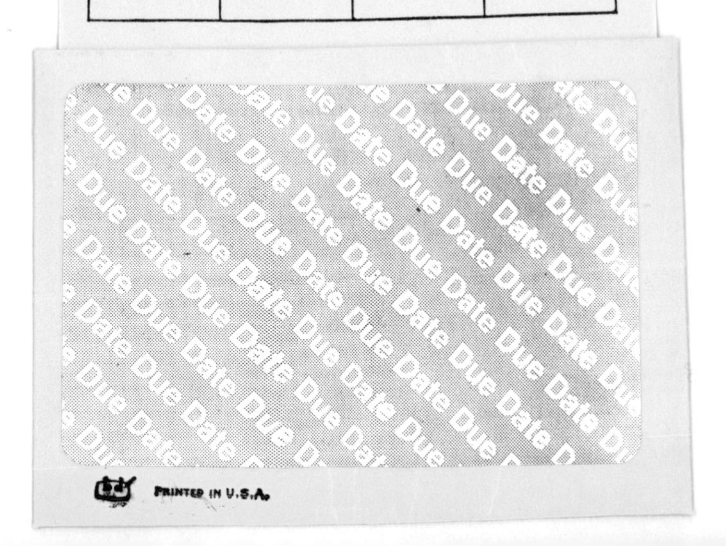
Date Due

The Wolves of North America

By

STANLEY P. YOUNG *and* EDWARD A. GOLDMAN

Senior Biologists, Section of Biological Surveys, Division of Wildlife Research, Fish and Wildlife Service, Department of the Interior.

PART II

Classification of Wolves

By

EDWARD A. GOLDMAN

DOVER PUBLICATIONS, INC.
NEW YORK

Published in the United Kingdom by Constable and Company, Limited, 10 Orange Street, London W.C. 2.

This Dover edition, first published in 1964, is an unabridged and corrected republication of the work first published in 1944 by the American Wildlife Institute. Certain plates which were color plates in the original edition are reproduced in black and white in this edition.

This work originally appeared in one volume but now appears in two volumes.

Library of Congress Catalog Card Number: 64-15510

Manufactured in the United States of America

Dover Publications, Inc.
180 Varick Street
New York 14, N.Y.

Part II

Classification of Wolves
by
Edward A. Goldman

CONTENTS

ILLUSTRATIONS

Plates

PLATE PAGE

Text Figures

Tables

Part II

Classification of Wolves

by

Edward A. Goldman

VIII

INTRODUCTION

THE WOLVES of the genus *Canis* belong to the carnivorous family Canidae, which is nearly world-wide in distribution. The present revision includes the larger wolves, *Canis lupus*, and the red wolves, *Canis niger*, of North America, but excludes the coyotes, *Canis latrans*, which are somewhat wolf-like North American members of the same genus. Much evidence indicates that *Canis lupus*, the true wolf, as it may be called to distinguish it from other wolf-like species, is the progenitor of the domestic dog, *Canis familiaris*, the animal selected by Linné to typify the genus.

The true wolf (*Canis lupus*) is a living species formerly circumpolar in the Arctic land areas. From the Far North it extended south in the Old World to southern Eurasia, and in America from northern Greenland to the southern end of the interior plateau of Mexico, south of the 20th parallel of north latitude. It seems doubtful whether any other species of land mammal has exceeded this geographic range, and this wolf may, therefore, be regarded as the most highly developed living representative of an extraordinarily successful mammalian family.

The species *Canis lupus* forms a compact assemblage of closely allied geographic races. Complete intergradation is evident in numerous cases, and the relative values and combinations of characters presented indicate such close relationships that intergradation can be safely assumed where lack of material for study leaves gaps in the known ranges of continental forms. The wolf populations of Newfoundland, now extinct, and of Vancouver Island, still living, represent geographic detachment, but agree so closely with mainland races in their combinations of essential characters that sub-specific treatment seems fully warranted.

In America, the races of *Canis lupus* have received various colloquial names. Some of these are regional in application but are used to distinguish representatives of *Canis lupus* from the red wolves, *Canis niger*, and from the coyotes, *Canis latrans*, which are overlapped in geographic range. Perhaps most widely used is the common name "gray wolf" in reference to the grayish color tones that tend to prevail in the larger wolves; but colors vary from white through numerous shades of gray, buff, tawny, and brown to black. The term "brown wolf" was appropriately applied by Lewis and Clark to the dark-colored wolves of the forested region of western Oregon and Washington. The appellation "buffalo wolf" became extensively used for the wolves that were known to prey on the buffalo in the Great Plains region of the West. In the Southwest the Spanish name "lobo" is commonly used to designate the gray wolf. Gray wolves far exceed the coyotes in size, and as a rule contrast strongly with the red wolves also in this respect; but small gray wolves may be equaled by large red wolves in general dimensions.

The living red wolf, *Canis niger*, is much more restricted in distribution than the gray wolf. At the time of exploration and early settlement of the country, it inhabited the Mississippi River Valley and affluents from the Gulf of Mexico north at least to Warsaw, Ill., and Wabash, Ind., and from the Pecos River Valley, Tex., on the west to the Atlantic coast in Georgia and Florida on the east. The species is divisible into three subspecies. The reddish or tawny coloration tends to be distinctive, but owing to the range of individual variation, cranial features afford more reliable indices in making specific determination. West of the Mississippi River, the range of the red wolf is overlapped by that of the coyote. These two species are normally quite distinct, but small red wolves, especially in parts of central Texas, resemble coyotes very closely, and some specimens appear to be hybrids.

In revising the wolves of North America, twenty-three subspecies of *Canis lupus* are accorded recognition. *Canis niger* is subdivided into three geographic races. The revision is based mainly on a study of the extensive wolf material brought together especially in connection with the predatory animal control work conducted since 1915 by the Fish and Wildlife Service (formerly the Biological Survey), and other collections in the United States National Museum, now numbering 1,190 specimens. Many of these are skulls without skins, and in some cases skins without skulls. These specimens have been augmented by 178 from other American museums, making a total of 1,368 examined. (See "Acknowledgments," p. VII.) The assemblage has included the type or topotypes of most of the described forms. This unparalleled wealth of material has afforded a basis for accurate appraisal of the range of individual and geographic variation, and has led to satisfactory conclusions in most cases.

When the manuscript was about to go to press the descriptions of three new Arctic races were published (Anderson, 1943). These were added to the list of recognized forms on the basis of representations made by their describer who is well known as an eminent authority in his field. No opportunity was afforded, however, to obtain illustrations or to include cranial measurements in tables that had been prepared.

IX

HISTORY

The history of the Canidae, or dog family, as shown by the fossil record, extends, with many ramifications, far back in geologic time. The phylogeny of the family has been clearly traced by Matthew (1930, p. 133) to common ancestry with other carnivora in the Miacid family of Creodonts or Primitive Carnivora of the early Tertiary. The Canidae are primarily a group of carnivora, with long slender limbs and non-retractile claws, that became adapted for speed on open ground and acquired long jaws for snapping and slashing at prey. Development of hunting methods led to association in groups, teamwork, and finally to the highly complex social instincts and intelligence shown in modern dogs, wild and domestic. The dog family thus presents a wide contrast with the Felidae, or cat family, which represents another and even more exclusively carnivorous offshoot of Miacid ancestry. Unlike the dogs, the cats as a group developed shorter limbs with retractile claws and short jaws adapted to seizing and holding prey. Along with this physical equipment came the habits of concealment and lying in wait to pounce on a victim that could be quickly overpowered and killed. The cats evolved with similar success but as a group more solitary in habits and lacking the social behavior exhibited by the dogs. From the genus *Cynodictis*, a Miacid derivative of Oligocene time in both the Old and New Worlds, slow evolution brought the typical line of the dog family through the Miocene period to the genus *Canis* in the upper Pliocene or lower Pleistocene period. Originating in the northern hemisphere, the family became nearly world-wide in dispersal, but was absent from Australasia until the introduction of the dingo, probably by man.

Pleistocene deposits reveal the occurrence of wolves closely allied to the gray and red wolves of today that were transcontinental in distribution, as shown by finds in Cumberland Cave, Maryland, the Rancho Le Brea tar pits, California, and elsewhere. Apparently contemporaneous were wolves of the somewhat aberrant *Canis* (*Aenocyon*) *dirus* group which ranged from Alaska to the Valley of Mexico and from California east to Indiana and Florida.

Colonial settlers along the Atlantic coast of North America soon came in contact with the wolf. Perhaps the earliest reference to an American wolf in literature is that of Captain John Smith (1608-1631, p. CVI). In describing the animals of Virginia about 1609-1610, he wrote: "Ther be in this cuntry Lions, Beares, woulues, foxes, muske catts, Hares, fleinge squirells, and other squirels." Other early references to the animal were by William Wood (1635, p. 17) and by Thomas Morton (1637, p. 79), who dealt with its occurrence in New England. The first use of a distinctive name for an American wolf was by Schreber (1775), who entered the name *Canis lycaon* on plate 89 of his great work on the *Saugthiere*. The name was further validated by its appearance in the index, p. 585, of a section published in 1778. *Canis lycaon* was based by Schreber on Buffon's description and figure (1761, pp. 362-370, pl. 41) of a "loup noir," a female, captured in Canada when very young, kept chained, and taken alive to Paris by a French naval officer. In considering the names of North American wolves, Miller (1912, p. 95) showed that *Canis lycaon* Schreber must stand for the animal occurring in eastern Canada.

A very early name for the Florida wolf is *Lupus niger*, which was applied by Bartram (1791, p. 199) to the animal met with on the Alachua Savanna, Florida, in 1774. This name had been generally overlooked by authors until Harper (1942, p. 339) directed attention to it. Many years later the Florida wolf was described as

Canis floridanus by Miller (1912, p. 95). The name was based on a single specimen which proved to be of the so-called "red wolf" group. Previous to Harper's detection of an earlier name the red wolf was regarded as typified by *Canis lupus* var. *rufus* of Audubon and Bachman (1851, p. 240), from Texas. In this combination Audubon and Bachman erroneously linked the true wolf with the red wolf. In treating the mammals of Texas, Bailey (1905, p. 174) employed a full specific name, *Canis rufus*, for the red wolf which he distinguished from both the true wolf, *Canis lupus*, and the coyote, *Canis latrans*. Since no true wolf is known to have occurred in Florida in recent time it is reasonable to assume, as pointed out by Harper, that the specific name *niger* of Bartram must displace the more appropriate specific name *rufus* of Audubon and Bachman for the red wolf group. Black individuals of the red wolf group are very common, however, and it was evidently one of these that Bartram had in mind in bestowing the name *niger* to the Florida animal.

The close resemblance of the American gray wolf to *Canis lupus* of the Old World was noted by Richardson (1829, p. 60) in describing *Canis lupus occidentalis*, and in characterizing forms that he regarded as varieties, including *Canis lupus* var. *nubilus*, which Say (1823, p. 169) had treated as specifically distinct. Ten years later Richardson (1839, p. 5) published *Canis lupus* var. *fusca*. Many subsequent authors, however, in dealing with American true wolves, used names implying specific separation from the wolves of the Old World, and in the unrevised condition of the group, nominal specific names multiplied. *Canis pambasileus* was described by Elliot in 1905, and *Canis tundrarum* by Miller in 1912. *Canis nubilus baileyi* was added by Nelson and Goldman (1929, p. 165), and *Canis occidentalis crassodon* by Hall (1932, p. 420).

In "The Races of Canis Lupus," Pocock (1935), reverting to the usage of some earlier authors, treated the true wolves of the world, including the North American geographic races with the exception of *Canis lycaon* Schreber, as subspecies of *Canis lupus* Linné of Sweden. Comparison of Old World and New World material, and geographic considerations, seem to warrant this intercontinental linkage of subspecies. Specimens from the Anadyr region, northeastern Siberia, perhaps representing *Canis lupus dybowskii* Domanieski of Kamchatka, appear to be smaller, but in cranial features and dental details are very similar to the wolves of Alaska. Evidence of the near relationship of Asiatic and American wolves is not surprising in view of the close approach of the two continents, and the probability that animals venturing out on the ice would become marooned on detached ice fields and, under favorable wind conditions, be carried across Bering Strait.

Six subspecies of *Canis lupus* and one of *Canis rufus* (= *C. niger*) were described and the forms assignable to the two species were listed by the writer in 1937; and three additional subspecies have been published in connection with preparation of the present revision. In "The Names of the Large Wolves of Northern and Western North America," the nomenclature of the group was given comprehensive consideration by Miller (1912a). His paper afforded a very satisfactory basis for the work of subsequent authors.

Several names have erroneously been applied to wolves or may require clarification of status: The name *Canis mexicanus* Linné (1766, p. 60) was based on the *Xoloitzcuintli* of Hernandez (1651, p. 479) and was generally assumed by authors to refer to a Mexican true wolf until shown by G. M. Allen (1920, p. 478) to apply to the Mexican "hairless" dog. The early name *Canis lupus griseus* was proposed by Sabine (1823, p. 654) for the wolf of the vicinity of Cumberland House, Saskatchewan, Canada. Commonly treated as of full specific rank, it was accepted by authors for many years to designate wolves from regions as far south as Texas. However, as pointed out by Rhoads (Amer. Nat. 28: 524, 1894), by Bangs (Amer. Nat. 32: 505, July 1898), and by Miller (1912a, p. 2), the name is preoccupied by *Canis griseus* Boddaert (Elench. Anim., p. 97, 1784), a synonym of *Urocyon cinereoargenteus*. *Canis lycaon* B *americana*, applied by Hamilton Smith (Griffith's Cuvier, Anim. King. 5: 144, 1827) to the Florida wolf, was antedated by *Canis americanus* of Gmelin (Syst. Nat. 1 (13th ed.): 69, 1788) for an American Indian dog. Apparently combining the names *Canis* (*Lupus*) *griseus* and *Canis* (*Lupus*) *albus* of Sabine (Franklin's Journ., 1823, pp. 654 and 655 respectively) as *Canis occidentalis* var. *griseo-albus*, Baird (1857, p. 104) seems to have entertained a somewhat composite concept of a widely ranging race varying in color from "pure white to grizzled gray." No type was mentioned, and the name does not appear to be valid or clearly assignable to the synonymy of any particular race.

Reference is made by Baird (1859, p. 15) to the "lobo wolf, described in the Berlandiere MSS. as *Canis torquatus*," and he says: "The skull of Dr. Berlandiere's specimen (1379) is smaller than 2193, but similar in all essential features." No. 2193 was a specimen from Santa Cruz, Sonora, collected by C. B. Kennerly. Recourse to the U. S. National Museum catalog shows the entry dated January 26, 1855, as follows: "1379/*Lupus* young/ skull/7-3/4 in./Lt. D. N. Couch/Coll. L. Berlandiere/'*Lupus torquatus*.'" The unpublished Berlandiere manuscript, in the library of the U. S. National Museum, contains a very full description in Berlandiere's handwriting of an animal regarded by him as a wolf. Under the name *Canis torquatus* he placed *Canis mexicanus* Desmarest in synonymy. The species was assigned to a range on the coastal plains along the Gulf of Mexico in Tamaulipas. In the description reference is made to a nuchal band commonly discernible in both wolves and coyotes. The dimensions given of the young animal might be of either wolf or coyote. It seems clear that Baird (l.c.) in effect fixed on skull No. 1379, from Saltillo, Coahuila, as lectotype of the animal named *Canis torquatus*. As this skull cannot be found, its determination by Baird as that of a wolf is uncertain. It may be pointed out that the skull came from territory from which there appear to be no other authentic wolf records. The name *Canis torquatus* is not, therefore, satisfactorily assignable.

Canis frustror Woodhouse (Proc. Acad. Nat. Sci. Phila. 5: 147, 1851) from Cimarron River, about 100 miles west of Fort Gibson, Okla., was described as the American jackal believed to have been previously confounded with *Canis latrans*. In his Revision of the Coyotes or Prairie Wolves, Merriam (1897, p. 26) regarded *frustror* as a coyote, full specific rank being retained for it in accordance with his treatment of the other coyotes. On the basis of specimens collected later at Redfork, Okla., Bailey (1905, p. 175) concluded that *frustror*, instead of being a coyote, is more nearly related to the red wolf, *Canis rufus* (= *C. niger rufus*). This opinion was later shared by others, including the writer. The specimen regarded as the type in the U. S. National Museum is the stuffed skin without skull of an animal that was very young when collected. More critical comparison of this skin with those of red wolves and coyotes of similar age has convinced me that it is that of a coyote.

X

GENERAL CHARACTERS

The present revision includes the so-called true wolves, *Canis lupus*, and the red wolves, *Canis niger*, of North America. It excludes the coyotes, *Canis latrans*, the only other North American species currently assigned to the genus *Canis*. The species of the genus *Canis* are all larger and more robust than those of the foxes of the genera *Vulpes*, *Urocyon*, and *Alopex*, which are the other living representatives of the family Canidae in North America. In general structural characters, including the possession of glands on the upper basal part of the tail, all of the genera are very similar, but they differ in important details. In the wolves the normal number of mammae is ten. In *Canis*, in contrast with other North American canids, the pelage is elongated in a mane, erectile and conspicuous in anger, extending along the median line from the nape to a point behind the shoulders where it ends abruptly; the tail is more pointed than in *Vulpes* and *Alopex*, and more rounded, less crested than in *Urocyon*. The non-retractile claws are more blunt than in the foxes. As in the foxes, there are four toes on each hind foot and five on each front foot, the first short and rudimentary but bearing a well-developed claw, and a prominent callosity is present near the outer side on the posterior surface of the lower part of the forearm. In the wolves the tail gland is usually marked by a narrow patch of black-tipped hairs which are somewhat shorter and more bristly than those of surrounding areas. Even in Arctic wolves, in nearly pure white pelages, a few black-tipped hairs usually persist over this gland.

In the wolves, much as in the foxes, the cranium is elongated and tapered anteriorly, the jaws are very long, and the postorbital processes of the frontals and the zygomata are short, leaving a wide opening between them. Cranial characters distinguishing the wolves and coyotes of the genus *Canis* from the foxes of the genera *Vulpes*, *Urocyon*, and *Alopex* are presented by the frontals and adjoining bones. In *Canis* the postorbital processes are smoothly rounded above and evenly decurved, without depressions behind elevated edges, the posterior borders turning more obliquely inward and backward to form a sagittal crest than in the foxes. In addition, the median groove of the frontals ends farther forward, and the inion projects farther posteriorly than in the foxes. Compared with *Urocyon*, the genus *Canis* also differs notably in the union of the temporal ridges to form a long sagittal crest instead of their wide separation in a shield-shaped design, and in the absence of the prominent keel present in *Urocyon* on the under side of the lower jaw. Another differential cranial feature in *Alopex* compared with *Canis*, and in fact with the other foxes, is the encroachment of the squamosal arm of the zygoma over the jugal, so that the short postorbital process of the zygomatic arch is formed by the squamosal instead of by the jugal.

The dental formula in *Canis* is usually $\text{I.}\ \frac{3\text{-}3}{3\text{-}3};\ \text{C.}\ \frac{1\text{-}1}{1\text{-}1};\ \text{P.}\ \frac{4\text{-}4}{4\text{-}4};\ \text{M.}\ \frac{2\text{-}2}{2\text{-}2} = 42$, as in *Vulpes*, *Urocyon*, and *Alopex*, the other genera of North American Canidae. In dental sculpture, only minor details distinguish *Canis* from the other living Canids of the region. The upper carnassial ($P.^4$) is elongated antero-posteriorly, the crown partially cleft behind the middle consists of two main elements, an anterior lobe with a high conical point (paracone) directed backward, and a posterior lobe (metastyle) forming a laterally compressed shearing ridge; the protocone is variable but usually present as a small, blunt, antero-internal cusp in the red wolves and coyotes, and usually absent or rudimentary in the true wolves. The first upper molar is a large tooth transverse to the cranial axis in greatest diameter; the higher outer part is divided into two large conical cusps (protocone and hypocone), of which the anterior, the protocone, is the larger: the inner lobe is lower, with two small variable cusps, the posterior one obsolescent in the true wolves, and a low, crescentic ridge extends along the inner border. The lower carnassial (M.1) is longer (antero-posterior diameter) than the upper, with a laterally compressed paraconid-protoconid blade, the protoconid being much the higher of these two main divisions of the crown; the metaconid is a small but prominent conical cusp standing against the postero-internal base of the protoconid; a broad, low, posterior heel normally bearing two small cusps occupies about one-third of the crown surface. The posterior lower molars are very small, and not infrequently absent on one or both sides.

It is not surprising that some of the wolves of the recent past should be closely allied to living representatives of the gray and red species. *Canis armbrusteri* Gidley (Proc. U. S. Nat. Mus. 46: 98, 1913) from Pleistocene deposits in Cumberland Cave, Maryland, appears to have been allied to the red wolf, *Canis niger*, and other material from the same deposits indicates the occurrence of a close relative of the gray wolf. *Canis occidentalis furlongi* J. C. Merriam (Univ. Calif. Publ. Bull. Dept. Geol. 5: 393, 1910), from the Rancho La Brea tar pits, southern California, had many cranial characters in common with the gray wolves of today. Other remains from the tar pits suggest relationship to *Canis niger*. It may be of interest to point out that neither gray nor red wolves have been known in that region in recent time.

Associated with the material already mentioned from Rancho La Brea were the much more abundant remains of the widely ranging, somewhat aberrant, so-called Dire wolf, *Canis* (*Aenocyon*) *dirus* Leidy. The characteristics of this species have been fully described by J. C. Merriam (1912, pp. 218-246). The similarity in dentition and other general cranial features suggest that *Canis dirus* stood not far from the trunk line of evolution that led to *Canis lupus*. The skull exceeded that of *Canis lupus* in maximum size and massiveness, but some skulls of *dirus* are approached in general dimensions by *C. l. pambasileus* and some of the other large races of northern wolves. *Canis dirus* differs notably from *Canis lupus* in the shortness of the basicranial region behind the glenoid fossae. The posterior palatine foramina are situated farther back, near the posterior plane of the upper carnassials, instead of near or in front of a line drawn across the palate near the middle of these teeth. The lateral borders of the squamosals behind the zygomata slope slightly downward, instead of curving backward and upward to a point over the mastoids. The supraoccipital shield is narrower, and the inion is more prominent and projects farther posteriorly than usual in *Canis lupus;* these features are, however, approached in *Canis lupus nubilus.* In dentition, *C. dirus* is very similar to *C. lupus.* Points of general agreement in dental sculpture are the absence or rudimentary condition of the protocone in the upper carnassial, and the simple crown of the first upper molar. In the latter tooth the cingulum on the outer side is reduced to an inconspicuous line as in *lupus,* but the inner border of the inner lobe is distinctly lower than in the modern wolf. Despite the resemblance to *Canis lupus,* the departure in important cranial and dental details seems to warrant the recognition of the name *Aenocyon* as a genus or subgenus to include the wolves of the *dirus* group.

The gray wolves, *C. lupus,* red wolves, *C. niger,* and coyotes, *C. latrans,* form a compact group in North America, the three species differing from one another in characters that are usually distinctive, but quantitative rather than qualitative in value. The greater gross size is one of the best distinguishing characteristics of the gray wolf in contrast with the red wolf and the coyote; and in the same way the red wolf may usually be known from the coyote. Owing to geographic and individual variation, however, size alone is not always a safe index to specific determination. Large individuals of large subspecies of the red wolf about equal in size small examples of small races of the gray, and small red wolves closely approach large specimens of the coyote. And the resemblances are not confined to size, as is pointed out in describing the species. (Pls. 130-131.)

In the wolves, most of the sutures of the skull are clearly discernible at birth. The supraoccipital and interparietal become fused at a very early age. Soon to follow is closure of the sutures of the basicranial segment surrounding the foramen magnum. The supraoccipital, exoccipitals, and basioccipital are all firmly united, and the sutures have disappeared before the permanent dentition is fully in place. The union between most of these bones and the remainder of the skull, however, remains visible until finally closed with advancing age. The fusion of the interparietal and parietals is irregular, as it may come early or somewhat late in life. The jugals unite with the maxillae earlier than with the squamosals. Some of the sutures, however, remain distinct until extreme old age. Among the last to fuse are those between the nasals, maxillae, and premaxillae, forming the anterior segment of the skull, and the zygomatic union of the jugals and squamosals. The suture between the two halves of the lower jaw remains open. The temporal ridges unite to form a sagittal crest in both sexes early in life. The crest is usually more prominent in the males, than in the females, and reaches its highest development on the median line of the interparietal. The height of the crest and extent of closure of sutures are indices of age.

In the wolves, as in many other widely-ranging species, subspecific distinctions rest upon combinations of relatively slight characters indicating close relationships. The characters do not stand out very conspicuously as a rule, and allowance should be made for wide range of individual variation, but they are maintained with a fair degree of constancy over areas often of considerable extent. Individual variation in the color of both gray and red wolves is extraordinary. It ranges in some of the northern races of gray wolves from nearly pure white through mixtures of gray and buff to nearly pure black; and in the red wolves from grayish through more or less distinctly tawny to nearly pure black. Cranial characters are also variable, but within narrower limits, and are therefore more reliable than color in determining systematic relationships. The gray wolves, *Canis lupus*, and the red wolves, *Canis niger*, present specific patterns in dental sculpture, but the subspecies differ only in minor dental details.

In tracing the relationships of the subspecies or geographic races in the gray and the red wolves, the principal characters of taxonomic value are the following: Gross average size; general color, whether light or dark, plain grayish overlaid with black, or mixed with varying shades from pinkish buff to tawny; general form and massiveness of the skull, including height of brain case, frontal profile, posterior extension of inion, length of rostrum, and size of auditory bullae; size and relative length and breadth of molariform teeth. The males are usually decidedly larger than the females in all dimensions, with more prominent sagittal crests, but large females sometimes exceed small males, and females of a large race may exceed in size males of a smaller race.

Cranial abnormalities in the large number of specimens examined are few. In the skull of a young *C. l. irremotus* (No. 224445, U. S. Nat. Mus.) from Ingomar, Mont., in which the teeth of the permanent series were being acquired, the crowns were uncovered with enamel, leaving the dentine fully exposed. The small posterior lower molars may be absent, and the small anterior premolars may be lacking in either jaw. In a skull of *C. l. occidentalis* (No. 34447, Amer. Mus. Nat. Hist.) from Great Bear Lake, Mackenzie, a small additional upper premolar is present on the left side. In *C. l. lycaon* (No. 77344, Mus. Vert. Zool.) from Whitney, Ontario, three upper molars are present on each side. The supernumerary teeth are small, rounded, and very similar to the small corresponding molars normally present in the lower jaw. They are partially opposed to the lower molars and appear to have been functional to some extent.

XI

PELAGE AND MOLT

The pelage in the gray and red wolves is very similar in general character. In both species it consists of long guard hairs and much shorter and softer under-fur. The pelage is much longer and denser in the northern, than in the southern, races of gray wolves, in obvious response to climatic conditions. In the southern wolves the pads on the feet are entirely naked, and the hairs between the toes relatively short. In Arctic wolves, on the contrary, the edges of the pads are encroached upon by hairs to some extent, and long tufts between the toes doubtless afford additional support in passing over soft snow.

The annual molt seems to be somewhat irregular but, in the gray wolves at least, extends over a lengthy period during the summer. The new pelage, rather short in early fall, becomes longer in winter. The color is modified by wear of the tips of the guard hairs, or the complete removal of these hairs over large patches in some cases, thus exposing more of the under tone. This commonly results in a reduction of the black on the upper parts in the pelages of both gray and red wolves. In the red wolves the rufescent tone is most vivid in prime winter pelage, becoming duller through wear at other seasons. In the gray wolves, very old individuals tend to be somewhat grayer than those of younger age. Owing to greater length and density, the fur of northern wolves is much more valuable than that of the races inhabiting more southern territory.

XII

VARIATION

Variation in the wolves is assignable to several categories, of which perhaps the most obvious are geographic and individual.

GEOGRAPHIC

The gray wolves, *Canis lupus*, are all very similar in the more essential features and are believed to intergrade through the vast range of the species on the North American mainland. The component subspecies are the expressions of geographic variation in size, weight, color, and minor details of structure in response to environmental and genetic influences. The subspecies of wolves are based mainly on characteristic patterns of cranial structure, in which the gross size is combined with general agreement in certain proportions, and details that prevail with a fair degree of constancy over a geographic unit or area. Such areas may be either of limited or of vast extent. Some of the insular forms, such as *C. l. crassodon* from Vancouver Island and *C. l. beothucus* from Newfoundland, may present a somewhat greater degree of differentiation owing to isolation; but, as the trinomial names indicate, are not regarded as distinct species. The largest geographic races, *C. l. pambasileus*, *C. l. alces*, and *C. l. occidentalis*, inhabit Alaska, Yukon, and Mackenzie, and large wolves range south along the continental backbone to include

C. l. youngi of Utah, Colorado, and northern New Mexico. The gray wolves of the Arctic islands and eastern North America are somewhat reduced in size; and the smallest, *C. l. baileyi*, is from the Sierra Madre of Mexico. This small race was connected with the much larger subspecies *C. l. youngi* by *C. l. mogollonensis*, a rather compact form intermediate in geographic range, size, and detailed characters. The evidence presented by ample material shows that while there was intergradation, *C. l. baileyi* passed into the distinctly larger form *C. l. mogollonensis* within a restricted area in southeastern Arizona and southwestern New Mexico. This abrupt transition is probably due to the circumstance that the Sierra Madre and the Mogollon Mountain region were centers of wolf population not far apart, separated by a belt of less attractive desert or semi-desert terrain, entered by wolves only in small numbers. The contrast between the two races occupying such closely adjoining ranges seems most remarkable in view of the fact that wolves are known to include points 100 miles or more apart in the course of their regular movements.

Other geographic races, as *C. l. ligoni* of the Alexander Archipelago, and *C. l. alces* of the Kenai Peninsula, Alaska, appear to pass through narrow transitional areas into forms inhabiting adjoining territory. On the other hand, *C. l. occidentalis*, which ranges over an area of very great extent, apparently merges more gradually with the related forms. The boundaries of the ranges of such subspecies can only arbitrarily be fixed along lines representing the nearest apparent approach to scientific accuracy, as shown by specimens examined.

Geographic variation in color in *C. lupus* is shown in the lighter, less buffy tones in the normal grizzled grayish color phase, and the prevalence of nearly white or black individuals. Plain grayish colors tend to prevail in the wolves inhabiting the northern lowlands and the Great Plains east of the Rocky Mountains as far south as Oklahoma. From the Rocky Mountains to the Pacific Coast in the Northwest, the grizzled gray is usually more or less suffused with buff or cinnamon, and the muzzle, ears, and limbs are more vividly colored, the tones becoming more intense to the southward, and varying to tawny in *C. l. baileyi* of Mexico. Perhaps the most distinctively colored geographic race is *C. l. fuscus* of the forested region mainly west of the Cascade Range in Washington and Oregon. This race is dark "cinnamon" or "cinnamon buff" in general tone, with the back profusely overlaid with black. In Arctic wolves, white, usually with a varying admixture of thinly distributed dark hairs, prevails. Nearly white wolves, interspersed with those normally colored, are common east of the continental divide, and along the Rocky Mountains as far south as New Mexico and extreme eastern Arizona where individuals in this phase are referable to *C. l. mogollonensis.*

In *C. niger* the subspecies are based in part on geographic variation in size. Subspecies *rufus* of central Texas is small and closely resembles the coyote of the region. Increase in size is rapid toward the east, and some of the larger individuals of *C. n. gregoryi* from the Mississippi River Valley about equal small examples of *C. l. lycaon* of eastern Canada. The species was evidently based on the observation of individuals in the black phase such as are numerous in *C. n. gregoryi,* but appear to be rare in *C. n. rufus* of Texas.

INDIVIDUAL

Individual variation refers to the extent of divergence from the mean exhibited in a series of specimens from any given locality. In the wolves the range of this variation in size, color, and cranial details is very wide and should be carefully considered in the identification of specimens. While subspecies with confluent ranges may differ considerably in size, an unusually large individual of a small form may be similar in size to an unusually small individual of a large form.

Individual variation in color in most of the races of *C. lupus* is extraordinary, as it may extend through several color phases from nearly pure white to nearly pure black. Between these extremes are the grizzled grayish phase, which may be regarded as normal; a plain, more uniform gray phase in which the white and black are reduced and the buff eliminated; and a rufescent phase. While it is often convenient to refer to these color variations as color phases, there is no sharp line of demarcation between them. The races of the red wolf, *C. niger,* present two principal color phases. In one of these, the normal phase, "cinnamon buff," "cinnamon," or "tawny" tends to predominate, and the muzzle, ears, and outer surfaces of limbs, especially, exhibit the rufescent tones that led to the name for the species. Variation of this phase extends to individuals that are quite plain grayish owing to reduction of the rufescent element. In the other phase nearly black individuals resemble those in the corresponding phase of *C. lupus*.

The skulls of males, compared with those of females, are usually decidedly larger and more angular, as shown especially by the more prominent development of the sagittal crest and the heavier dentition. Individual variation, however, extends to cases in which there is little or no discernible sex difference. Irregular individual variations in the relative size of the large cheek teeth are not infrequent. Owing to individual deviations from the subspecific pattern, some specimens from unknown localities may be difficult to identify.

One or both of the small anterior premolars or posterior molars in either jaw may be absent, and in a few skulls supernumerary teeth were noted. In a skull of *C. n. rufus* from Kerr County, Tex. (No. 146744, U. S. National Museum), two small additional posterior upper molars are present. These have triangular crowns and are three-rooted. Similar additional posterior upper molars are in evidence in a skull of *C. n. gregoryi* from Solo, Pope County, Tex. (No. 243306, U. S. National Museum). These have nearly oval crowns, transverse in greatest diameter to the longitudinal axis of the skull. In another skull of *C. n. gregoryi* from Cooks Station, Mo. (No. 244426, U. S. National Museum), a supernumerary incisor placed slightly behind and between the second and third normal upper incisors on the right side projects slightly beyond the other teeth.

XIII

EXPLANATIONS

MEASUREMENTS

All measurements of specimens are in millimeters. The weights given are in pounds. Owing to the limited number of specimens of which external measurements and weights were available, more reliance is placed on conclusions based on the measurements of skulls. The external measurements, unless otherwise stated, were taken in the flesh by the collector, as follows: *Total length,* nose to end of terminal vertebra; *tail vertebrae,* upper base of tail to end of terminal vertebra; *hind foot,* back of heel to end of longest claw. Adult males usually exceed females in size, and the measurements are, therefore, presented according to sex. In some cases, so few nearly typical examples are available that the measurements given may not represent the normal range of individual variation, and too broad generalizations should not be based on them. The following cranial measurements of typical adults, unless otherwise stated, were taken with vernier calibers by the author. In measuring irregularly curved contours the vernier reading is apt to be altered with each slight change in the application of the points, or even the degree of pressure exerted. The calipers were, therefore, always held in as nearly the same position as possible; and whenever practicable, the vernier was read before the calipers were removed.

Greatest length.—Length from anterior tip of premaxillae to posterior point of inion in median line over foramen magnum.

Condylobasal length.—Length from anterior tip of premaxillae to posterior plane of occipital condyles.

Zygomatic breadth.—Greatest distance across zygomata.

Squamosal constriction.—Distance across squamosals at constriction behind zygomata.

Width of rostrum.—Width of rostrum at contriction behind canines.

Interorbital breadth.—Least distance between orbits.

Postorbital constriction.—Least width of frontals at constriction behind postorbital processes.

Length of mandible.—Distance from anterior end of mandible to plane of posterior ends of angles, the right and left sides measured together.

Height of coronoid process.—Vertical height from lower border of angle.

Maxillary tooth row, crown length.—Greatest distance from curved front of canine to back of cingulum of posterior upper molar.

Upper carnassial, crown length (outer side), and crown width.—Antero-posterior diameter of crown on outer side, and transverse diameter at widest point anteriorly.

First upper molar, antero-posterior diameter, and *transverse diameter.*—Greatest antero-posterior diameter of crown on outer side, and greatest transverse diameter.

Lower carnassial (crown length).—Antero-posterior diameter at cingulum.

COLORS

Owing to the banding of the individual hairs, the pelage of wolves, like that of many other mammals, presents blended colors difficult to segregate and describe. The names employed of colors in quotation marks are from Ridgway's "Color Standards and Nomenclature, 1912." They represent approximations to color tones and are supplemented by generally understood modifying or comparative terms.

SPECIMENS EXAMINED

Specimens examined, unless otherwise indicated, are in the United States National Museum, including the Biological Surveys collection.

USE OF DISTRIBUTION MAPS

No attempt has been made to present keys to the subspecies of wolves. The construction of satisfactory keys to closely intergrading subspecies is not very practical, and it is suggested that recourse to the distribution maps will afford more reliable clues to the identification of specimens.

XIV

LIST OF NORTH AMERICAN SPECIES AND SUBSPECIES, WITH TYPE LOCALITIES

Subspecies of *Canis lupus:*

Canis lupus tundrarum Miller—Point Barrow, Alaska.
Canis lupus pambasileus Elliot—Susitna River, region of Mount McKinley, Alaska,
Canis lupus alces Goldman—Kachemak Bay, Kenai Peninsula, Alaska.
Canis lupus occidentalis Richardson—Fort Simpson, District of Mackenzie, Northwest Territories, Canada.
Canis lupus hudsonicus Goldman—Head of Schultz Lake, District of Keewatin, Canada.
Canis lupus arctos Pocock—Melville Island, District of Franklin, Northwest Territories, Canada.
Canis lupus orion Pocock—Cape York, northwestern Greenland.
Canis lupus labradorius Goldman—Fort Chimo, Quebec, Canada.
Canis lupus beothucus Allen and Barbour—Newfoundland, Canada.
Canis lupus lycaon Schreber—Quebec, Quebec, Canada.
Canis lupus nubilus Say—Engineer Cantonment, near Blair, Nebr.

Canis lupus irremotus Goldman—Red Lodge, Carbon County, Mont.

Canis lupus columbianus Goldman—Wistaria, north side of Ootsa Lake, Coast District, British Columbia.

Canis lupus ligoni Goldman—Head of Duncan Canal, Kupreanof Island, Alexander Archipelago, Alaska.

Canis lupus fuscus Richardson—Banks of the Columbia River, below the Dalles, between Oregon and Washington.

Canis lupus crassodon Hall—Tahsis Canal, Nootka Sound, Vancouver Island, British Columbia, Canada.

Canis lupus youngi Goldman—Harts Draw, north slope of Blue Mountains, 20 miles northwest of Monticello, San Juan County, Utah.

Canis lupus mogollonensis Goldman—S. A. Creek, 10 miles northwest of Luna, Catron County, N. Mex.

Canis lupus monstrabilis Goldman—Ten miles south of Rankin, Upton County, Tex.

Canis lupus baileyi Nelson and Goldman—Colonia Garcia (about 60 miles southwest of Casas Grandes), Chihuahua, Mexico (altitude 6,700 feet).

Canis lupus bernardi Anderson—Cape Kellett, southwestern part of Banks Island, District of Franklin, Northwest Territories, Canada.

Canis lupus mackenzii Anderson—Imnanuit, west of Kater Point, Bathurst Inlet, District of Mackenzie, Northwest Territories, Canada.

Canis lupus manningi Anderson—Hantzsch River, east side of Foxe Basin, west side of Baffin Island, District of Franklin, Northwest Territories, Canada.

Subspecies of *Canis niger:*

Canis niger niger Bartram—Alachua Savanna (now Payne's Prairie), Alachua County, Fla.

Canis niger gregoryi Goldman—Mack's Bayou, 3 miles east of Tensas River, 18 miles southwest of Tallulah, La.

Canis niger rufus Audubon and Bachman—Fifteen miles west of Austin, Tex.

XV

CANIS LUPUS AND SUBSPECIES

CANIS LUPUS Linné

[Synonymy under American subspecies treated]

[*Canis*] *lupus* Linné, Syst. Nat. 1 (10th ed.): 39, 1758. Type from Sweden.

Distribution.—The original range of *C. lupus* was circumpolar in the Arctic land areas. From the Far North it extended south in the Old World, including Ireland and the British Isles in the West and Japan in the East, to southern Eurasia; in America it ranged from Cape Morris Jesup, Greenland, the most northern point of land in the world, 380 miles from the Pole, to the Valley of Mexico at the southern end of the high interior plateau of Mexico. Outlying islands included are Vancouver near the west coast and Newfoundland off the Atlantic coast. Throughout most of the vast general range of the species in America, wolves were formerly well distributed, but were absent in the extremely arid desert sections of the Far West and Southwest, particularly in central Washington, central Oregon, much of Nevada, the Great Salt Lake basin in Utah, southwestern Arizona, most of California, Baja California, and

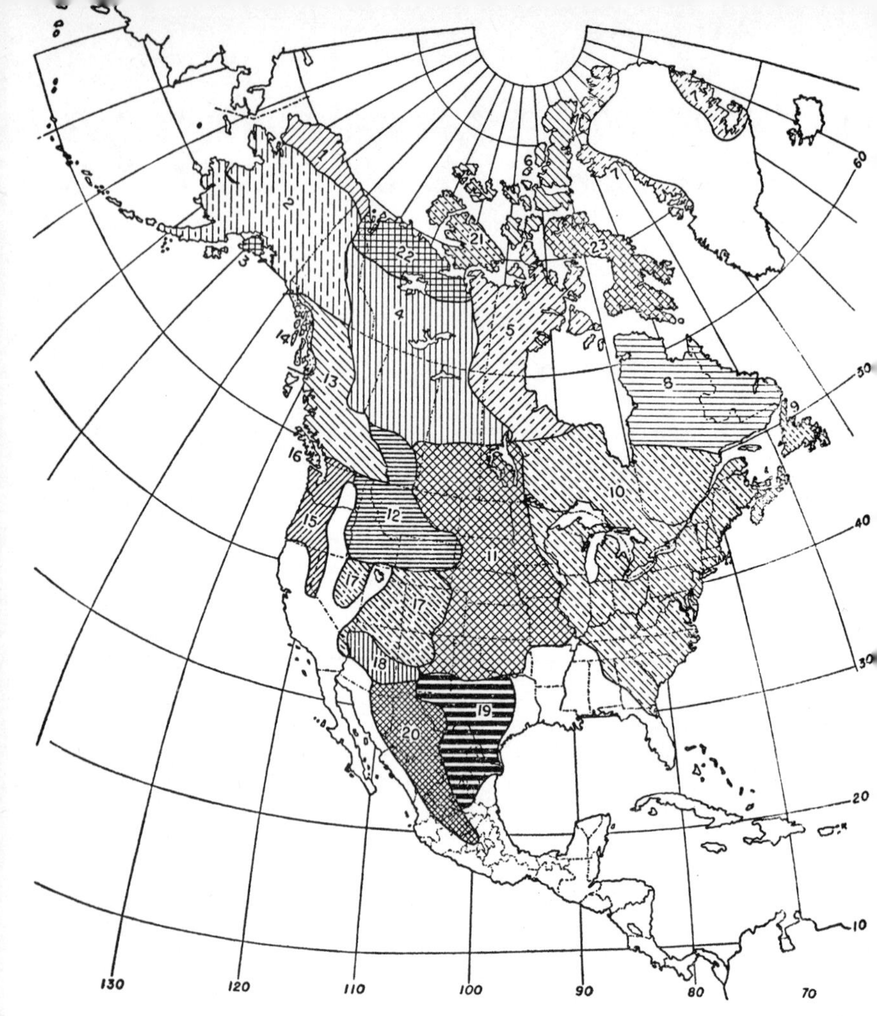

Figure 14. Distribution of subspecies of *Canis lupus*

1. *Canis lupus tundrarum*
2. *C. l. pambasileus*
3. *C. l. alces*
4. *C. l. occidentalis*
5. *C. l. hudsonicus*
6. *C. l. arctos*
7. *C. l. orion*
8. *C. l. labradorius*
9. *C. l. beothucus*
10. *C. l. lycaon*
11. *C. l. nubilus*
12. *C. l. irremotus*
13. *C. l. columbianus*
14. *C. l. ligoni*
15. *C. l. fuscus*
16. *C. l. crassodon*
17. *C. l. youngi*
18. *C. l. mogollonensis*
19. *C. l. monstrabilis*
20. *C. l. baileyi*
21. *C. l. bernardi*
22. *C. l. mackenzii*
23. *C. l. manningi*

western Sonora. They were absent also west of the Sierra Nevada in California where conditions were apparently favorable, and did not enter the tropical parts of Mexico. The species has been extirpated from many regions formerly occupied, but is still present over vast areas, especially in the Far North.

General characters.—Size largest of the existing feral species of the genus; form robust; color variable, from mixtures of white with gray, brown, cinnamon, tawny, and black, to nearly uniform black in some color phases, and nearly pure white in Arctic races; skull heavy; first upper molar with cingulum on outer side indistinct.

Color.—*North American races in normal phase:* Upper parts in general widely varying mixtures of white with black and intermediate shades of gray, "cinnamon" or "cinnamon-buff," and brown; the back is usually more or less profusely overlaid with black; light posthumeral and nuchal bands are usually discernible where the black-tipped hairs thin out, but these bands are commonly interrupted along the median line; the muzzle, ears, and limbs, especially in the more southern forms, incline toward "cinnamon," "cinnamon-buff," or even tawny; under parts varying from whitish to "pinkish buff"; tail above similar to back, the black conspicuous over tail gland, paler below to tip which is black all around. *Black phase:* Upper parts brownish black to nearly pure black, with varying admixtures of white as a rule; under parts somewhat lighter in tone; a pure white median pectoral spot often present. *Young in first pelage:* Upper parts "drab-gray" to "drab," overlaid with brownish black; under parts usually somewhat paler, but chin blackish; ears blackish varying to buffy in some subspecies.

Skull.—Size large, and form massive. Comparison with *C. niger:* Size usually much larger, but small individuals may be exceeded by large ones of *niger;* form more massive; large molariform teeth with crowns less deeply cleft, the cusps more rounded and conical, less compressed laterally, the points and shearing edges less trenchant; upper carnassial with protocone, or antero-internal cusp more frequently absent, or if present usually less prominent; first upper molar with less prominent cingulum and with postero-external cusp less distinctly smaller as compared with antero-external cusp, also inner lobe bearing more reduced cusplets and enamel ridges; second upper molar variable but usually smaller.

Remarks.—The gray wolves are readily distinguished from any other North American canid, except possibly the red wolf, *C. niger*, in certain cases. In central Texas, gray wolves, *C. l. monstrabilis*, and red wolves, *C. n. rufus*, overlapped in geographic range. Specimens of the two from the same localities contrast strongly in size and present other differential characters that are unmistakable. Some specimens of *C. l. lycaon*, however, are of about the same size as *C. n. gregoryi* and *C. n. floridanus*, and while the pelage is longer, the color may not be very different. Similarity is also remarkably close in most other respects. Even the skulls are very much alike in form and in dental details. The most reliable distinguishing characters seem to be the reduction of the cingulum on the outer side in the first upper molar, the less deeply cleft crowns and more rounded, less laterally compressed cusps of the large molariform teeth. All discernible characters are subject to individual variation that may tend to obscure true relationship. It seems evident, however, that the cranial and dental similarities are superficial, with no direct bearing on specific distinction.

Gray wolves are often similar in external appearance to some of the large domestic dogs with which they readily cross, especially in the Far North. In cranial and dental details, however, wolves and dogs usually present marked contrasts. Among points of difference, the skulls of wolves tend to be flatter, with less elevated frontal region, and as a result the orbital angle, measured across orbits or at postorbital processes of frontals and jugals, rises less steeply. The orbits are more elliptical, less evenly rounded, owing to lesser concavity of the frontal border near the lachrymals, and are directed more obliquely outward. The auditory bullae are larger, more rounded and fully inflated, instead of flattened, with surface smoother, less rugose than in dogs. In dental sculpture the two animals are much alike, but in wolves the canines are longer, and the crowns of the upper carnassials, or large cheek teeth, exceed those of dogs in antero-posterior diameter.

CANIS LUPUS TUNDRARUM Miller
Alaska Tundra Wolf (Pls. 88-89)

Canis tundrarum Miller, Smiths. Misc. Coll. 59 (15): 1, June 8, 1912.

Type locality.—Point Barrow, Alaska.

Type specimen.—No. 16748, probably female, skull only, U. S. National Museum; collected by Lt. P. H. Ray.

Distribution.—Tundra region bordering Arctic coast of northwestern Alaska; south to Noatak River Valley. Intergrading on the south with *pambasileus,* and on the east along the Arctic coast with *mackenzii.*

General characters.—Size large; color light; pelage and claws very long; skull with heavy dentition. Closely allied to *pambasileus* of Mount McKinley region, but color paler and grayer, the white less mixed with brown or buff on head, and back more sparingly overlaid with black; skull with heavier dentition. Similar also to *occidentalis* and *mackenzii* of Mackenzie in size, but color darker, the general dorsal area more extensively mixed with black, and the tendency toward pure white less evident than in *occidentalis;* dentition heavier.

Color.—*Winter pelage:* Upper parts in general from nape to rump a mixture of white and black, the overlying black rather thinly distributed (compared with *pambasileus*); short pelage on top of head a grizzled mixture of white and black, faintly suffused in one specimen with "pale pinkish buff." Lip blackish in one specimen, white in another; entire under parts white; upper surface of muzzle pale buffy; ears pale buffy, mixed with black; outer surfaces of legs and feet faintly suffused with buff; soles and interdigital spaces "onion skin pink"; tail above similar to back, white below to tip which is blackish all around. No specimens in the black phase from the vicinity of the type locality have been examined, but two in this phase from the Noatak River appear to be referable to *tundrarum.*

Skull.—In close agreement with that of *pambasileus* in size and general structure, but dentition usually heavier, the difference most noticeable in the molariform teeth; crowns of second and third upper premolars, and of second, third, and fourth lower premolars usually distinctly longer. Not very unlike that of *occidentalis,* but dentition usually heavier.

Measurements.—*Body measurements approximated from tanned skins:* An adult male and female from Meade River, near Point

Barrow, respectively: Total length, 2020, 1940 mm.; tail vertebrae, 500, 475; hind foot, 295, 286. *Skull:* Type specimen (adult, probably female): Greatest length, 258.7; condylobasal length, 138.5; squamosal constriction, 76.1; width of rostrum, 43.2; interorbital breadth, 47.3; postorbital constriction, 41.9; length of mandible, 188.1; height of coronoid process, 74.7; maxillary toothrow, crown length, 110.6; upper carnassial, crown length (outer side), 25.9, crown width, 15; first upper molar, antero-posterior diameter, 17.7; transverse diameter, 24.7; lower carnassial, crown length, 30.5. An adult male and female from Meade River, near Point Barrow, respectively: Greatest length, 267.5, 270.5; condylobasal length, 248, 244.2; zygomatic breadth, 143.7, 140.5; squamosal constriction, 81.4, 77.2; width of rostrum, 47.1, 47; interorbital breadth, 46.9, 50.5; postorbital constriction, 43.7, 46.2; length of mandible, 199.4, 195.5; height of coronoid process, 84, 80; maxillary toothrow, crown length, 112.9, 112.6; upper carnassial, crown length (outer side), 27.2, 24.5, crown width, 16.3, 13.4; first upper molar, antero-posterior diameter, 18, 15.9; transverse diameter, 25.3, 21.1; lower carnassial, 30.9, 28.4.

Remarks.—Specimens examined indicate that *tundrarum* is a rather slightly differentiated, but recognizable subspecies. It appears to be most closely allied to *pambasileus*, but probably meets the range of *mackenzii* along the Arctic coast to the eastward. No specimens are available for study from the Arctic coast of Alaska east of the type locality of *tundrarum*. Wolves are known to occur, however, and in view of the close agreement of *tundrarum* with *mackenzii*, the intergradation of the two may safely be assumed. Six skins from points near the head of the Noatak River are variable in color: Two are similar to *pambasileus* in the gray phase, two resemble that subspecies in the black phase, and two are paler and more like typical specimens of *tundrarum*. The two skulls available from the Noatak area agree closely, especially in dental details, with *tundrarum*. These specimens are probably somewhat intermediate, but seem more properly referable to *tundrarum* than to *pambasileus*.

Specimens examined.—Total number, 13, all from Alaska, as follows: Meade River (near Point Barrow), 2[1]; Noatak River (near head), 6 (4 skins without skulls)[2]; Point Barrow (type locality), 5 (skulls only).

---

[1]Colo. Mus. Nat. Hist.

[2]One in Stanley P. Young coll.

CANIS LUPUS PAMBASILEUS Elliot

Interior Alaskan Wolf (Pls. 90-91)

Canis pambasileus Elliot, Proc. Biol. Soc. Washington 18: 79, February 21, 1905.

Canis lupus pambasileus Goldman, Jour. Mamm. 18 (1): 45, February 14, 1937.

Type locality.—Susitna River, region of Mount McKinley, Alaska.

Type specimen.—No. 13481, ♂ adult, skin and skull, Field Museum of Natural History; collected by C. F. Periolat.

Distribution.—Interior and most of western and southwestern Alaska, including the Seward Peninsula, the Yukon, Kuskokwim, and Susitna river valleys, and the Mount McKinley region; ranging east into southern Yukon. Intergrades with *occidentalis* on the east, with *tundrarum* toward the northwest, and probably with *alces* near the base of the Kenai Peninsula.

General characters.—Size among the largest of North American wolves; black color phase frequent; upper parts in gray phase mainly white moderately overlaid with black, with a buff suffusion in some specimens; pelage long; skull very large with elongated rostrum. Similar in size to *occidentalis* of Mackenzie, but color usually darker; upper parts in normal gray phase more profusely overlaid or mixed with black, and more or less suffused with pale buff, instead of the more uniform white or grayish shades exhibited by *occidentalis;* black color phase more prevalent; skull with longer palate. Similar in size to *tundrarum* of the Arctic coast of Alaska; color darker, the white more extensively mixed with brown or buff on head, and back more extensively overlaid with black; skull very similar in general form, but dentition lighter. Much larger and paler, in normal gray color phase, and *pelage* longer than in *ligoni* of the Alexander Archipelago. Size apparently smaller than *alces* of the Kenai Peninsula, and cranial details different.

Color.—*Winter pelage:* Upper parts from nape to rump a mixture of white and black, the black moderately extensive near the median line, thinning out along sides, more or less suffused in some specimens with "ivory yellow"; longer guard hairs near top of shoulders 130 to 140 mm. in length, tipped with black for about 25 mm., below which there is a white band, interrupted again by black giving way to white toward base; short pelage on top of head a grizzled mixture of white and black, varying in some specimens to white and "cinnamon-buff"; chin more or less distinctly brownish or blackish; under side of neck finely flecked with black, the rest of under parts white; upper surface of muzzle "cinnamon-buff" varying to blackish; ears "pinkish buff" or "cinnamon-buff" mixed with black; outer surfaces of legs and feet near "pale pinkish buff," a narrow blackish line present on forearm in some specimens, absent in others; tail above similar to back, below whitish near base, usually becoming suffused with "pinkish buff," and distinctly black all around at tip. *Summer pelage:* Shorter and much worn, but not materially different in color. In the black phase, while black or brownish black is predominant, especially over the back, specimens commonly present varying combinations of black or brown, thinly mixed with white in a grizzled pattern. The grizzled areas usually include the under parts, limbs, sides of head and lips, but intermingled white hairs may be present anywhere. According to Stanley P. Young, the recently-born pups are often of a light maltese slate color. Five very young pups from Toklat River are nearly uniform very dark brownish black everywhere, except for a small pure white pectoral spot on each.

Skull.—Closely approaches that of *occidentalis* in size and general form, but rostrum and palate slightly longer; maxillary tooth row longer. In close agreement with that of *tundrarum* in size and general structure, but molariform teeth usually smaller. Decidedly larger, more massive than in *ligoni,* with relatively heavier dentition. Differs from that of *alces* in apparently smaller size and less extreme elongation; rostrum and palate shorter; nasals narrower, less divergent anteriorly; supraoccipital shield narrower; molariform teeth relatively broader. Distinguished from *columbianus* by larger usual size; supraoccipital shield narrower; postorbital processes broader, less tapering, more bluntly pointed; carnassials relatively broader, less elongated (antero-posteriorly); second lower molars larger, less elongated.

Measurements.—An adult male from the Mount Hayes region, about 100 miles northeast of the type locality: Total length, 1753 mm. Two adult males from White River, Yukon, respectively: Total length, 1880, 1829; tail vertebrae, 532, 507. An adult female from same locality: Total length, 1765; tail vertebrae, 482. *Skull:*

An adult male from Gold Creek, a tributary of the Susitna River in the region of the type locality, and an adult male from Sushana River, north of Mount McKinley, respectively: Greatest length, 281.4, 286.9; condylobasal length, 261.4, 268.4; zygomatic breadth, 147.3, 151.6; squamosal constriction, 85.5, 82.8; width of rostrum, 48.6, 46.4; interorbital breadth, 47.3, 47.4; postorbital constriction, 45.8, 42.8; length of mandible, 203.7, 210.3; height of coronoid, 85.3, 89.1; maxillary tooth row, crown length, 120.4, 119; upper carnassial, crown length (outer side), 29.5, 27.1; upper carnassial, crown width, 14.7, 13.6; first upper molar, antero-posterior diameter, 19.7, 17.8; transverse diameter, 25.2, 24.1; lower carnassial, crown length, 33.8, 29.4. Two adult females, one from Tanana and the other from Fairbanks, Alaska, respectively: Greatest length, 269, 265.9; condylobasal length, 246.8, 245.5; zygomatic breadth, 129.4, 133; squamosal constriction, 79.8, 74.9; width of rostrum, 41.1, 44.6; interorbital breadth, 46.1, 44.3; postorbital constriction, 40.5, 40.7; length of mandible, 191.1, 191.3; height of coronoid process, 74.6, 71.6; maxillary tooth row, 111, 111.9; upper carnassial, crown length (outer side), 25.7, 25.4, crown width, 14.5, 14.8; first upper molar, antero-posterior diameter, 17, 17.1, transverse diameter, 23.2, 22.8; lower carnassial, 27.7, 28.7.

Remarks.—*C. l. pambasileus* agrees closely with *occidentalis* in size, and differs only slightly in cranial details, but is apparently distinguished by darker color in the normal color phase. It also differs in darker color from skins of *tundrarum* from the vicinity of the type locality, Point Barrow, Alaska. The type of the subspecies, *pambasileus*, is a black wolf. Individuals in the black phase are numerous.

Specimens examined.—Total number, 84, as follows: Alaska: Anchorage, 1 (skull only); Beaver, 2 (skulls only); Big Creek, Mount McKinley National Park, 1 (skull only); Big Delta, Tanana River, 2 (skulls only); Birch Creek (14 miles southwest of Circle), 1 (skull only); Chicken (Mesquite Forks, Forty-Mile River), 4 (skulls only); Cook Inlet (headwaters), 1 (skull only);[1] Cordova Bay (head), 1 (skull only)[2]; Dry Creek, north of McKinley National Park, 2 (skulls only); Eagle, 1 (skull only); East Fork, Mount McKinley National Park, 1 (skull only); Etchepuk River, Golovin Reindeer Range, Seward Peninsula, 1; Fairbanks, 2 (1 skull without skin); Fairbanks (100 miles north), 1; Farewell Mountain (south fork of Kuskokwim River), 1 (skull only); Fort Yukon, 1 (skull only); Fort Yukon (100 miles northwest), 1; Fort Yukon (head of Salmon Fork of Black River 120 miles northwest), 1 (skull only);[2] Gold Creek (near head; tributary of Susitna River above Curry), 1 (skull only); Jarvis Creek, 1 (skull only); Kenai Peninsula (probably near base), 1 (skull only);[2] Little Delta River, 2 (skulls only); Matanuska River (mouth), 1; Mount Hayes (headwaters Little Delta River), 2 (skulls only); Mount Hayes region, 9 (6 skulls without skins); Mount McKinley National Park, 5 (skulls only); O'Brien Creek (tributary of Forty-Mile River), 1 (skull only); Old Rampart House, 1 (skull only);[3] Savage River, 1 (skull only); Seventy Mile, 1 (skull only); Sushana River (north of Mount McKinley), 1 (skull only); Susitna River, 1 (skull only);[4] Tanana, 2 (skulls only); Tanana River (above Salcha River), 1 (skull only); Teklanika River (north of Mount McKinley National Park), 6 (skulls only); Toklat River, 6 (skins only); White River Glacier (near), Wrangell Mountains, 1; Yukon River (35 miles below Beaver), 3 (skulls only).

Yukon: Hoole Canyon, Pelly River, 1 (skull only); Hoole River, 1 (skull only); New Rampart House (6 miles north), 1 (skull only); Pelly River (mouth of Trummell River), 1 (skull only); White River, 8 (skulls only).[5]

CANIS LUPUS ALCES Goldman

Kenai Peninsula Wolf (Pls. 92-93)

Canis lupus alces Goldman, Proc. Biol. Soc. Washington 54: 109, September 30, 1941.

Type locality.—Kachemak Bay, Kenai Peninsula, Alaska.

Type specimen.—No. 147471, ♀ adult, skull only, U. S. National Museum (Biological Surveys collections); collected by C. A. Lambert, 1904. X-catalog number 5133.

[1]Kans. Univ. Mus. Nat. Hist.
[2]Mus. Vert. Zool.
[3]Stanley P. Young Coll.
[4]Field Mus. Nat. Hist.
[5]6 in Royal Ont. Mus. Zool.; 2 in Mus. Vert. Zool.

Distribution.—Known only from the type locality near the south-end end of the Kenai Peninsula.

General characters.—Size large, perhaps the largest of North American wolves; skull elongated with broad rostrum and narrowly spreading zygomata; canines large, but molariform teeth comparatively small. Similar in general to *pambasileus* of the Mount McKinley region, but apparently larger and differing in cranial details.

Color.—No skins available and color undetermined.

Skull.—Similar in general to that of *pambasileus*, but apparently larger, more elongated; rostrum and palate longer; nasals broader, more divergent anteriorly; supraoccipital shield broader; dentition similar, but molariform teeth relatively narrower.

Measurements.—No body measurements available. *Skull:* type, and an adult female topotype, respectively: Greatest length, 280.5, 272; condylobasal length, 263.5, 253.2; zygomatic breadth, 141.3, 141.4; squamosal constriction, 82.2, 81.8; width of rostrum, 47.4, 46.6; interorbital breadth, 49, 45.9; postorbital constriction, 44.3, 42.1; length of mandible, 201.3, 194.3; height of coronoid process, 79.1, 82; maxillary tooth row, crown length, 118.5, 112.3; upper carnassial, crown length (outer side), 25.5, 24.5, crown width, 12.8, 13; first upper molar, antero-posterior diameter, 17.1, 17.1, transverse diameter, 22.3, 22.3; lower carnassial, 30.3, 29.1. Two immature male topotypes (canines not fully in place), respectively: Greatest length, 263, 262.8; condylobasal length, 245, 250; zygomatic breadth, 133.8, 130.5; squamosal constriction, 80.7, 82.3; width of rostrum, 44.7, 45.7; interorbital breadth, 43.9, 42.5; postorbital constriction, 42.4, 40.9; length of mandible, 185, 190; height of coronoid process, 76.5, 74; maxillary tooth row, 108.6, 113.2; upper carnassial, crown length (outer side), 26, 27.5, crown width, 14.4, 15.4; first upper molar, antero-posterior diameter, 16.8, 17.3, transverse diameter, 23.3, 23.3; lower carnassial, 28.9, 31.1.

Remarks.—Five skulls without skins, from Kachemak Bay, Kenai Peninsula, not satisfactorily assignable to any of the races described, have accordingly been regarded as representatives of a new subspecies. This peninsular race reaches the maximum size attained by the species in North America. The skulls of two adult females are longer than those of any others examined, and present other peculiarities pointed out. Skulls of three immature males are not widely different from those of *pambasileus* of comparable age, but differ uniformly in the greater width of the supra-occipital shield. The new subspecies may range throughout the Kenai Peninsula, which at its base is narrowly connected with the mainland of Alaska. Specimens from north of Turnagain Arm of Cook Inlet are assignable to *pambasileus*. The principal natural prey of the Kenai wolf is doubtless the giant moose of the region. The large size of the wolf may be the result of adaptation enabling it to cope with so large an animal.

Specimens examined.—Total number, 5 (skulls only), all from Kachemak Bay, Kenai Peninsula, Alaska.

CANIS LUPUS OCCIDENTALIS Richardson

Mackenzie Valley Wolf (Pls. 94-95)

Canis lupus occidentalis Richardson, Fauna Boreali-Americana 1: 60, 1829.

Canis lupus-albus Sabine, Franklin's Narr. Jour. Polar Sea, p. 655, 1823. From Fort Enterprise, Mackenzie, Canada.

[*Canis lupus occidentalis*] var. C, *Lupus sticte* Richardson, l. c., p. 68. From banks of the Mackenzie River, Canada.

[*Canis lupus occidentalis*] var. E, *Lupus ater* Richardson, l. c., p. 70. From banks of the Mackenzie and Saskatchewan Rivers, Canada.

Type locality.—Name restricted by Miller (1912: 4) to subspecies occurring at Fort Simpson (now Simpson near mouth of Liard River), Mackenzie, Canada.

Type specimen.—Not designated.

Distribution.—Upper Mackenzie River Valley, north to Great Bear Lake, south over the vast lowlands interior of Mackenzie to central Alberta (Edmonton), Saskatchewan, and central Manitoba (Norway House); west in the Peace River Valley to eastern British Columbia. Intergrades on the west with *pambasileus*, and *columbianus*; on the north with *mackenzii*; on the east with *hudsonicus*; on the south with *nubilus*.

General characters.—Size among the largest of North American wolves; ratio of black to normally colored individuals apparently lower than in some of the other subspecies; upper parts in normal color phase varying from nearly pure white to white thinly overlaid or mixed with black or shaded with gray, usually lacking any buffy suffusion; skull very large and massive. Similar in size to *pambasileus* of Alaska, and somewhat larger than *columbianus* of British Columbia, but lighter, more predominantly white or plain grayish in normal color phase, without the buffy suffusion of upper parts seen in *pambasileus and columbianus.* Similar in size to *tundrarum* of the Arctic coast of Alaska, but color lighter, the tendency toward pure white more prevalent or the white less extensively mixed with black; dentition usually lighter. Apparently larger than *mackenzii* of northern Mackenzie and differs from *arctos,* the little-known race of Melville Island, Arctic America, in larger size and cranial details, including the broader brain case. Differs from *hudsonicus* of Keewatin in larger size and distinctive cranial features. Differs from *nubilus* of Nebraska most notably in larger size and more predominantly white pelage.

Color.—Very similar to *nubilus* in range of variation presented, but usually more extensively white; black patch on tail gland present, but black tip of tail usually inconspicuous. A skin from Fort Simpson, Mackenzie, in winter pelage is nearly uniform brownish black, the guard hairs with concealed white at base over dorsum.

Skull.—About the size of that of *pambasileus,* but rostrum and palate slightly shorter; maxillary tooth row shorter. About like that of *tundrarum* in size and general structure, but molariform teeth usually smaller. Very similar to that of *columbianus,* but usually larger; postorbital processes stouter, less tapering, more bluntly pointed; dentition as a whole heavier, but second lower molars smaller. Apparently larger than that of *mackenzii.* Compared with *arctos:* Size larger, more massive; brain case broader; frontal region decidedly broader and flatter, less highly arched and convex in profile, more broadly and deeply V-shaped along median line; postorbital processes stouter, more bluntly pointed; auditory bullae smaller, less fully inflated; dentition similar. Compared with *hudsonicus:* Size decidedly larger; postorbital processes stouter, more bluntly pointed, the posterior borders turned less abruptly inward. Differs from that of *nubilus* most noticeably in larger size, supraoccipital shield usually broader, less projecting posteriorly, with a lesser tendency to develop a descending terminal hook.

Measurements.—A young adult male from Fort Simpson (type locality), Mackenzie: Total length, 1680 mm.; tail vetebrae, 480;

hind foot, 320. An adult male and an adult female from Wood Buffalo Park (10 miles from Slave River), Alberta, respectively: Total length, 1690, 1620; tail vertebrae, 430, 410; hind foot, 295, 290. *Skull:* Two adult males, one from Fort Simpson, Mackenzie, and the other from Wood Buffalo Park (10 miles from Slave River), Alberta, respectively: Greatest length, 292.8, 278.2; condylobasal length, 266, 262.5; zygomatic breadth, 156.5, 145.5; squamosal constriction, 85.4, 90.5; width of rostrum, 50.1, 47.2; interorbital breadth, 53.2, 46.2; postorbital constriction, 44.9, 44.6; length of mandible, 204.8, 197.6; height of coronoid process, 85.3, 80.8; maxillary tooth row, crown length, 116, 114.1; upper carnassial, crown length (outer side), 30.6, 27.2, crown width, 17.1, 14.4; first upper molar, antero-posterior diameter, 18.8, 17.6, transverse diameter, 24.8, 24.2; lower carnassial, crown length, 33.8, 30.8. Two adult females from Great Bear Lake, Mackenzie, and Wood Buffalo Park (10 miles from Slave River), Alberta, respectively: Greatest length, 249.5, 257.3; condylobasal length, 233, 237.5; zygomatic breadth, 130, 143; squamosal constriction, 75.5, 83.1; width of rostrum, 42.7, 44.6; interorbital breadth, 42.3, 42.3; postorbital constriction, 36, 45; length of mandible, 176.7, 185.5; height of coronoid process, 70.1, 76.4; maxillary tooth row, crown length, 106.6, 104.8; upper carnassial, crown length (outer side), 26.5, 25.8, crown width, 14.2, 14.2; first upper molar, antero-posterior diameter, 18, 17, transverse diameter, 24.1, 23.4; lower carnassial, crown length, 29, 29.7.

Remarks.—The wolves of the vast area here assigned to *occidentalis* are still very imperfectly known. Study of more ample material, when available, may result in a revision of range boundaries. The few body measurements at hand may suggest that *occidentalis* is smaller than *pambasileus,* but the skull dimensions of a larger number indicate that the two are very similar in size. The most obvious cranial difference appears to be the somewhat shorter rostrum and palate usually shown in *occidentalis* by the shorter maxillary tooth row. The prevailing color in the present race, like that of the other far northern subspecies ranging east of the continental divide, is white mixed to a very limited but widely varying extent with black or gray. In pallid general coloration, *occidentalis* closely resembles the paler specimens of *nubilus,* and contrasts rather strongly with *pambasileus*, *columbianus*, and other subspecies ranging mainly west of the continental divide. *Canis lupus-albus* Sabine, from Fort Enterprise, Mackenzie, as has been shown by Miller (1912, p. 1), is preoccupied by *C*[*anis*] *lupus albus* Kerr, 1792 (*Animal Kingdom*, p. 137), applied to the wolf of the Yenisei Region, Russia. *Lupus sticte* and *Lupus ater* are names applied by Richardson to color phases and are assignable to the synonymy of *occidentalis*.

Specimens examined.—Total number, 42, as follows:

Alberta: Edmonton, 1 (skull only); Smith landing (50 miles southwest), 1; Wood Buffalo Park (10 miles from Slave River), 7 (skulls only).[1]

British Columbia: Cache Creek, Peace River District, 2 (skulls only);[2] Cameron River, Peace River District, 1 (skull only);[2] Carbon River (35 miles west of Hudson Hope), Cariboo District, 2 (skulls only); Fort McLeod, Cariboo District, 1 (skull only);[1] Henry River (above Tuchade Lake), 1 (skull only).

Mackenzie: Artillery Lake, 1; Aylmer Lake, 1 (skull only);[1] Caribou Point, Great Slave Lake, 1 (skull only);[1] Fort Rae, Great Slave Lake, 1 (skull only); Fort Resolution, 1 (skull only); Fort Simpson, 5 (4 skulls without skins); Fort Smith, 1 (skull only); Great Slave Lake, 1 (skull only).[1]

Manitoba: Norway House (near north end of Lake Winnipeg), 1 (skull only).

Yukon: Crow Base (35-40 miles southeast), 3 (skulls only); Macmillan River (north fork), 2 (skulls only); Pelly Lakes, 7 (skulls only); Riddell River, 1 (skull only).

CANIS LUPUS HUDSONICUS Goldman

Hudson Bay Wolf (Pls. 96-97)

Canis lupus hudsonicus Goldman, Proc. Biol. Soc. Washington 54: 112, Sept. 30, 1941.

Type locality.—Head of Schultz Lake, Keewatin, Canada.

---

[1]Amer. Mus. Nat. Hist.

[2]Brit. Col. Prov. Mus.

Type specimen.—No. 180281, made adult, skin and skull, U. S. National Museum (Biological Surveys collection); collected by H. V. Radford, January 4, 1912. Original number 92.

Distribution.—Northern Keewatin, including the northwestern coast of Hudson Bay (Cape Fullerton), and west to northeastern Mackenzie (Back's River, 20 miles below Lake Beechey).

General characters.—A light-colored subspecies of medium size; winter pelage nearly white, but hairs becoming grayish or brownish toward base over dorsum; skull with rather broad postorbital region and narrow, acutely pointed postorbital processes. Similar in general to *Canis lupus occidentalis* of the upper Mackenzie River Valley, but smaller, and cranial features distinctive. Apparently larger than in *mackenzii* of the lower Mackenzie River Valley. Size and color about as in *Canis lupus arctos* of Melville Island, but cranium flatter, less highly arched, the frontal outline much less strongly convex in lateral view, and differing in other details. Differs from *Canis lupus lycaon* of Quebec in larger size and whiter coloration.

Color.—*Type* (*winter pelage*): Upper parts in general yellowish white, or "cream color"; top of head and middle of face with dark brown under color faintly showing through; guard hairs over dorsum with a brownish band near middle below which they are whitish to base, the shorter under fur on the same area brownish at base, becoming pale yellowish toward tips; under parts overlaid with yellowish white, the under tone whitish to base of hairs; limbs about like under parts; feet "onion-skin pink" between the toes, as usual in the group; tail "cream color," except on the median line near upper base, where black-tipped hairs form a conspicuous, elongated patch on glandular area. A skin from Cape Fullerton, Hudson Bay, is whiter, the yellowish tone being absent, and the tail lacks the dusky spot on gland. Three April skins from Back's River, 20 miles below Lake Beechey, Mackenzie, are essentially white, with thinly distributed dark hairs on ears and over back, black tail gland, and scantily black-tipped tail.

Skull.—Similar in general to that of *occidentalis*, but differs in decidedly smaller size; postorbital processes more slender and more acutely pointed, the posterior borders turned more abruptly inward. Apparently larger than that of *mackenzii*. Similar in size to that of *arctos* but flatter, the frontal region less highly arched and convex in lateral view, more deeply V-shaped along median line in posterior view; zygomata tending to spread more widely; auditory bullae slightly larger, more fully inflated; postorbital processes narrow and acute as in *arctos;* dentition similar, but antero-internal cusps of upper carnassials less prominent. Compared with that of *lycaon,* the skull is much larger, with relatively broader rostrum.

Measurements.—Type: Total length, 1720 mm.; tail vertebrae, 519; hind foot, 323; height at shoulder, 848; weight, 101 pounds. An adult female topotype: Total length, 1570; tail vertebrae, 420; hind foot, 290. Three apparently adult males (skins only) from Back's River (20 miles below Lake Beechey, Mackenzie), respectively: Total length, 1593, 1650, 1605; tail veterbrae, 413, 431, 368; hind foot, 298, 307, 282. *Skull* (type and an adult female topotype, respectively): Greatest length, 258.3, 251; condylobasal length, 241, 228.8; zygomatic breadth, 146.4, 134.8; squamosal constriction, 83.9, 77.4; width of rostrum, 46, 42.4; interorbital breadth, 47.2, 44.4; postorbital constriction, 41.8, 43.2; maxillary tooth row, 110.1, 104.1; upper carnassial, crown length (outer side), 26.8, 24.5 crown width, 14.2, 13.8; first upper molar, anteroposterior diameter, 17.4, 17.4, transverse diameter, 24.2, 22.6; lower carnassial, crown length, 32.6, 27.6.

Remarks.—The wolves of northern Keewatin and Back's River drainage in Mackenzie, and the northwest coast of Hudson Bay, are closely allied to *occidentalis,* the geographic neighbor on the west, but the differential characters pointed out seem to warrant the recognition of a regional race. Comparison with a skull from Ellesmere Island, assumed to represent *arctos,* indicates more distant relationship.

Specimens examined.—Total number, 9, as follows:

Keewatin: Cape Fullerton, 1[1]; Hudson Bay (without definite locality), 1;[1] Schultz Lake, 3 (2 skulls without skins); Wager River, 1 (skull only).[1]

Mackenzie: Back's River (20 miles below Lake Beechey), 3 (skins only).

---

[1]Amer. Mus. Nat. Hist.

CANIS LUPUS ARCTOS Pocock

Melville Island Wolf (Pl. 98)

Canis lupus arctos Pocock, Zool. Soc. London Proc., part 3, p. 682, September 1935.

Type locality.—Melville Island, Arctic America.

Type specimen.—No. 55.11.26.4, adult, probably male, skull only, British Museum; collected on Sir E. Belcher's expedition, 1853-54.

Distribution. — Melville Island and probably neighboring islands; north and east to Ellesmere Island.

General characters.—A nearly white subspecies of medium size. Differs from *occidentalis* of Mackenzie in smaller size, more predominantly white coloration, and narrower braincase. Closely resembles *orion* of Greenland in coloration, but may be larger; skull with more elevated frontal region.

Color. — A female from Ellesmere Island (*winter pelage, April*): General coloration white, with blackish-tipped hairs thinly and inconspicuously distributed along median line of dorsum and across upper side of tail near base; sides of muzzle and small areas near angles of mouth mixed with dusky; throat yellowish; underfur over dorsum "light mouse gray"; soles of feet and interdigital areas near "buff-pink" on fore feet and "shell pink" on hind feet.

Skull.—Compared with *occidentalis:* Size smaller, less massive; braincase narrower, more highly arched; frontal region decidedly narrower, more convex in profile, less broadly and deeply V-shaped along median line; postorbital processes slenderer, more acutely pointed; auditory bullae larger, more fully inflated; dentition similar, but rather light; protocone of upper carnassial prominent. Compared with *orion:* Very similar in general form, but frontal region less elevated and less convex in outline.

Measurements. — Tanned skin of a female from Ellesmere Island: Total length, 1515; tail vertebrae, 360; hind foot, 225. *Skull:* From original description of type specimen: "Total length, 255; condylobasal length, 232; zygomatic width, 142; postorbital width, 43; interorbital width, 47; maxillary width above fourth upper premolar, 76; maxillary width at canines, 48; palate length, 114;

width of upper incisors, 39; upper cheek teeth, 108; mandibular length, 185; fourth upper premolar, 27 x 15.5; first upper molar, 18 x 21; first lower molar, 31." An adult male from Ellesmere Island: Greatest length, 264.7; condylobasal length, 236.9; zygomatic breadth, 138.7; squamosal constriction, 79.4; width of rostrum, 46; interorbital breadth, 45.6; postorbital constriction, 40.4; length of mandible, 186.8; height of coronoid process, 76.1; maxillary tooth row, crown length, 108.6; upper carnassial, crown length (outer side), 26.4; upper carnassial, crown width, 15.3; first upper molar, antero-posterior diameter of crown, 17.6, transverse diameter of crown, 23; lower carnassial, crown length, 30.1.

Remarks.—In describing *arctos*, Pocock referred to it a skull from Discovery Bay, Ellesmere Island. A somewhat larger skull from Ellesmere Island in the collection of the American Museum of Natural History also seems to agree with the original description, especially in the elevation of the frontal region, and is assumed to be representative. Characters differentiating *arctos* from *occidentalis* appear to be well marked, but relationship to *orion* is not so clear, owing to the lack of adequate material for comparison.

Specimens examined.—Two (one skin without skull, one skull without skin),[1] from Ellesmere Island.

CANIS LUPUS ORION Pocock

Greenland Wolf (Pl. 99)

Canis lupus orion Pocock, Zool. Soc. London Proc., part 3, p. 683, September 1935.

Type locality.—Cape York, on Baffin Bay, northwestern Greenland.

Type specimen.—No. 97.3.5.1, skin and skull, apparently male adult, British Museum.

Distribution.—Northern Greenland, Arctic America; limits of range unknown. Donald B. MacMillan writes me that wolves were found by his party at Cape Morris Jesup, the most northern point of land in the world, 380 miles distant from the Pole. He points out

[1]Amer. Mus. Nat. Hist.

their apparent absence at present in southern Greenland, but also evidence of their former occurrence, as the Norsemen arriving in 986 reported finding wolf traps, such as are built by Eskimos today.

General characters.—Described as a "whitish gray" subspecies, perhaps smaller than *arctos;* skull with less elevated frontal region.

Color.—From original description: "The coat is everywhere long and densely thickened with underwool about 60 mm. in length, the length of the contour hairs (in mm.) being approximately as follows: Back 70, flank 65, shoulder-mat 134, nape 105. There are also long hairs, from 60 to 70 mm., on the backs of the legs above the paws, the latter being long-haired round the margins and between the pads, which are completely overlapped and concealed. The general colour is a uniform whitish grey, except for the tolerably extensive marbling and streaking of the black-tipped contour hairs of the upper side, but the ears are pale buff, turning to drab towards the point; the top of the head, as far as the angle of the eye, and of the muzzle, apart from its white tip, is very pale brownish grey; there is some buff about the lower jaw and some black hair-tips on the hind throat; the rest of the underside and the legs are white; the tail has a black tip, but the rest of its upper side is not so conspicuously black and white as the back. Judging from the condition of the coat, and especially the hairiness of the backs of the legs and the soles of the feet, this skin is in winter coat." Two skins in the American Museum of Natural History were taken on the Crockerland Expedition from "Greenland." One of these is marked female, March 26, 1914, and both are almost entirely white. In one a few inconspicuous dark-tipped hairs appear on the lower part of the rump, and the upper side of the tail near the base. In the other, dark-tipped hairs are restricted to a few over the tail gland. In both of these skins the concealed woolly under-fur is pale gray, near "pallid mouse gray." Tufts of hairs between the median toes on the fore feet are about 55 millimeters in length, tinted basally with "shell pink."

Skull.—Type skull of doubtful sex, described as smaller than that of *arctos*, with less elevated and convex frontal profile. The skull of a female from "Greenland" is very similar to that of a male believed to represent *arctos* from Ellesmere Island in general form. The frontal region is less elevated, and thus in accord with the description of the type, but the range of individual variation is unknown.

Measurements.—No external measurements of specimens from very near the region of the type locality are available. Measurements of two wolves (sex and age not stated) shot by the Denmark Expedition on the east coast of Greenland in latitude between 75° and 83° 10′ N., furnished by Donald B. MacMillan, are respectively as follows: Total length, 1,500, 1,530 mm.; length of tail, 420, 440; height at shoulder, 760, 730; circumference of chest, 750, 670; weight, 63.8, 45.1 pounds. *Skull* (type specimen from original description): "Total length, 235; condylobasal length, 220; zygomatic width, 130; postorbital width, 40; interorbital width, 43; maxillary width above fourth upper premolars, 68; maxillary width at canines, 42; palate length, 110; palate between second upper premolars, 32; width of upper incisors, 34; upper cheek-teeth, 101; mandibular length, 171; fourth upper premolar, 23 x 14; first upper molar, 16 x 19; first lower molar, 27." An adult female from "Greenland": Greatest length, 242.4; condylobasal length, 227.5; zygomatic breadth, 132.8; squamosal constriction, 74.7; width of rostrum, 39.6; interorbital breadth, 42.1; postorbital constriction, 35.8; length of mandible, 173.4; height of coronoid process, 71; maxillary tooth row, crown length, 102.6; upper carnassial, crown length (outer side), 24.5, crown width, 13.8; first upper molar, anteroposterior diameter, 16.2, transverse diameter, 2.2; lower carnassial, crown length, 28.

Remarks.—The Greenland wolf was not fully characterized by its describer, and owing to lack of adequate material for comparison, its relationship to *arctos* remains somewhat uncertain. General conditions, however, point to the probable occurrence of more than one geographic race on the great island of Greenland. Degerbol (1927, p. 23) refers in comparative remarks to the wolves of the northwestern coast and the Scoresby Sound region on the east side of Greenland.

Specimens examined.—Two (one skin without skull) from Greenland (without definite locality).[1]

---

[1]Amer. Mus. Nat. Hist.

CANIS LUPUS LABRADORIUS Goldman

Labrador Wolf (Pls. 100-101)

Canis lupus labradorius Goldman, Mamm. Jour. 18 (1): 38, Feb. 14, 1937.

Type locality.—Vicinity of Fort Chimo (now Chimo), Quebec, Canada.

Type specimen.—No. 23136, probably ♀, adult skull only, U. S. National Museum; collected by Lucien M. Turner in 1882 or 1883. Original number 2190.

Distribution.—Northern Quebec and Labrador, Canada.

General characters.—Size medium; color light; frontals remarkably broad behind postorbital processes (usually broader than between orbits). Most closely allied to *lycaon* of southern Quebec, but larger; color lighter; cranial details, especially the greater postorbital width of the frontals, distinctive.

Color.—Varying from "dark somewhat grizzly gray to almost white" (Turner manuscript).

Skull.—Compared with that of *lycaon*, the skull is larger, more massive; rostrum heavier; postorbital region relatively broader (broader than interorbital region in most skulls examined); dentition heavier.

Measurements.—No body measurements available. *Skull.*—An adult, probably male, from Hopedale, Labrador, and the type, an adult, probably female, from Fort Chimo, Quebec, respectively: Greatest length, 262.2, 247.1; condylobasal length, 243.5, 222.7; zygomatic breadth, 141.5, 132.7; squamosal constriction, 78.8, 73; width of rostrum, 49.5, 41.7; interorbital breadth, 46.6, 43.5; postorbital constriction, 46.9, 46.9; length of mandible, 189.6, 175.5; height of coronoid process, 81.8, 73.8; maxillary tooth row, crown length, 110.1, 98.4; upper carnassial, crown length (outer side), 25.7, 25; upper carnassial, crown width, 13.7, 12.4; first upper molar, antero-posterior diameter, 17.1, 15.3, transverse diameter, 23.3, 21.3; lower carnassial, crown length, 29.4, 28.1.

Remarks.—The Labrador wolf appears to be an inhabitant of the barren grounds, requiring close comparison only with *lycaon* of the forested region of eastern Canada and the northeastern United States. A skull, probably of a female, from Hopedale, Labrador, agrees closely in general size and proportions with some examples of *lycaon* from southern Quebec, but the frontals are broader and the dentition is decidedly heavier. The skull, conforming so closely in many of the more essential details, suggests the probability of intergradation.

Specimens examined.—Total number, 11, as follows:
Labrador: Adlavik, 1 (skull only);[1] Hopedale, 3 (skulls only);[1] Kippokak, 1 (skull only);[1] Porcupine (near Cartwright), 1 (skull only).
Quebec: Fort Chimo, 5 (skulls only).

CANIS LUPUS BEOTHUCUS Allen and Barbour

Newfoundland Wolf (Pl. 102)

Canis lupus beothucus Allen and Barbour, Mamm. Jour. 18 (2): 230, May 14, 1937.

Type locality.—Newfoundland.

Type specimen.—No. 351, adult, probably ♂, skull only, Museum of Comparative Zoology; collected by J. M. Nelson, about 1865.

Distribution.—Confined to Newfoundland; now extinct.

General characters.—A white subspecies of medium size, with rather robust skull. Compared with *labradorius* of northern Labrador: Size and perhaps color similar; cranial details distinctive. Compared with *lycaon* of Quebec: Size larger; color whiter; skull heavier, the rostrum decidedly broader.

Color.—From original description of a skin from north of Grand Lake, Newfoundland, collected many years ago by Dr. Elwood Worcester: "Entirely pure white with a slight tinge of ivory yellow on the head and limbs. The under fur is dense and woolly, about 45 mm. deep on the shoulders, while the overlying guard hairs in the same region are about 160 mm. long. The short ears are densely hairy. According to Dr. Worcester, black individuals may occur."

Skull.—Similar to that of *labradorius* in size and general form including the broad rostrum, but differs in structural detail; frontal region more deeply groved, or V-shaped, along median line; postorbital processes less tapering, more obtusely pointed; supraoccipital

[1]Mus. Comp. Zool.

shield narrower; ascending branches of premaxillae shorter and broader; nasals less deeply excised to the median line anteriorly, leaving the narial borders more broadly U-shaped, instead of V-shaped; dentition similar. Exhibits a departure from that of *lycaon* in decidedly heavier rostrum and larger carnassials, and differs otherwise in about the same details as from *labradorius*.

Measurements.—From original description of a nearly complete skin collected many years ago north of Grand Lake, Newfoundland: "The ears measure about 80 mm. in length and hardly exceed the surrounding long guard hairs. This skin measures in head and body length, in its present condition, about 1390 mm." *Skull.*—From original description of type, regarded as a male, and a Newfoundland skull believed to be of a female, respectively: "Greatest length, 265, 245; basal length, 238, 227; palatal length, 125, 120; zygomatic width, 140, 130; mastoid width, 79.2, 71.8; width outside pm^4, 82, 75; upper cheek teeth, c-m^2, 107, 103; lower cheek teeth, c-m_3, 118, 126; length of upper pm^4, 24.2, 23; length of alveoli, pm^4, 21.8, 20.6; length of lower molar m_1, 28, 27.9." A larger skull, doubtless of an adult male from Newfoundland (also from original description): "Greatest length, 276; zygomatic width, 143. Skull of an adult, probably male (measured by author), from Newfoundland: Greatest length, 254; condylobasal length, 230; zygomatic breadth, 138.7; squamosal constriction, 78.2; width of rostrum, 44.1; interorbital breadth, 46.7; postorbital constriction, 45.4; length of mandible, 182.7; height of coronoid process, 78.6; maxillary tooth row, crown length, 104; upper carnassial, crown length (outer side), 26.2, crown width, 14.7; first upper molar, antero-posterior diameter, 17.5, transverse diameter, 23; lower carnassial, crown length, 29."

Remarks.—The Newfoundland wolf appears to have been more closely allied to *labradorius* than to *lycaon*. Its natural prey was the native caribou. With the settlement of the island, however, much injury to young cattle was reported, and a price put by the legislature on its head. This wolf probably became extinct during recent years.

Specimens examined.—Four skulls and one skin are known to exist. All of these were in the Museum of Comparative Zoology, but one skull of this lot has recently passed to the U. S. National Museum (Biological Surveys collection) in exchange. The exchanged skull is the only one examined by the author.

CANIS LUPUS LYCAON Schreber
Eastern Wolf (Pls. 103-104)

Canis lycaon Schreber, Die Saugthiere, theil 2, heft 13, pl. 89, 1775; name *Canis lycaon* also appears in Nachtrag zum 26 heft, theil 3, p. 585, 1778.

Canis lupus canadensis Blainville, Ostiogr. Mamm. Recents et Foss., vol. 2, facs. 13 (Atlas), Genre Canis, p. 45, pl. 7, 1843. Presumably from Canada.

Canis lupus canadensis Allen and Barbour, Jour. Mamm. 18 (2): 230, May 14, 1937.

Canis lupus lycaon Goldman, Jour. Mamm. 18 (1): 45, Feb. 14, 1937.

Canis tundrarum ungavensis Comeau, Ann. 1, Acfas, Montreal, 6: 121, 1940.

Type locality.—Vicinity of Quebec, Quebec, Canada. Type locality fixed by Goldman (Jour. Mamm. 18 (1): 38, Feb. 14, 1937).

Type.—Name used by Schreber in plate illustration (l.c.) derived from Buffon's description and figure (1761, pp. 362-370, pl. 41) of a "loup noir," a female, captured in Canada when very young, kept chained, and taken alive to Paris by a French naval officer.

Distribution.—Formerly southern Quebec, Ontario, north probably to Hudson Bay, eastern Minnesota, Michigan, Ohio, northeastern and middle Atlantic states; southern limit of range indefinitely determined but believed to extend to Florida. Still present in southern Quebec, Ontario, and parts of northern Minnesota, Wisconsin, and northern Michigan. Doubtless intergrading with *labradorius* and *hudsonicus* on the north, east and west of Hudson Bay, respectively, and formerly with *nubilus* west of the Great Lakes.

General characters.—A small, dark-colored subspecies; skull with remarkably slender rostrum. Size smaller than *labradorius* of northern Quebec, *hudsonicus* of Keewatin, or *nubilus* of Nebraska, and color darker than in any of them. Superficially similar to some specimens of large subspecies of *Canis niger*.

Color.—*Winter pelage:* Upper parts in general grayish, usually heavily overlaid with black from upper side of neck over back; head more or less suffused with "cinnamon"; under parts, including throat and thoracic area, varying from white to "pale pinkish buff," with scattered dark hairs intermingled, becoming clearer white on inguinal region; chin and space between lower jaws varying from white to blackish; ears "cinnamon" to near "tawny"; outer surfaces of limbs ranging from "cinnamon-buff" to rich "cinnamon," the forearms with a narrow black line, prominent in some specimens and obsolescent in others; feet near pinkish buff; tail grayish above, the guard hairs tipped with black, the black tending to mass over tail gland as usual in the group; under side of tail more or less distinctly suffused with buff to tip, which is black. *Summer pelage:* Similar to winter pelage, but somewhat paler, the black less in evidence.

The skin of a wolf taken on the grounds of the Tourelli Club, 50 miles north of Quebec, about November 1, 1916, and presented by Theodore Roosevelt, is mainly dark brown or brownish black, or more or less distinctly "fuscous," and may be not very unlike the animal figured as the type. In this specimen the upper parts from nape to rump are brownish black along the median line, but the guard hairs bear a nearly concealed subterminal buffy band about 10 millimeters wide, below which is a brownish section giving way to white at base. The under fur is brown. The sides of body are grayish brown. The muzzle and ears are clear brown or "fuscous," passing into a grizzled mixture of white and brown on the face. The throat and thoracic areas, except a pure white pectoral spot, are dark brown, becoming lighter, more grayish brown on abdominal region. The limbs are mainly brownish black. The tail is blackish above, grayish brown below.

Skull.—Similar in general to that of *nubilus*, but smaller, with much slenderer rostrum; supraoccipital shield less projecting posteriorly over foramen magnum; nasals usually more deeply emarginate anteriorly; upper carnassials smaller, the protocones prominent in some specimens, absent in others; posterior upper molars usually actually as well as relatively larger. Differs from that of *hudsonicus* in much smaller size and relatively slenderer rostrum. Compared with that of *labradorius*, the skull is much smaller and slenderer; frontal region narrower; nasals more deeply emarginate anteriorly; dentition in general lighter, but posterior upper molars relatively larger. Similarity in size and cranial details to large subspecies of *niger* is rather close; but in *lycaon* the skull is usually broader, with higher brain case and more massive in general form; zygomata more widely spreading; postorbital processes with posterior margins turned less abruptly inward; large molariform teeth with crowns less deeply cleft, the cusps more rounded, less compressed laterally, and the cingulum on the outer side in the first upper molar is less prominent.

Measurements.—An adult male from Montebello, Quebec, and one from Algonquin National Park, Ontario, respectively: Total length, 1575, 1626; tail vertebrae, 393, 419; hind foot, 323, 267. Average of three adult females from Montebello, Quebec: Total length, 1473 (1423-1524); tail vertebrae, 360 (356-368); hind foot, 269 (260-286). An adult female from Lucerne, Ontario: Total length, 1601; tail vertebrae, 482; hind foot, 253. *Skull:* Two adult males from Montebello, Quebec, respectively: Greatest length, 253, 250.5; condylobasal length, 233, 236; zygomatic breadth, 140.3, 136; squamosal constriction, 76.2, 78.8; width of rostrum, 41.4, 41.5; interorbital breadth, 45.3, 43.9; postorbital constriction, 38.1, 37.6; length of mandible, 181.7, 178.5; height of coronoid process, 75, 71; maxillary tooth row, crown length, 104.8, 106.6; upper carnassial, crown length, outer side, 23.7, 23.4, crown width, 13.7, 12.5; anterior upper molar, antero-posterior diameter, 16.3, 17.7, transverse diameter, 21.3, 21.9; lower carnassial, 27.9, 28.2. Two adult females from Montebello, Quebec, respectively: Greatest length, 213.6, 224.7; condylobasal length, 203.3, 211.4; zygomatic breadth, 118.2, 117.9; squamosal constriction, 69.6, 70.2; width of rostrum, 34.4, 35.3; interorbital breadth, 35.8, 37.2; postorbital constriction, 30.4, 33.8; length of mandible, 155, 157.7; height of coronoid process, 62.5, 65.8; maxillary tooth row, crown length, 91, 94.5; upper carnassial, crown length (outer side), 22.5, 21.8, crown width, 12, 12.4; first upper molar, antero-posterior diameter, 16, 15.8; transverse diameter, 19.5, 21; lower carnassial, crown length, 25.8, 25.9.

Remarks.—*Canis lupus lycaon* is characterized by small general size, and particularly the relative slenderness of the rostrum. Specimens from the Great Lakes region present a wide range of individual variation in size and cranial details, and grade toward the more robust plains wolf, *nubilus*. The color is grayer, but in size and even in many details of cranial structure, some examples of *lycaon* bear a rather close resemblance to certain of the larger specimens of *Canis niger*. The subspecies *lycaon* differs, however, from the subspecies of *Canis niger* in combination of cranial details, as pointed out, and the resemblances are evidently superficial. A skull (No. 11179, Mus. Comp. Zool.) labeled Florida, without definite locality, is quite unlike that of the type of *floridanus,* now regarded as representing typical *niger,* the red wolf of the region. In the height and massiveness of the cranium, obliquely directed temporal ridges and absence of well developed cingula on the outer borders of the first upper molar, this skull shows closer alliance with the true wolves. It is tentatively referred to *lycaon,* but is rather massive, with heavier but more narrowly spreading zygomata, shorter nasals, and heavier canines than usual in that form. More material might indicate that it represents an unrecognized extinct southeastern race of *C. lupus. Canis tundrarum ungavensis* was not compared by the describer with *lycaon,* the type locality of which had been fixed as Quebec, which is within 200 miles. The two names are undoubtedly synonymous.

The name *Canis lycaon* was first used by Schreber (l.c.) under the figure on plate 89 in 1775. The animal was regarded as a black fox, and in synonymy reference is made to the "loup noir" of Buffon in theil 3, p. 353 of his great work, published in 1776. The name *Canis lycaon* again appears, with further reference to the "loup noir" of Buffon, in Nachtrag zum 26 Heft, theil 3, p. 585, published in 1778. The name *Canis lupus canadensis* Blainville appears to be assignable to the synonymy of *lycaon,* as shown by Allen and Barbour (1937, p. 230).

Specimens examined.—Total number, 77, as follows:

Florida: Without definite locality, 1 (skull only).[4]

Michigan: Calderwood, 2 (1 skull without skin); Cusino, 1; Dickinson County, 1 (skull only); Duluth, 7 (skulls only);[5] Eckerman (9 miles north), 1; Escanaba River (west branch), Dickinson County, 2 (skulls only); Grand Isle, 1 (skin only); Hulbert, 1 (skull only); Kenton, 1 (skull only); L'Anse, 2 (skulls only); Mackinac County, 1; Marquette (30 miles northwest), 3; Marquette County, 1 (skull only);[6] Newberry (22 miles northeast), 1 (skin only); Pine Lake, Marquette County, 2 (skulls only); Randville, 1; Saul Sainte Marie, 1 (skull only); Taquamenaw River (east branch, 5 miles from mouth), 1 (skull only); Taquamenaw River (2 miles above falls), 1; Walsh, Schoolcraft County, 1 (skull only).[7]

Minnesota: Elk River, 2 (skulls only); Gunflint Lake (east of), Superior National Forest, 8 (skulls only).[8]

New York: Adirondack Mountains, 1 (skull only).
Ohio: Without definite locality, 1 (skull only).[9]
Ontario: Brent, Algonquin National Park, 1 (skull only);[1] Dacre, Renfrew, 1 (skull only);[1] Gaudette Twp., Algoma, 1 (skull only);[1] Hurkett, Thunder Bay, 1 (skull only);[1] Little Island Lake, Algonquin National Park, 1 (skin only);[1] Mattawa, Nipissing (40 miles northeast), 2 (skulls only); McCoy's Lake, Algonquin National Park, 1 (skull only); Norway Creek, Algonquin National Park, 1 (skin only);[1] Port Sydney, Muskoka, 1 (skull only);[1] Searchmont, Algoma, 1 (skull only);[1] Silver Islet, Thunder Bay, 1 (skull only);[1] Sundridge, Parry Sound, 1 (skull only);[1] Whitney, Nipissing, 1 (skull only).[2]
Pennsylvania: Without definite locality, 2 (skulls only).[9]
Quebec: Lucerne, Hull, 3 (skulls only);[3] Montebello, Papineau, 6 (skulls only);[1] Quebec (Tourelli Club, 50 miles north), Quebec, 1 (black skin).
Tennessee: Hamilton County, 1 (ramus of mandible only).
Wisconsin: Antigo, Langlade County, 1 (skull only);[6] Eagle River, 1 (skull only); Perkinstown, Taylor County, 1 (skull only); Vilas County, near Michigan line, 2 (skulls only).[6]

CANIS LUPUS NUBILUS Say

Great Plains Wolf; Buffalo Wolf; Loafer (Pls. 105-106)

Canis nubilus Say, Long's Expedition Rocky Mountains 1: 169, 1823.
Canis variabilis Wied, Reise in das innere Nord Amerika 2: 95, 1841. From Fort Clark, near Stanton, Mercer County, N. Dak.
Canis lupus var. *nubilus* Richardson, Fauna Boreali-Americana, p. 69, 1829.

---

[1]Royal Ontario Mus. Zool.
[2]Mus. Vert. Zool.
[3]2 in Mus. Vert. Zool.; 1 in Royal Ontario Mus. Zool.
[4]Mus. Comp. Zool.
[5]Amer. Mus. Nat. Hist.
[6]Field Mus. Nat. Hist.
[7]Stanley P. Young collection.
[8]Minn. Mus. Nat. Hist.
[9]Acad. Nat. Sci. Phila.

Type.—No type specimen designated.

Type locality.—Engineer Cantonment, near present town of Blair, Washington County, Nebr.

Distribution.—Formerly Great Plains region from southern Saskatchewan and Manitoba south to northeastern New Mexico and southern Oklahoma, and from near the eastern base of the Rocky Mountains east to western Minnesota, western Iowa, and Missouri; now probably extinct. Intergraded on the north with *occidentalis*, on the west with *irremotus* and *youngi*, on the east with *lycaon*, and on the south with *monstrabilis*.

General characters.—Size medium; color rather light; skull short, broad, and massive, with supraoccipital region narrow, the inion strongly projecting backward and tending to develop a descending hook. Averaging smaller than *youngi* of the southern Rocky Mountain region, with upper parts less suffused with buff; skull with supraoccipital region projecting farther posteriorly. Resembling *irremotus* of the northern Rocky Mountain region, but usually grayer, less inclining toward white; frontals narrower. Differs from *occidentalis* of Mackenzie in smaller size and shorter, less extensively white pelage. Similar in size to *monstrabilis* of Texas, but usually paler, pelage longer and denser; skull flatter. Differs from *lycaon* of southern Quebec in paler color and much more robust skull.

Color.—*Winter pelage:* Upper parts in general a mixture of white and varying shades of light buff, moderately overlaid with black, tending to produce a grayish tone; more distinctly grizzled black and white on face and top of head where the pelage is short; under parts varying from white to near "pale pinkish buff"; outer sides of limbs to feet "pale pinkish buff," becoming lighter, more whitish along inner sides; ears "pale pinkish buff" to near "cinnamon-buff," usually edged with black; tail above whitish to "pale pinkish buff," overlaid with black most profusely over gland near base, becoming pure white or buff below, and black all around with a few white hairs usually interspersed at tip. Many color variations are presented. Individuals may be nearly white at any season, except for a sprinkling of black hairs over the back, a small, narrow, but conspicuous black patch over the tail gland, and a more or less distinctly black tip. Black individuals may occur in the same litter with those normally colored. A male in winter pelage from Mizpah Creek, 65 miles southeast of Miles City, Montana, is light "tawny" in prevailing color of upper parts. *Young:* In first pelage, sooty brown or near "wood brown" in general tone, varying to blackish on lower part of rump and upper surface of tail; facial area and top of head suffused with "cinnamon-buff"; ears "ochraceous-tawny" edged with black. This pelage, short and velvety at first, grows rapidly, and thinly outstanding guard hairs appear. In about six to eight weeks it gives way to a new and shorter coat of a somewhat lighter shade, due to the removal of dusky guard hairs. In young specimens taken 20 miles south of Higbee, Colorado, on April 26, 1910, this first molt had advanced to the base of the tail, leaving this appendage in the earlier stage. In the new pelage the color markings of the adult, especially the post-humeral whitish areas and tendency to exhibit a whitish collar, become more clearly apparent. The black patch over the tail gland is more or less distinctly in evidence from early puppyhood.

Skull.—Relatively short and massive in general form, with heavy rostrum and narrow supraoccipital shield and inion prominently projected posteriorly. Similar in general form to that of *youngi,* but averaging smaller; rostrum shorter and supraoccipital shield narrower, rising less steeply, the inion projecting farther posteriorly over foramen magnum, and tending to develop a descending terminal hook. Compared with *irremotus:* Frontal region narrower, and differing otherwise in about the same characters as from *youngi.* Compared with *lycaon:* Larger, more massive; rostrum broader; supraoccipital shield and inion more projecting posteriorly; nasals less deeply emarginate anteriorly; dentition as a whole heavier, but posterior upper molars usually actually as well as relatively smaller. Differs from that of *occidentalis* most noticeably in smaller size. Compared with *monstrabilis:* Size similar, but more flattened; frontals less highly arched and less convex in profile; rostrum less depressed across middle, sloping more gradually upward to frontals; nasals with inner margins usually turned less strongly downward to form a V-shaped median trough.

Measurements.—An adult male from Douglas, Wyo.: Total length, 1,982; height at shoulder, 940. *Skull:* Two adult males from Kearney, Nebr., respectively: Greatest length, 258.4, 253.5; condylobasal length, 228.9, 232.3; zygomatic breadth, 137.7, 135.2; squamosal constriction, 80.4, 75.7; width of rostrum, 44.3, 42.2; interorbital breadth, 46.6, 48.1; postorbital constriction, 35.7, 40.3;

length of mandible, 180.3, 183.5; height of coronoid process, 81, 81.2; maxillary tooth row, 102.8, 106.3; upper carnassial, crown length (outer side), 26.1, 25.2, crown width, 13.1, 12.4; first upper molar, antero-posterior diameter, 15.9, 17.2, transverse diameter, 22.6, 22.7; lower carnassial, 29.2, 28.9. Two adult females, one from Kearney and the other from Platte River, Nebr., respectively: Greatest length, 228.7, 231; condylobasal length, 210.7, 212.5; zygomatic breadth, 119.4, 130.5; squamosal constriction, 70.6, 71.4; width of rostrum, 38.7, 40.9; interorbital breadth, 38.9, 40.3; post-orbital constriction, 34.8, 38; length of mandible, 161.7, 165.5 height of coronoid process, 66.5, 71.4; maxillary tooth row, crown length (outer side), 24.1, 24.2, crown width, 12.8, 14.1; first upper molar, antero-posterior diameter, 16.9, 15.5, transverse diameter, 23.2, 20.2; lower carnassial, crown length, 27.8, 28.

Remarks.—The Great Plains wolf was a well-marked race, mid-continental in geographic position. Its range included that of the greatest game herds of North America, which afforded an ample food supply. The individual cranial variation that may be expected in wolves is well shown by 88 skulls of this subspecies taken many years ago in the vicinity of Fort Union, Mont. Evidence of inter-gradation with neighboring races is shown by specimens from various localities along the borders of the general range. Specimens from eastern Minnesota and Michigan seem more properly referable to *lycaon,* but relationship to *nubilus* is shown in somewhat intermediate characters.

Specimens examined.—Total number, 191, as follows:

Colorado: Bent County, 15 (7 skulls only); Fort Massachusetts (now Fort Garland), San Luis Valley, near head of Rio Grande, 1 (skull only); Higbee, Otero County (20 miles south), 3; Republican Fork of Kansas River, 1 (skull only); Thatcher (11 miles north), 1 (skull only.)[1]

Kansas: Fort Harker, 1; Gove County, 1 (skull only).

Manitoba: Duck Mountain, 2 (skulls only).

Minnesota: Crookston, 1 (skull only).

Missouri: Without definite locality, 1 (skull only).[2]

Montana: Ekalaka, 1 (skull only); Fort Union, 88 (skulls only); Glendive, 1 (skull only); Kinsey, 1; Meredith, 5 (skin and skull); Miles City, 7 (1 skull only); Mizpah, 1; Mizpah Creek (65 miles southeast of Miles City), 1; Stone Shack, Custer

County, 3 (1 skull only); Upper Missouri River, 1 (skull only).
Nebraska: Fort Kearney, 14 (skulls only); Platte River, 5 (skulls only).
New Mexico: Carthage, 5; Gallo Canyon (40 miles southeast of Corona), 1 (skull only); Mountainair, Torrance County, 2 (skin and skull); Santa Rosa (18 miles north), 2 (skulls only).
North Dakota: Medora (20 miles south), 6 (skulls only).
Oklahoma: Afton, 1 (skull only); Beaver Creek, 1 (skull only);[3] Wichita Mountains, 4 (skulls only).
South Dakota: Dewey, Custer County, 1; Faith, Meade County, 1; Folsom, Custer County, 1; Fort Randall, 2 (1 skull only); Harding County, 1 (skull only); Imlay, Pennington County, 1.
Wyoming: Douglas, 5 (1 skull only); Natrona County, 2 (skulls only).

CANIS LUPUS IRREMOTUS Goldman
Northern Rocky Mountain Wolf (Pls. 107-108)

Canis lupus irremotus Goldman, Mamm. Jour. 18 (1): 41, Feb. 14, 1937.

Type locality.—Red Lodge, Carbon County, southwestern Montana.

Type specimen.—No. 214869, ♂ adult, skin and skull, U. S. National Museum (Biological Surveys collection); collected by M. E. Martin, April 19, 1916. X-catalog number 16243.

Distribution.—Formerly the northern Rocky Mountain region and high adjoining plains, from southern Alberta (Calgary) south through Idaho, and western Montana to western Wyoming; east to the Black Hills (Belle Fourche) of South Dakota.

General characters.—A light-colored subspecies of medium to rather large size, with narrow but flattened frontal region. Similar in size to *youngi* of the more southern Rocky Mountain region, but whiter, the upper parts less heavily overlaid with black; skull differs in detail, especially in the narrowness of the frontal region. Size larger and color whiter than in *nubilus* of Nebraska, or in *fuscus* of Oregon, and differs from both in cranial features, including the rela-

[1]Coll. Stanley P. Young.
[2]Coll. Acad. Nat. Sci. Phila.
[3]Coll. Amer. Mus. Nat. Hist.

tive narrowness of the frontal region. Differs from *occidentalis* of Mackenzie in decidedly smaller size. Differs from *columbianus* of central British Columbia in smaller average size, paler, less "cinnamon-buff" coloration, and narrower postorbital region of skull.

Color.—Winter pelage: Upper parts from nape to rump usually near "light buff" or varying shades of gray, sparingly overlaid with black, becoming nearly white on sides and limbs; short pelage on top of head light buffy white, the hairs tipped with black; ears and upper surface of muzzle light buffy; under parts in general more or less soiled white; tail above light buffy, thinly and inconspicuously overlaid with black, light buffy below to tip, which is a mixture of buff and black all around. Individuals in the black phase appear to be rare. In a skin from the vicinity of Kelly, Wyoming, the prevailing color is brownish black, extending down over the legs to the feet. A skin from near Elk, Wyoming, is unusual in "pale drab-gray" general tone, becoming whitish on legs and feet; ears brownish black in marked contrast with surrounding pelage; tail grayish, tipped with white.

Skull.—Very similar in size and spread of zygomata to that of *youngi*, but frontals usually narrower between orbits and behind postorbital processes; supraorbital shield tending to project farther posteriorly over foramen magnum. Usually larger than that of *nubilus*, but frontals narrower; supraoccipital shield broader and rising more steeply, less projecting posteriorly, over foramen magnum. Compared with *fuscus:* Size similar; frontal region flatter, less convex in profile, and distinctly narrower, less inflated behind postorbital processes; rostrum and nasals longer, the nasals usually ending well behind posterior plane of maxillae. Compared with *columbianus:* Size smaller; frontal region narrower, more constricted behind postorbital processes; supraoccipital shield narrower, more tapering toward apex; dentition similar.

Measurements.—Type (approximated from tanned skin): Total length, 1870 mm.; tail vertebrae, 410; hind foot, 240. An unusually large adult male from 15 miles south of Three Forks, Gallatin County, Montana (measured in flesh by collector): Total length, 1834; height at shoulder, 839; weight, 106 pounds. A male, not quite full grown, from Soda Springs, Idaho: Total length, 1904; tail vertebrae, 412; hind foot, 263. Two adult females from the same locality, respectively: Total length, 1929, 2046; tail vertebrae, 480, 440; hind foot, 236, 254. Two females, not quite full-grown, from Montpelier, Idaho, respectively: Total length, 1803, 1854; tail vertebrae, 440, 470; hind foot, 232, 242. *Skull:* Type and an adult male topotype, respectively: Greatest length, 259.2, 262; condylobasal length, 237, 241; zygomatic breadth, 144.9, 142.7; squamosal constriction, 81.1; 81; width of rostrum, 47.7, 49.5; interorbital breadth, 44.6, 43.1; postorbital constriction, 34.7, 35.5; length of mandible, 186, 193.5; height of rostrum, 74.4, 82.6; maxillary tooth row, 105.7, 106.2; upper carnassial, crown length (outer side), 25.7, 26.1, crown width, 13.9, 15.3; first upper molar, antero-posterior diameter, 17.6, 18.4; transverse diameter, 20.2, 24.1; lower carnassial, crown length, 28.8, 29.5. Two adult females from Dillon, Montana, respectively: Greatest length, 254.5, 244.5; condylobasal length, 237.7, 225.5; zygomatic breadth, 127, 123.3; squamosal constriction, 76.8, 69.1; width of rostrum, 42.8, 40.8; interorbital breadth, 45.7, 41.7; postorbital constriction, 39.7, 36.9; length of mandible, 179.4, 173; height of coronoid process, 73.5, 70.6; maxillary tooth row, 109.2, 102.3; upper carnassial, crown length (outer side), 26, 25.2, crown width, 13.4, 14.8; first upper molar, antero-posterior diameter, 16.8, 16.4, transverse diameter, 22.9, 23.7; lower carnassial, crown length, 30.3, 28.

Remarks.—*C. l. irremotus* occupied a section along the backbone of the continent extending northward from the United States into Canada. An individual was killed 15 miles south of Three Forks, Gallatin County, Mont., April 30, 1941, by Al Johnson of the Fish and Wildlife Service. This remarkable animal from a region in which the wolves were believed to have been extirpated was found to have the longest skull (285.3) of any measured from the entire United States. It equals some of the larger, more northern wolves (*pambasileus* and *occidentalis*) in general dimensions, but differs notably in lighter dentition. A few wolves may still persist in the mountainous region between southwestern Alberta and southeastern British Columbia. Specimens from northwestern Wyoming are somewhat intermediate between *irremotus* and *youngi*, which ranged to the southward. One of the largest wolf skulls from the United States is that of an old male referred to *irremotus* from 15 miles northwest of Manville, Wyo. Skulls from the Snake River Desert and other localities in central-southern and southwestern Idaho are rather small and variable. They do not appear to be typical, but agree more closely with *irremotus* than any other race. Specimens from the Black Hills region of Wyoming and South Dakota are variable and grade toward *nubilus*, the area forming an eastern salient loop in the range of the subspecies. In southern British Columbia, *irremotus* probably intergrades with *columbianus*.

Specimens examined.—Total number, 149, as follows:

Alberta: Calgary, 7;[1] Gleichen, 4 (skulls only);[1] Lethbridge, 3;[1] Lethbridge (25 miles southeast), 1.

Idaho: Aldridge, 5; Argora, Clark County, 1; Bear Park (35 miles northeast of Minidoka), 4 (skulls only); Boise National Forest, 1 (skull only); Castleford, Twin Falls County, 1 (skull only); Dry Valley (20 miles northeast of Soda Springs), 1; Hammett, Owyhee County, 3 (skins only); Leodore, 1; Leodore (10 miles south), 1 (skull only); Montpelier, 3; Priest River, 1 (skull only); Pocatello (head of Port Neuf River), 3 (skins only); Pocatello (10 miles east), 1; Soda Springs, 11 (4 skulls only); South Fork of Boise River, Elmore County, 1 (skull only); Spark's Well (23 miles northeast of Minidoka), 3 (skulls only); Tyhee Basin, Bannock County, 2 (1 skull only).

Montana: Beaverhead Mountains (12 and 25 miles southeast of Leadore, Idaho, respectively), 2; Belt, 5; Continental Divide (Montana side, 20 miles east of Leadore, Idaho), 1; Delphia 1 (skin only); Dillon, 2; Fort Conrad, 1 (skull only); Ingomar, 2 (1 skin without skull); Kruger, 1 (skull only); Lame Deer, Rosebud County, 1 (skull only); Little Belt Mountains, 4 (skulls only); Lodge Grass, Big Horn County, 1; Musselshell River, 1 (skull only);[1] Powderville, 4; Red Lodge (type locality), 3; Red Rock, Beaverhead County, 1; Riceville, 1 (skull only); Ridge, 1 (skull only); Spring Creek, Madison County, 1 (skin only); Sun River Valley, 1 (skull only); Three Forks (15 miles south), Gallatin County, 1 (skull and scalp); Warm Springs, deer Lodge County, 2; White Sulphur Springs (20 miles northwest), 1.

South Dakota: Belle Fourche, 1 (skull only).

Wyoming: Arvada, Sheridan County, 2 (1 skull only); Barber, 2 (skulls only); Big Piney, Sublette County, 4; Cokeville, Lincoln County, 1 (skull only); Converse County, 4 (skulls only); Cora, Sublette County, 6; Elk and vicinity, Teton County, 5; Fort Washakie, 1; Gillette, 1 (skull only); Glenrock, Converse

County, 1; Hell Roaring Creek, 7; Howard, 1; Kelly (Bacon Creek Ridge), Teton County, 1; Lenore, Fremont County, 3; Lost Springs (10 miles north), Converse County, 3 (1 skull without skin); Manville (15 miles northwest), 1; Otto, 1 (skull only);[1] Pinedale, 1 (skull only); Sand Creek Canyon, Black Hills, 1 (skull only); Shell, 1 (skin only); Split Rock, 2; Yellowstone National Park, 3 (skulls only).

CANIS LUPUS COLUMBIANUS Goldman
British Columbia Wolf (Pls. 109-110)

Canis lupus columbianus Goldman, Proc. Biol. Soc. Wash. 54: 110, September 30, 1941.

Type locality.—Wistaria, north side of Ootsa Lake, Coast District, British Columbia.

Type specimen.—No. 3559, ♂ adult, skull only, British Columbia Provincial Museum; collected by J. C. Shelford, November 1938.

Distribution.—Greater part of British Columbia, west of the Rocky Mountains and the Stikine Mountains, passing into *fuscus* near the southwestern coast and into *ligoni* along the coast bordering the Alexander Archipelago of southwestern Alaska; grades into *occidentalis* in the Peace River region, and farther south into *irremotus*.

General characters.—Size large; upper parts rather dark; ears light "cinnamon buff"; skull with broad supraoccipital shield and narrow carnassials. Approaches *pambasileus* of Alaska and *occidentalis* of Mackenzie in size, but reaches less extreme maximum cranial dimensions; color similar to *pambasileus*, less uniformly grayish or whitish than in *occidentalis*. Differs from *irremotus* of Montana in larger usual size, more buffy coloration, and broader postorbital region of skull. Differs from *fuscus* of Oregon in larger size, paler color, and cranial features, especially the longer nasals. Differs from *crassodon* of Vancouver Island in paler color and lighter dentition. Differs from *ligoni* of the Alexander Archipelago, Alaska, mainly in greater average size.

Color.—Variable but similar to *pambasileus*. A somewhat worn skin from Chezacut, north shore of Chilcotin Lake: Upper parts in

[1]Amer. Mus. Nat. Hist.

general mixed white and black with a pale buffy or yellowish suffusion, the back moderately overlaid with black; short pelage on middle of face a grizzled mixture of white and black, becoming suffused pith "pinkish buff" at top of head; upper surface of muzzle "pinkish buff"; under parts across middle of abdomen thinly overlaid with pale buff, the under color near "avellaneous" showing through; middle and sides of chest white; the hairs white to roots; ears "cinnamon-buff" mixed with black near tips; outer sides of limbs "pinkish buff," the usual narrow black line on anterior surface of forearm narrow and indistinct; tail above similar to back, a black line over glandular area, below "pale pinkish buff."

In another, a female in fresh pelage from Chezacut, the buffy element is darker and richer in tone and the color in detail as follows: Upper parts in general suffused wtih light "cinnamon-buff," purest and most intense on sides of shoulders, flanks, and thighs; top of head "cinnamon-buff" mixed with black, becoming abruptly grizzled grayish on forehead and face; muzzle and chin brownish; under side of neck "pale pinkish buff" slightly darkened by black tips of longer hairs; chest and thorax "pinkish buff"; inguinal region white; ears "cinnamon" mixed with black; lower part of legs "pinkish buff," a narrow blackish line along anterior surface of forearm; upper side of tail near base suffused with "pale pinkish buff," the glandular area heavily overlaid with black, passing distally into "cinnamon-buff" more moderately darkened by black-tipped hairs, becoming black at end as usual in the species; under side of tail "pale pinkish buff" on proximal two-thirds, passing into a "pinkish-buff" suffusion overlaid with black toward tip. Three from Chezacut and others from the vicinity of Takla and Bear Lakes in the black phase are similar to those of *pambasileus* and *ligoni* in the same color phase. In these the hairs are more or less distinctly buff-banded along the median line of the back, and brown rather than black is predominant. A skin from near the south end of Bear Lake presents an unusual coarsely grizzled mixture of black and white or gray, the blend producing an "iron-gray" general tone, with no trace of a buffy element, and resembling a similar color phase seen in *ligoni* and other subspecies. A female taken in August on the Little Tahltan River, Cassiar District, is intensively suffused with "cinnamon-buff," and the ears are near light "cinnamon-rufous."

Skull. — Closely resembles that of *pambasileus,* but usually smaller; subpraoccipital shield broader; postorbital processes slenderer, more tapering and acutely pointed; carnassials relatively narrower, more elongated (antero-posteriorly); second lower molars larger, more elongated. Very similar to that of *occidentalis,* but usually smaller; postorbital processes slenderer, more tapering; dentition as a whole lighter, but second lower molars larger; canines slenderer; carnassials relatively narrower. Compared with *irremotus:* Size larger; frontal region broader, less constricted behind postorbital processes; supraoccipital shield usually broader, more rounded near apex; dentition similar. Compared with *fuscus:* Size larger; nasals relatively longer, extending farther posteriorly beyond ends of maxillae; second lower molar relatively larger. Differs from that of *crassodon* in lighter dentition, especially the narrower carnassials. Differs from that of *ligoni* most obviously in greater average size.

Measurements.—Approximated from tanned skin of a female from Chezacut: Total length, 1600 mm.; tail vertebrae, 370. *Skull: Type* (male) and an adult male topotype, respectively: 272.9, 263.9; condylobasal length, 260, 244.4; zygomatic breadth, 148.4, 147.7; squamosal constriction, 82.5, 80.8; width of rostrum, 46, 45; interorbital breadth, 48.8, 43.1; postorbital constriction, 45.7, 38.3; length of mandible, 196.2, 193; height of coronoid process, 75, 80.9; maxillary tooth row, 112.1, 107.3; upper carnassial, crown length (outer side), 27.1, 26.8, crown width, 13.8, 14; first upper molar, antero-posterior diameter, 17.3, 16.4, transverse diameter, 24.1, 22.9; lower carnassial, crown length, 31.1, 29.5. Two adult female topotypes, respectively: Greatest length, 262.2, 266.5; condylobasal length, 235.8, 246.4; zygomatic breadth, 140, 133.8; squamosal constriction, 79.3, 79.5; width of rostrum, 45.4, 43.1; interorbital breadth, 46.8, 42.7; postorbital constriction, 44.6, 37; length of mandible, 185.3, 188.7; height of coronoid process, 73.6, 73, maxillary tooth row, 105.8, 108.4; upper carnassial, crown length (outer side), 25.6, 24.7, crown width, 12.9, 13.4; first upper molar, antero-posterior diameter, 16.7, 17.1, transverse diameter, 22, 21.8; lower carnassial, 29, 28.2.

Remarks.—The British Columbia wolf, *columbianus,* approaches its larger northern neighbors in size but differs in its combination of color and cranial details. Two skulls from Iskut summit, 60 miles south of Telegraph Creek, are large for *columbianus*, but present somewhat mixed characters in detail. They probably represent intergradation with *pambasileus* or *occidentalis*. Although from a locality not far distant from the range of *ligoni*, which is mainly confined to the Alexander Archipelago, these specimens exhibit a marked departure from those of that race in size and detailed characters. The British Columbia subspecies is believed to be increasing in numbers in some of the more remote sections of the country.

Specimens examined.—Total number, 25, as follows:

British Columbia: Bear Lake (5 miles north and 4 miles east of south end, respectively), 2 (skins only);[1] Bear Lake (12 miles northeast and 6 miles northwest, respectively), 2 (skins only);[1] Bowron Lake, Cariboo District, 1 (skull only)[2]; Chezacut, north shore of Chilcotin Lake, 5 (2 skins without skulls);[2] Iskut Summit (60 miles south of Telegraph Creek), 2 (skulls only)[3]; Kettle River, 2 (skulls only);[4] Little Prairie, Horsefly River, Cariboo District, 1 (skull only);[2] Little Tahltan River, Cassiar District, 1 (skin only);[5] Pemberton, Lillooet District, 1 (skull only);[2] Roche River (tributary of Similkameen River), Yale District, 1 (skull only); Tacla Lake (18 miles northwest of north end), 1 (skin only);[1] Telegraph Creek, 1 (skull only);[2] Vernon, Yale District, 1 (skull only);[2] Wistaria, north side of Ootsa Lake, Coast District, 4 (skulls only).[2]

CANIS LUPUS LIGONI Goldman

Alexander Archipelago Wolf (Pls. 111-112)

Canis lupus ligoni Goldman, Mamm. Jour. 18 (1): 39, Feb. 14, 1937.

Type locality.—Head of Duncan Canal, Kupreanof Island, Alexander Archipelago, Alaska.

Type specimen.—No. 243323, ♂ adult, skin and skull, U. S. National Musenum (Biological Surveys collection); collected by J. Stokley Ligon, November 7, 1922. X-catalog number 23022.

---

[1]John F. Stanwell-Fletcher Coll.

[2]Provincial Museum of British Columbia.

[3]Mus. Vert. Zool.

[4]Kansas Univ. Mus. Nat. Hist.

[5]Amer. Mus. Nat. Hist.

Distribution.—Alexander Archipelago, and adjacent mainland of southeastern Alaska; northward along the coast to Yakutat Bay.

General characters.—A dark-colored subspecies of medium size; pelage short. Differs from *columbianus*, of central British Columbia, in smaller usual size and paler buff suffusion of upper parts. Similar in general to *fuscus*, of the lower Columbia River Valley, but somewhat larger; ratio of blackish to normally colored individuals higher; upper parts in normally colored examples similarly overlaid with black, but usually less suffused with buff; skull more elongated and differing in detail. Much smaller and darker in normal gray color phase and pelage shorter than in *pambasileus* of the Mount McKinley region, Alaska. Similar to *crassodon* of Vancouver Island, British Columbia, in size and color, but differs in cranial details, notably the smaller auditory bullae.

Color.—Type (winter pelage, November): Short pelage on top of head a mixture of black and white, producing a grizzled effect; upper parts from nape to rump pale buff heavily overlaid with black, the black giving way to purer buff along sides; outer surfaces of legs cinnamon buff, paling gradually to near pinkish buff on feet; upper surface of muzzle cinnamon buffy; ears rich tawny, mixed with black; under parts in general buffy white; tail above about like back, becoming buffy below and deep black all around at tip.

Specimens from Zarembo, Kuiu, and Prince of Wales Islands present two distinct color phases—one which may be regarded as normal, and the other predominantly black. Four of the five skins available from Zarembo Island are in the blackish phase. In the latter the muzzle and feet usually are nearly pure black, but in one a mixture of black and white or gray includes the entire body in a combination suggesting the peculiar color of the glacier bear, which also inhabits the coast region of southern Alaska.

Skull. — Rather closely resembling that of *columbianus*, but smaller; auditory bullae usually larger, more fully inflated. Decidedly smaller, less massive than *pambasileus*, with relatively lighter dentition. Similar in size and general form to *crassodon*, but auditory bullae smaller, less inflated; upper carnassials distinctly smaller and narrower, the anterior borders more transverse to longitudinal axis of skull, instead of oblique and directed inward and backward as in *crassodon*.

Measurements.—Type: Total length, 1733 mm.; tail vertebrae, 477; hind foot, 300; weight (stomach empty), 91 pounds. An adult female topotype: 1556; 457; 285. Two adult males from Wrangell, Alaska, respectively: Total length, 1650, 1683; tail vertebrae, 453, 492; hind foot, 298, 292. Two adult females from Wrangell, Alaska, respectively: 1585, 1496; 435, 406; 279, 270. An adult female from Baker Island, Alaska: 1499; 393; 279. *Skull:* Type and an adult male from Wrangell, respectively: Greatest length, 262.1, 262; condylobasal length, 251, 239.4; zygomatic breadth, 145.3, 146.4; squamosal constriction, 80, 84.4; width of rostrum, 43.4, 47.9; interorbital breadth, 49.1, 47; postorbital constriction, 43.4, 41.5; length of mandible, 197, 184.5; height of coronoid process, 72.9, 73.3; maxillary tooth row, crown length, 112.8, 110.3; upper carnassial, crown length (outer side), 25.2, 25; upper carnassial, 13.9, 14.2; anterior upper molar, antero-posterior diameter, 17.7, 16.3; anterior upper molar, 24.5, 23.3; lower carnassial, crown length, 30.4, 28.3. An adult female topotype and an adult female from Wrangell, respectively: Greatest length, 250, 244; condylobasal length, 232.8, 229; zygomatic breadth, 135.5, 132.2; squamosal constriction, 76.1, 77.4; width of rostrum, 42.4, 43.4; interorbital breadth, 41.2, 43.9; postorbital constriction, 36.4, 41.6; length of mandible, 185.3, 178.5; height of coronoid process, 73.4, 66.7; maxillary tooth row, crown length, 106.1, 104.6; upper carnassial, crown length (outer side), 23.9, 22.8; upper carnassial, crown width, 12.9, 12.8; anterior upper molar, antero-posterior diameter, 16.4, 16.3; anterior upper molar, transverse diameter, 22.9, 21.6; Lower carnassial, crown length, 28.7, 27.5.

Remarks.—The wolf of the Alexander Archipelago and closely adjoining mainland of southeastern Alaska is a well-marked subspecies, differing from the wolves of the interior in smaller size, shorter pelage, and darker normal coloration. In the normal, or gray, color phase, the back is more profusely overlaid with black than in *pambasileus.* In the varying mixtures presented in the black phase, however, the two are much alike. Its principal natural prey is probably the black-tailed deer (*Odocoileus columbianus sitkensis*) of the region.

Specimens examined.—Total number 37, all from Alaska, as follows: Baker Island, 2; Conclusion Island, 1 (skull only); Dry

Bay, Alsek River, 1 (skull only);[1] Eleanor Cove, Yakutat Bay, 1 (skull only);[1] Juneau, 1 (skull only);[2] Ketchikan, 2; Kuiu Island, 7 (5 skulls without skins); Kupreanof Island (type locality), 5; Prince of Wales Island, 8 (6 skulls without skins; 2 skins without skulls); Revillagigedo Island, 1 (skull only); Wrangell, 3 (1 skin without skull); Zarembo Island, 5.

CANIS LUPUS FUSCUS Richardson

Cascade Mountains Wolf (Pls. 113-114)

Canis lupus var. *fusca* Richardson, Zool. Capt. Beechey's Voyage of the Blossom, 1839, p. 5. Reference is made to his earlier description under *Canis lupus occidentalis* (1829, p. 61).

Lupus gigas (Townsend), Acad. Nat. Sci. Phila., Ser. 2, vol. 2, Art. 8, p. 75, Nov. 1850. From near Vancouver, Clark County, Washington.

Canis gigas Miller, Smiths. Misc. Coll. 59 (15): 4, June 8, 1912.

Type.—Not designated.

Type locality.—Banks of the Columbia River, below the Dalles, between Oregon and Washington.

Distribution.—Formerly the forested region from the Cascade Range in Oregon and Washington west in places to the Pacific coast; south to undetermined limits along the Sierra Nevada in northeastern California, and probably northwestern Nevada, north along the coast of British Columbia to undetermined limits; on the east intergradation with *columbianus* and *irremotus* can safely be assumed. Probably still extant in some of the wilder sections near the coast of southwestern British Columbia and the Siskiyou Mountains of southern Oregon.

General characters.—A dark cinnamon or cinnamon-buffy subspecies, with dorsum profusely overlaid with black; size medium; skull rather short; rostrum and nasals short, the nasals usually ending near posterior plane of maxillae. Similar in size to *youngi* of Utah and *irremotus* of Montana, but color darker, more suffused with "cinnamon-buff" than either, the back more heavily overlaid with black; cranial details, especially the shorter nasals, distinctive.

---

[1]Roy. Ont. Mus. Zool.

[2]Field Mus. Nat. Hist.

Similar in size to *crassodon* of Vancouver Island, but ground color less grayish, more cinnamon-buffy; cranial and dental details different. Differs from *columbianus* of British Columbia in smaller size, darker color, and cranial features, especially the shorter nasals.

Color.—Winter pelage: Upper parts in general usually suffused with "cinnamon" or "cinnamon-buff," the top of head and entire back profusely overlaid with black; under parts varying from "cinnamon-buff" to "pinkish cinnamon," becoming white in some specimens on inguinal region; chin blackish; outer surfaces of fore and hind legs ranging from "cinnamon-buff" to rich "cinnamon," becoming somewhat paler on feet; ears externally suffused with "cinnamon," the hairs tipped with black; inner surfaces of ears more thinly clothed with "cinnamon-buff" hairs; tail above "cinnamon" or "cinnamon-buff," overlaid with black; tail below whitish or "pinkish buff" near base, passing gradually to "cinnamon-buff" overlaid with black toward tip which is black all around, as usual in the group. A skin from Sycan, Oregon, is nearly pure white, except for a sprinkling of dark hairs over rump and a black patch on tail gland. In one skin a few hairs white to roots are intermingled with the black on the tip of the tail.

Skull.—Similar in size to that of *youngi*, but frontal region more inflated behind postorbital processes; nasals shorter, less extended posteriorly, more nearly conterminous with maxillae. Compared with *irremotus:* Size similar; frontals broader between orbits and broader, more inflated behind postorbital processes; rostrum and nasals shorter, the nasals usually ending nearer the posterior plane of maxillae. Compared with *crassodon:* Size and general form similar; nasals usually shorter, more nearly conterminous with maxillae posteriorly; auditory bullae smaller, less inflated; dentition, especially the larger molariform teeth, lighter; upper carnassial narrower anteriorly, with border of crown more nearly transverse to longitudinal axis of skull (anterior border of crown directed more obliquely inward and backward in *crassodon*). Compared with *columbianus:* Size smaller, nasals relatively shorter, less extended posteriorly; second lower molars relatively smaller.

Measurements.—Two adult males from Cascadia, Oregon (approximated from tanned skins), respectively: Total length, 1670, 1800 mm.; tail vertebrae, 390, 470; hind foot, 230, 260. Two adult females from the same locality (tanned skins), respectively:

Total length, 1610, 1562; tail vertebrae, 390, 377; hind foot, 220, 240. An adult male from Elwha River, 22 miles south of Port Angeles, Washington: Weight, 86 pounds. *Skull:* Two adult males from Cascadia, Oregon, respectively: Greatest length, 256.5, 256; condylobasal length, 235.5, 238.3; zygomatic breadth, 137, 141.1; squamosal constriction, 78.8, 75.6; width of rostrum, 45, 44.3; interorbital breadth, 47.8, 50.3; postorbital constriction, 44.3, 44; length of mandible, 187, 187.2; height of coronoid process, 85, 83.3; maxillary tooth row, crown length, 109.1, 107.6; upper carnassial, crown length (outer side), 25.6, 25.5, crown width, 14.2, 12.3; first upper molar, antero-posterior diameter, 16.8, 16.9; transverse diameter, 22, 23.1; lower carnassial, crown length, 30.1, 28.4. Two adult females from Cascadia, Oregon, respectively: Greatest length, 239.8, 237.5; condylobasal length, 218.5, 222.8; zygomatic breadth, 128.3, 131.8; squamosal constriction, 75.4, 72; width of rostrum, 44, 40.6; interorbital breadth, 45, 46.8; postorbital constriction, 41.7, 43; length of mandible, 170.5, 172.4; height of coronoid process, 72.8, 71.8; maxillary tooth row, crown length, 98.6, 101.4; upper carnassial, crown length (outer side), 21.9, 22.8, crown width, 12.9, 12.5; first upper molar, antero-posterior diameter, 15.1, 15, transverse diameter, 21.3, 20.8; lower carnassial, crown length, 26.3, 26.4.

Remarks.—The Cascade wolf is distinguished by peculiar dark coloration in combination with cranial details in marked contrast with those presented by its geographic neighbors. Owing, no doubt, to the dark "cinnamon" or "cinnamon-buff" general ground color, the animal was referred to as the "brown wolf." This wolf undoubtedly passed gradually into *irremotus* in the region east of the Cascade Range, in northeastern Washington, and may still intergrade with that subspecies in southeastern British Columbia.

The name *Canis lupus fusca* Richardson (1839, p. 5) for the "large brown wolf" of Lewis and Clark, said to inhabit "California and the banks of the Columbia" River, seems to have been overlooked until brought to attention by Allen and Barbour (1937, p. 230). This name, proposed by Richardson, clearly takes precedence over *gigas* described by Townsend from the same general region in 1850. Lewis and Clark (Thwaites ed., 1905, p. 94) state that "The large brown wolf is like that of the Atlantic States, and are found only in the woody country on the Pacific Ocean embracing the

Mountains which pass the Columbia between the Great Falls an[d] Rapids of the same." The type region may, therefore, be restricted to the banks of the Columbia River below the Dalles, between Oregon and Washington.

The first naturalist to obtain a specimen of the Cascade Mountains wolf seems to have been David Douglas. According to his journal published in 1914 (p. 59), he procured in the summer of 1825, along with other mammals, a "new species of *Canis*" on the banks of the Santiam River, a branch of the Willamette River in Oregon. In this connection, there is a bare manuscript reference, no page being given, to Richardson's Fauna Boreali-Americana. It seems probable from the context that the "*Canis*" was the wolf. Mammals collected by Douglas, including a hunter's skin of *Arctomys? (Spermophilus?) douglasi* (equals *Citellus beecheyi douglasii*), were listed by Richardson; but he says (l. c., p. 61), "I have seen none of these brown wolves," and there seems to be no evidence that any wolf material taken by Douglas reached Richardson.

Specimens examined.—Total number, 28, as follows:

British Columbia: Burrard Inlet, 1 (skull only);[5] Calvert Island, 1 (skull only);[5] Swindle Island, 1 (skull only).[5]

California: Litchfield, Lassen County, 1 (skull only).[1]

Oregon: Cascadia, 3; Clackamas River (28 miles above Cazadero), 1;[2] Crane Prairie (25 miles northeast of Ashland), 1 (skull only); Estacada, 1; Foster, Linn County, 1 (skull only);[3] Foster (6 miles northeast), 1 (skin only);[2] Glide, 2 (one 40 miles east; one 15 miles northeast); Glide (north fork of east fork of north fork of Rock Creek, 20 miles northeast of Glide), 1;[2] Glide, 3;[4] Molalla River (at source), Clackamas County, 1;[2] Rogue River (Peavine Mountain, 40 miles northeast), 2; Tiller (15 miles southeast on Elk Creek), 2; Sycan (30 miles south of Silver Lake), 1.

Washington: Bitter Cottonwood, 1 (skull only); Elwha River (22 miles south of Port Angeles), 1 (skull only); Hoh River (base of Olympic Mountains), 1; Twin Peaks, Chelan County, 1.

---

[1]Mus. Vert. Zool.

[2]Oregon Agr. College Coll.

[3]Stanley P. Young Coll.

[4]One in Oregon Agr. College Coll.

[5]Provincial Mus. of British Columbia.

CANIS LUPUS CRASSODON Hall
Vancouver Island Wolf (Pls. 115-116)

Canis occidentalis crassodon Hall, Univ. Calif. Pub. Zool. 38 (12) 420, November 8, 1932.

Type locality.—Tahsis Canal, Nootka Sound, Vancouver Island, British Columbia.

Type.—No. 12456, ♂ adult, skull only, Museum of Vertebrate Zoology; collected during winter of 1909-10 by Carl Leiner, from whom procured on July 26, 1910, by Harry S. Swarth. Original number 8419, H. S. S.

Distribution.—Vancouver Island, British Columbia.

General characters.—An insular subspecies; size medium; upper parts gray, heavily overlaid with black; skull with postorbital region broad; dentition heavy; upper carnassial with outer side longest, the anterior border of crown directed obliquely inward and backward to protocone. Most closely allied to *fuscus* of adjacent mainland, but color grayer, apparently lacking the "cinnamon" or "cinnamon-buff" suffusion of the latter; cranial details distinctive. Differs from *columbianus* of British Columbia in darker upper parts and heavier dentition.

Color.—A skin from Nootka Sound, in winter pelage: Upper parts in general a drab grayish mixture, the top of head and dorsal area heavily overlaid with black; under parts in general dull white; throat grayish; chin blackish; outer surfaces of fore and hind legs "pinkish buff"; ears brownish; tail grayish overlaid with black above, the black most extensive near base, below dull white, becoming black all around at tip about 120 millimeters in length.

Skull.—Similar in size and general proportions to that of *fuscus*; nasals usually longer, extending farther beyond posterior plane of maxillae; auditory bullae larger, more inflated; dentition, especially the larger molariform teeth, heavier; upper carnassial distinctly broader anteriorly, with border of crown directed more obliquely inward and backward (anterior border of crown more nearly transverse to cranial axis in *fuscus*). Differs from that of *columbianus* in about the same details as from *fuscus*.

Measurements.—A tanned skin from Nootka Sound: Total length, 1885; tail vertebrae, 470; hind foot, 310. *Skull:* Type (from original description): "Condylobasal length, 240.1; length of tooth-rows, 126.6; postpalatal length, 98.1; greatest width across upper toothrows, 89.2; mastoid breadth, 88; depth of mandible through coronoid process, 70.5." An adult male from Tahsis Canal, Nootka Sound, and an adult female from Quatsino Sound, Vancouver Island, respectively: Greatest length, 256.2, 241.9; condylobasal length, 239.6, 222.1; zygomatic breadth, 143.4, 132; squamosal constriction, 80.1, 79; width of rostrum, 44.8, 40.8; interorbital breadth, 50.1, 43.3; postorbital constriction, 45.6, 43; length of mandible, 183.5, 170.8; height of coronoid process, 72.1, 70.1; maxillary tooth row, crown length, 107.5, 101.8; upper carnassial, crown length (outer side), 26.2, 24.9, crown width, 15.9, 14.6; first upper molar, antero-posterior diameter, 17.6, 17.2, transverse diameter, 24.6, 21.7; lower carnassial, 30.4, 28.8.

Remarks.—The Vancouver Island wolf is most closely allied to *fuscus* of the adjacent mainland, as might be expected. Color differences appear to be well marked, however, as are the cranial and dental features, especially the size and form of the upper carnassial.

Specimens examined.—Total number, 12, all from Vancouver Island, as follows: Alberni, 1 (skull only);[1] Cowichan Lake, 1 (skull only);[1] Englishman's River, 1 (skull only);[2] Nootka Sound, 1 (skin only);[2] Quatsino, 2 (skulls only); Quatsino Sound, 4 (skulls only); Tahsis Canal, Nootka Sound, 2 (skulls only).[2]

CANIS LUPUS YOUNGI Goldman

Southern Rocky Mountain Wolf (pls. 117-118)

Canis lupus youngi Goldman, Mamm. Jour. 18 (1): 40, February 14, 1937.

Type locality.—Harts Draw, north slope of Blue Mountains, 20 miles northwest of Monticello, San Juan County, Utah.

Type specimen.—No. 224001, ♂ adult, skin and skull, U. S. National Museum (Biological Surveys collection); collected by Bert Brown Turner, December 11, 1916. X-catalog number 17413.

Distribution.—Formerly numerous in Rocky Mountain region from northern Utah and southern Wyoming south through Utah and western Colorado to northern Arizona and northern New Mexico;

[1]Brit. Col. Prov. Mus.
[2]Mus. Vert. Zool.

west irregularly to central Nevada (Gold Creek, Elko County), and sporadically at least to southeastern California (Providence Mountains). Now extremely rare and restricted mainly to the rugged territory bordering the upper Colorado River in southeastern Utah and southwestern Colorado. Intergraded on the north with *irremotus*, on the east with *nubilus*, and on the south with *mogollonensis*.

General characters.—A light-colored subspecies of medium to rather large size. Averaging larger than *nubilus* of the prairie region of Nebraska, with upper parts usually more suffused with buff; skull with supraoccipital region much less prominently projecting posteriorly. Similar in size to *irremotus* of the more northern Rocky Mountain region, but upper parts more suffused with buff; skull differs in detail, especially the greater breadth of the frontal region. Larger than *mogollonensis* of the Mogollon Mountain and plateau region of New Mexico and Arizona, with upper parts usually paler, less extensively overlaid with black and more suffused with buff.

Color.—Similar to that of *nubilus*, some specimens being indistinguishable, but upper parts usually more suffused with buff. An unusually light colored skin from Salt Creek (about 22 miles north of Fruita, Colorado), is buffy white over nearly entire body, except a narrow thin line of black-tipped hairs along median line of back, a black patch on tail gland, and a few dark hairs on tip of tail.

Skull.—Averaging larger than that of *nubilus;* rostrum and palate longer; supraoccipital shield broader, rising more steeply, less projecting posteriorly over foramen magnum, usually without the descending terminal hook so frequently present in *nubilus*. Similar in most dimensions to that of *irremotus*, but frontals usually broader between orbits and behind postorbital processes; supraoccipital shield tending to rise more steeply with lesser posterior projection of apex. Larger, more massive than that of *mogollonensis;* zygomata relatively less widely spreading; fronto-nasal profile usually straighter, the rostrum and nasals less depressed across middle; nasals flatter, the inner margins less decurved to form a V-shaped median groove; dentition relatively as well as actually heavier.

Measurements.—*Type* (approximated from tanned skin): Total length, 1800 mm.; tail vertebrae, 470; hind foot, 255. An adult male from Castle Peak (Burns Hole, 15 miles northeast of Eagle),

Colorado: Total length, 1777; height at shoulder, 806; weight, 125 pounds. An adult female from Salt Creek (22 miles north of Fruita), Colorado: Total length, 1701; height at shoulder, 724; weight, 110 pounds. An adult male from Laramie, Wyoming: Total length, 1600; tail vertebrae, 420; hind foot, 270. *Skull:* Type and an adult male from Salt Creek (about 22 miles north of Fruita), Colorado, respectively: Greatest length, 258.5, 265; condylobasal length, 243.5, 248.5; zygomatic breadth, 136.7, 148; squamosal constriction, 82.8, 82.5; width of rostrum, 47.7, 48.2; interorbital breadth, 44.3, 51.5; postorbital constriction, 40.6, 45.4; length of mandible, 187.7, 193.4; height of coronoid process, 77.1, 82.1; maxillary tooth row, 107.8, 110.3; upper carnassial, crown length (outer side), 26.5, 25.2, crown width, 14.1, 13.4; first upper molar, antero-posterior diameter, 17.3, 17.1, transverse diameter, 23.7, 24.8; lower carnassial, 30, 29.1. Two adult females from Piceance, Rio Blanco County, Colorado, respectively: Greatest length, 244.5, 242.8; condylobasal length, 228.7, 226.5; zygomatic breadth, 130.9, 128.8; squamosal constriction, 73.2, 72.5; width of rostrum, 42.7, 40; interorbital breadth, 43.2, 44.1; postorbital constriction, 39, 39.9; length of mandible, 175.8, 172.2; height of coronoid process, 70.6, 70.4; maxillary tooth row, crown length, 106.7, 104; upper carnassial, crown length (outer side), 24.6, 24.5, crown width, 12.7, 13.4; first upper molar, antero-posterior diameter, 16.1, 15.3, transverse diameter, 22, 22.1; lower carnassial, 28, 27.8.

Remarks.—*C. l. youngi* was evidently the wolf of the southern part of the Rocky Mountains and high adjacent plains, displacing *nubilus* west of the prairie region of Nebraska and Kansas. It appears to have been most typical in the Colorado River drainage along the western side of the continental divide. Its range marked the western limit of wolves in the arid Southwest. Small numbers extended into Nevada. One only, perhaps a wanderer from southern Nevada, was trapped in the Providence Mountains, southeastern California, in 1922.

Specimens examined.—Total number, 111, as follows:

California: Providence Mountains (Old Barnett Mine, 12 miles west of Lanfair), 1 (skull only).[1]

Colorado: Castle Peak (Burns Hole, 15 miles northeast of Eagle), 1 (skin only);[2] Chico Creek (near Dove Creek), Dolores County, 1; Glade Park (Black Ridge), Mesa County, 3; Piceance, Rio Blanco County, 3 (1 skull without skin); Pueblo (20 miles northeast), 2 (skulls only); Redvale (25 miles northwest), 1 (skull only);[2] Salt Creek (about 22 miles north of Fruita), 2;[3] Sulphur, Rio Blanco County, 1 (skull only); Turman's Creek, Rio Blanco County, 1; West Creek, Garfield County, 2.

Nevada: Gold Creek, Elko County, 1 (skull only).[1]

New Mexico: Abiquiu, 3;[4] Canjilon, 4; Cuba, 3; Dulce (35 to 45 miles southwest), 14; El Rito, 2; El Vado (20 miles south), Rio Arriba County, 6; Haynes, 6; Jemez, 1; Jemez Mountains, 1; Lamy, 2 (1 skull without skin); La Plata, San Juan County, 1; San Mateo, 5; San Mateo Mountains, 1; Senorito, 12;[5] Tusas, 1.

Utah: Duchesne, 3; Greasewood Valley (10 miles southeast of LaSal, San Juan County), 1; Grouse Creek, Boxelder County, 1 (skull only); Harts Draw (type locality—north slope of Blue Mountains, 20 miles northwest of Monticello), San Juan County, 2; South Eden, Weber County, 1.

Wyoming: Dry Lake (15 miles north of Rawlins), 1 (skull only);[2] Federal, 7 (2 skulls without skins); Jelm, Albany County, 5 (2 skins without skulls); Laramie, 2 (1 skull without skin); Rock Springs, 5 (4 skulls without skins); Wagon Creek (Southwestern Wyoming), 2.

CANIS LUPUS MOGOLLONENSIS Goldman
Mogollon Mountain Wolf (Pls. 119-120)

Canis lupus mogollonensis Goldman, Mamm. Jour. 18 (1): 43, Feb. 14, 1937.

Type locality.—S. A. Creek, 10 miles northwest of Luna, Catron County, N. Mex.

Type specimen.—No. 224548, ♂ adult, skin and skull, U. S. National Museum (Biological Surveys collection); collected by Bart Burnam, July 1, 1916. X-catalog 18119.

---

[1]Mus. Vert. Zool.
[2]Stanley P. Young Collection.
[3]One in Stanley P. Young Collection.
[4]One skull without skin in Field Mus. Nat. Hist.
[5]Four skulls without skins in Field Mus. Nat. Hist.

Distribution.—Formerly the Mogollon Plateau region, extending nearly across central Arizona, and east through the Mogollon Mountains of central western New Mexico; now rare, if not extinct. On the north *mogollonensis* gave way to *youngi*, and east of the Rio Grande to *nubilus* and *monstrabilis*. On the south it passed rather abruptly into *baileyi*, which still inhabits the Sierra Madre of Mexico.

General characters.—A rather small, usually dark-colored, but varying to nearly white, subspecies. Similar in general to *youngi* of the Rocky Mountain region to the northward, but smaller and usually darker in color. Decidedly larger and usually lighter in color than *baileyi* of the Sierra Madre of Mexico. Closely resembles *monstrabilis* of Texas, but differs in cranial characters, especially the more elevated frontal region. Differs from *nubilus* of Nebraska mainly in darker color and cranial details.

Color.—*Winter pelage:* Upper parts from nape to rump varying from dull white to "cinnamon-buff," rather heavily overlaid with black; short pelage on middle of face a mixture of "light buff" and black, tending to become "cinnamon-buff" on top of head; under parts and inner sides of legs mainly dull white, the under side of neck thinly mixed with black in some specimens; outer sides of legs varying from "pale pinkish buff" to "cinnamon-buff," usually becoming somewhat paler on feet; anterior surface of forearm with a narrow dusky line present in some specimens, absent in others; upper surface of muzzle near "cinnamon-buff"; ears "cinnamon-buff" to "ochraceous tawny," tinged with black; tail above similar to back, the black patch on tail gland conspicuous; tail dull white below on basal two-thirds, becoming more or less suffused with buff toward tip, which is black all around with a few white hairs often intermixed. In an unusually colored skin from 50 miles west of Chloride, New Mexico, the upper parts from muzzle to base of tail are overlaid with clear "pinkish cinnamon" instead of black; a few scattered black hairs appear on the upper surface and tip of the tail.

Skull.—Resembles that of *baileyi*, but is larger, more massive; rostrum distinctly broader. Smaller, less massive than that of *youngi;* zygomata relatively more widely spreading; inner margins of nasals tending to decurve more strongly to form a deeper V-shaped median groove; sagittal and lambdoid crests forming supraoccipital shield usually projecting farther posteriorly over foramen magnum; dentition lighter. Very similar in size to that of *nubilus*, but usually less flattened; rostrum more depressed near middle, sloping upward more steeply to frontals; inner margins of nasals usually more decurved. Differs from that of *monstrabilis* mainly in less elevated frontal region.

Measurements.—Two adult males, one from Fairview and the other from Reserve (25 miles northwest), N. Mex., respectively: Total length, 1,600, 1,470; tail vertebrae, 406, 420; hind foot, 254, 255. Two adult females from Chloride (24 miles northwest), respectively: Total length, 1,455, 1,480; tail vertebrae, 400, ------; hind foot, 245, 235; weight, 58, 49 pounds. An adult female from Escudilla Mountains, Ariz., 1,416; 394; 241. *Skull: Type* (male) and an adult male from Escudilla Mountains, Ariz., respectively: Greatest length, 253.5, 257; condylobasal length, 236.3, 238.7; zygomatic breadth, 142.1, 137.5; squamosal constriction, 80.8, 78.1; width of rostrum, 43.7, 44; interorbital breadth, 46.1, 45.2; postorbital constriction, 36.8, 41.6; length of mandible, 184.7, 184.5; maxillary tooth row, 107, 105.6; upper carnassial, crown length (outer side), 25.1, 24.4, crown width, 13.9, 14.2; first upper molar, antero-posterior diameter, 16.7, 15.9, transverse diameter, 22.8, 22.9; lower carnassial, crown length, 30, 27.9. Two adult females, a topotype and one from Escudilla Mountains, Ariz., respectively: Greatest length, 240.2, 238.3; condylobasal length, 222.4, 219; zygomatic breadth, 133.5, 129.7; squamosal constriction, 75.2, 73.5; width of rostrum, 44.1, 42.1; interorbital breadth, 46, 41.1; postorbital constriction, 42.3, 39.8; length of mandible, 174, 168.7; maxillary tooth row, 101.3, 96.1; upper carnassial, crown length (outer side), 24.7, 23.9, crown width, 14.3, 13.5; first upper molar, antero-posterior diameter, 16.7, 15.9, transverse diameter, 22.9, lower carnassial, crown length, 27.8, 27.4.

Remarks.—The Mogollon Mountain wolf is somewhat intermediate in characters, as well as in geographic position, between *youngi* and the smaller race *baileyi* which ranged north from the Sierra Madre and the high plateau region of Mexico into southeastern Arizona and southwestern New Mexico. It stands somewhat apart in combination of features, however, as a fairly well-marked regional race. Evidence of intergradation is clear, but the geographic transition from *mogollonensis* to the neighboring races, especially to *youngi* in northern New Mexico, and from *mogollonen-*

sis to *baileyi* in the southwestern part of the State, was remarkably abrupt.

Specimens examined.—Total number, 111, as follows:

Arizona: Aguila, Maricopa County, 1 (skull only);[1] Cibecue, 1; Clifton, 3; Cooney Tank (south of Springerville), 3; Escudilla Mountains, 5 (skulls only); Galiuro Mountains, 1 (skull only); Heber, 1; Kendrick Peak, 1 (skull only); Peloncillo Mountains, 1 (skull only).[1]

New Mexico: Alma (25 miles southwest), 1; Black Range, Socorro County, 7 (2 skulls only); Chloride (24-50 miles west), 14 (2 skins without skulls; 2 skulls without skins); Capitan Mountains, 2 (skulls only); Datil, 1; Datil Mountains, 1 (skull only); Datil National Forest, 2 (skulls only); Fairview, 5; Gila National Forest, 39 (skulls only); Head of Mimbres River, 2 (1 skull without skin); Hurley, 1; Luna, 2; Magdalena, 4; Monticello, 1; Reserve, 3 (2 skulls without skins); Reserve (20 miles northwest), 2 (skulls only); S. A. Creek (type locality—10 miles northwest of Luna), 1; Silver City, 6.

CANIS LUPUS MONSTRABILIS Goldman

Texas Gray Wolf (Pls. 121-122)

Canis lupus monstrabilis Goldman, Mamm. Jour. 18 (1): 42, Feb. 14, 1937.

Type locality.—Ten miles south of Rankin, Upton County, Texas.

Type specimen.—No. 209497, ♂ adult, skin and skull, U. S. National Museum (Biological Surveys collection); collected by W. F. DeLong, September 3, 1915. X-catalog number 12646.

Distribution.—Formerly southern and most of western Texas (apparently replaced by *baileyi* in extreme western part), southeastern New Mexico, and south into northeastern Mexico (Matamoros); now probably extinct. Intergraded on the north with *nubilus*, and on the west with *mogollonensis* and *baileyi*.

---

[1]Stanley P. Young Collection.

General characters.—Size medium; color usually dark, but varying to nearly white; skull with highly arched frontal region. Resembles *baileyi* of the Sierra Madre of Chihuahua but is larger and grayer, less strongly inclined toward buffy or tawny along flanks and on outer surfaces of limbs. Similar in size to *nubilus* of Nebraska, and *mogollonensis* of New Mexico, but usually darker than the former; pelage thinner and coarser; cranial characters, especially the more highly arched frontal region, differing from either.

Color.—About as in *mogollonensis.* An unusually colored skin from Mayhill, New Mexico, taken in April, is entirely pale yellowish, except a few black hairs on tail gland and along upper terminal two-thirds of tail.

Skull.—Most closely resembles that of *baileyi* in general form, but is decidedly larger and heavier; frontal region usually more highly arched; nasals strongly depressed along inner sides, tending to form a deep median groove as in *baileyi.* Similar in size to that of *nubilus,* but less flattened; frontal region more highly arched and fully inflated; nasals more depressed along median line. Differs from that of *mogollonensis* in higher, more inflated frontal region.

Measurements.—*Type* (adult male, approximated from tanned skin): Total length, 1,620 mm.; tail vertebrae, 423, hind foot, 230. Two adult females from 15 miles north of Elk, New Mexico, respectively: Total length, 1,372, 1,499; tail vertebrae, 419, 406; hind foot, 241, 254. An adult female from Mescalero, New Mexico: 1,422; 368; 222. *Skull: Type* (male) and an adult male topotype, respectively: Greatest length, 260, 255.5; condylobasal length, 236.8, 237.8; zygomatic breadth, 137.5, 131.5; squamosal constriction, 80.4, 74.7; width of rostrum, 43.7, 46.2; interorbital breadth, 45.4, 46.9; postorbital constriction, 39.5, 40.7; length of mandible, 184.4, 178.2; height of coronoid process, 83.9, 79.1; maxillary tooth row, crown length, 103.8, 106.3; upper carnassial, crown length (outer side), 24.7, 25.8, crown width, 14.3, 14.8; first upper molar, antero-posterior diameter, 15.1, 17.1, transverse diameter, 22.5, 24.2; lower carnassial, 28, 30. Two adult female topotypes, respectively: Greatest length, 250.4, 251.7; condylobasal length, 231.3, 228.1, zygomatic breadth, 138.5, 126; squamosal constriction, 78.1, 74.3; width of rostrum, 45.3, 39.3; interorbital breadth, 45.2, 45.1; postorbital constriction, 40.3, 40.3; length of mandible, 178.8,

171.3; height of coronoid process, 73.5, 69.2; maxillary tooth row, crown length, 103.3, 104.2; upper carnassial, crown length (outer side), 24.8, 24.2, crown width, 13.8, 13.8; first upper molar, antero-posterior diameter, 17.1, 17, transverse diameter, 22.1, 22.5; lower carnassial, crown length, 28, 27.7.

Remarks.—The distribution of the Texas gray wolf, extending to northeastern Mexico, marks the southern limit of the range of the species south over the great plains. Gray wolves were formerly plentiful in Texas, but apparently were never very numerous in northeastern Mexico. In central Texas, the range of the gray wolf meets that of the Texas red wolf (*Canis niger rufus*), but these forms are specifically distinct. The gray wolf is distinguished externally from the red wolf by decidedly larger size and more robust form. It is usually grayer, less rufescent as the common name implies, but owing to wide variation in both species, color is not always diagnostic. The skull of the Texas gray wolf, compared with that of the Texas red wolf, is much more massive and more highly arched. The dentition is very similar, but somewhat simpler. The larger molariform teeth above and below tend to be less deeply cleft, with less prominent cusp development. In the upper carnassial the antero-internal cusp when present is usually smaller, and is less frequently obsolete or absent. In the first upper molar, the large external cusps forming the high part of the crown are less unequal in size, the posterior one being less distinctly the smaller of the two. A small postero-median cusp in the first upper molar, absent or very small in the gray wolf, is more prominently developed in the red wolf. The posterior upper molars are relatively smaller than in *rufus* as a rule.

Specimens examined.—Total number, 41, as follows:

New Mexico: Capitan Mountains, (skulls only); Elk, 2; Mayhill, 1; Mescalero, 2; Sacramento Mountains, 7.

Tamaulipas: Matamoros, 1 (skull only).

Texas: Big Lake, Reagan County, 1; Fort Richardson, 1 (skull only); Guadalupe Mountains, 1 (skull only); Kimble County, 1 (skull only); Llano, 1 (skull only); Monahans, 1 (skull only); Nueces River, Edward County, 1 (skull only); Ozona N. H. Ranch, 25 miles west), 10; Rankin, 9 (10 miles south, 3; Harris Ranch, 18 miles southeast, 6).

CANIS LUPUS BAILEYI Nelson and Goldman
Mexican Wolf (Pls. 123-124)

Canis nubilus baileyi Nelson and Goldman, Mamm. Jour. 10 (2): 165, May 9, 1929.

Canis lupus baileyi Goldman, Mamm. Jour. 18 (1): 45, Feb. 14, 1937.

Type locality.—Colonia Garcia (about 60 miles southwest of Casas Grandes), Chihuahua, Mexico (altitude 6,700 feet).

Type specimen.—No. 98312, ♂ adult, skin and skull, U. S. National Museum (Biological Surveys collection); collected by E. W. Nelson and E. A. Goldman, July 10, 1899. Original number 13895.

Distribution.—Sierra Madre and adjoining tableland region of western Mexico, formerly extending north to southeastern Arizona (Fort Bowie), southwestern New Mexico (Hatch), and western Texas (Fort Davis), south to the Valley of Mexico; still living in the northern part of the Sierra Madre, the exact southern and eastern limits undetermined.

General characters.—Size smallest of the American subspecies of *Canis lupus;* color dark; skull small, with slender rostrum and widely spreading zygomata. Size smaller and color usually darker than *mogollonensis* of New Mexico. Compared with *monstrabilis* of Texas: Smaller and less grayish, more strongly inclining toward buffy or tawny along flanks and on outer surfaces of limbs.

Color.—*Winter pelage:* Upper parts varying from "pinkish buff" to "pale pinkish buff" rather heavily overlaid with black; short pelage on head and face, a grizzled mixture of varying shades of buff and black; upper surface of muzzle and ears "cinnamon-buff" to tawny, more or less mixed with black; under parts, inner sides of legs, and lower surface of tail mainly "light buff" to "pinkish buff"; outer sides of legs ranging from rich "tawny" to "pinkish buff," becoming paler on feet; tail above about like back, with the usual black patch on gland, the tip black all around. In the usual pattern of coloration, as shown by topotypes, the muzzle, top of head, ears, and outer sides of limbs incline toward tawny, but these parts vary in occasional pallid examples to near "pale pinkish buff." A skin from Helvetia, Arizona, is unusually rich rufescent. The upper surface of the muzzle and the ears are deep "tawny," the upper parts in general are suffused with "cinnamon," and the under parts are "cinnamon-buff." One from 18 miles east of Parker Canyon, Huachuca Mountains, Arizona, presents an unusual mixture of black and gray, with the black predominating above and below.

Skull.—Closely resembling that of *monstrabilis* in general form, but decidedly smaller and more slender in proportions; zygomata widely spreading, frontal region rather high and nasals depressed along inner sides, much as in *monstrabilis;* dentition rather light. Similar to that of *mogollonensis,* but distinctly smaller, less massive; rostrum relatively slenderer.

Measurements.—Type specimen (adult male): Total length, 1,570 mm.; tail vertebrae, 410; hind foot, 260. An adult male from Canelo Hills, 4 miles south of Canille, Arizona: Total length, 1,520; tail vertebrae, 400; hind foot, 270, weight, 98 lbs. An adult female from same vicinity; weight, 65 lbs. An adult male from Walnut Canyon, 35 miles southeast of Animas, New Mexico: Total length, 1,486; weight, 51 lbs. *Skull:* Two adult males, type specimen, and a topotype: Greatest length, 232.1, 246.5; condylobasal length, 221.4, 231.5; zygomatic breadth, 129.7, 144.7; squamosal constriction, 74.8, 82.8; width of rostrum, 39.5, 43.4; interorbital breadth, 44.5, 46.2; postorbital constriction, 38.9, 44.8; length of mandible, 171, 183; height of coronoid process, 70.4, 77.8; maxillary tooth row, crown length, 100.2, 104.2; upper carnassial, crown length (outer side), 24.7, 25.1, crown width, 12, 14.6; first upper molar, antero-posterior diameter, 15.8, 15.9, transverse diameter, 21.5, 22.2; lower carnassial, crown length, 27.2, 27. Two adult females from type locality: Greatest length, 224.4, 234.2; condylobasal length, 209.5, 215.9; zygomatic breadth, 126.1, 130.9; squamosal constriction, 74.1, 74.6; width of rostrum, 37.9, 38.1; interorbital breadth, 43.1, 40; postorbital constriction, 42.8, 40.3; length of nasals, 165, 168; height of coronoid process, 69, 69; maxillary tooth row, 95.4, 99.3; upper carnassial, crown length (outer side), 24.5, 23.4, crown width, 12.2, 12.1; first upper molar, antero-posterior diameter, 15.1, 15.5, transverse diameter, 20.4, 19.5; lower carnassial, 26.3, 24.9.

Remarks.—The range of *baileyi* marks the southern limits of the gray wolf group in geographic distribution. Wolves formerly occupied the plateau or tableland region to its southern extremity near the Valley of Mexico. Owing to their inroads on domestic stock, strychnine was used, and elaborate pit traps were constructed. As a result, the wolves were believed for many years to have been extingunished on the southern part of the plateau, but remained fairly numerous in the Sierra Madre as far south as Durango. Some recent reports have, however, indicated their reappearance in the mountains not far north of the Valley of Mexico. The Mexican wolf is similar in small size to geographically remote *lycaon*, and both are notable for the slenderness of the rostral portion of the skull; but they differ in other respects. In *baileyi* the zygomata are decidedly heavier than in *lycaon*. In southeastern Arizona and southwestern New Mexico, *baileyi* intergraded with *mogollonensis*. Although wolves are known to wander over considerable distances, the transition from *baileyi* to *mogollonensis* is remarkably abrupt. An adult female was recently killed 16 miles northwest of Fort Davis, Tex., in a section from which wolves were believed to have been extirpated. The animal is clearly referable to *baileyi*, which was previously unknown from Texas, and was taken under conditions suggesting that it may have been a wanderer from northern Chihuahua.

Specimens examined.—Total number, 61, as follows:

Arizona: Arivaca, 3;[1] Canelo Hills (4 to 6 miles south of Canille), 2; Chiricahua, 1; Fort Bowie, 1; Helvetia, 2; Parker Canyon (18 miles east, southwest side Huachuca Mountains), 1; Parker Ranch (Santa Rita Mountains), 2; Patagonia (15 miles west), 1; Santa Rita Mountains, 1 (skull only); Seep Springs (35 miles east of Douglas), 1.

Chihuahua: Casas Grandes, 2 (skulls only);[2] Colonia Garcia, 13 (5 skulls without skins); Colonia Juarez, 1; Gallego, 1; Rio Alamos, 1;[3] Sierra Madre (near Guadalupe y Calvo), 1 (skull only).

Durango: El Salto, 1.

New Mexico: Animas, 4; Animas Valley, 1; Animas Mountains, 1; Cloverdale, 7 (2 skulls without skins); Hachita, 8; Hatch, 1; San Luis Mountains, 2.

Sonora: Santa Cruz, 1 (skull only).

Texas: Fort Davis (16 miles northwest), 1.

---

[1]Stanley P. Young Collection.
[2]Field Mus. Nat. Hist.
[3]Amer. Mus. Nat. Hist.

CANIS LUPUS BERNARDI Anderson
Banks Island Tundra Wolf

Canis lupus bernardi Anderson, Journ. Mamm. 24 (3): 389, August 17, 1943.

[*Canis lupus*] *banksianus* Anderson, Journ. Mamm. 24 (3): 390, August 17, 1943.

Type locality.—Cape Kellett, southwestern part of Banks Island, District of Franklin, Northwest Territories, lat. about 72° N., long. 125° W., Canada.

Type specimen.—No. 2796, ♂ adult, skin and skull, National Museum of Canada; collected by Peter Bernard, February 27, 1916.

Distribution.—Known only from Banks Island, but probably occurs also on Victoria Island, at least on the northwestern part, as suggested by Anderson.

General characters.—From original description: "Color mostly whitish, with less buffy than shown by average specimens of *mackenzii* and *manningi;* all specimens examined showing a greater or lesser number of blackish-tipped hairs forming a more or less distinct median dorsal line. A rather large rangy wolf, with long narrow skull, slender rostrum and exceedingly large upper and lower carnassials."

Color.—From original description: "In the type specimen the general color is white with no yellowish tinge, except on back of ears. Top of head from nose to nape with hairs dusky gray at base and with short white tips, giving the hair a clean grayish appearance; a darker gray streak under each eye; cheeks and side of nose dull whitish, more grayish under chin. Mane very long, with hairs whitish at base, distal to this a broad black band, sometimes with white tip, but many of the hairs have a second black band at tip, making a hair with four distinct bands; blackish-tipped dorsal area overlapping on shoulders and hips, narrower medially and fading out on shoulders and thighs; tail thickly intermixed on dorsal surface with black-tipped hairs; white below and with tip black and the usual black spot on top of tail; feet white; claws blackish. No. 3505, adult female (allotype), Dec. 15, 1915, is almost completely white; ears light buffy at base, duller at tips; a faint trace of black-tipped hairs along median dorsal line from nape to tail; tail white, with the usual black spot on top, but with no black at tip of tail; claws horn color. One additional male and one adult female and a subadult male and female are between the above extremes. One young wolf of the year, taken September 9, 1914, at Cape Kellett, is remarkable in having no buffy coloring; whitish, with a fairly well-defined median dorsal area produced by sparse black-tipped hairs on dull whitish background; tail white with a few black-tipped hairs, black spot on top and black tip; in almost all respects a miniature of the adult male type."

Skull.—From original description: "Distinguished by great comparative length, narrow zygomatic breadth, long, slender rostrum, and exceedingly large carnassials. Nasals narrower than in *tundrarum* and extending much farther behind posterior extensions of maxillaries and with shorter distance across postorbital processes. From its nearest neighbor on the north, *Canis lupus arctos* (of Melville Island, Sverdrup Islands, and Ellesmere Island) with which it might be expected to have the closest relationship, *bernardi* differs the most widely, with skull of only slightly less length, but much less massive, with narrower rostrum, lesser zygomatic breadth, lighter lower mandible, of less depth and more nearly straight. The tooth-row is about the same length as in *arctos*, but the molars and premolars are all longer, broader, and heavier; canines and incisors project forward at a noticeably greater angle. Coronoid process slender, sloping backward more than in *mackenzii* and *tundrarum*; ramus of mandible lower than in *mackenzii* and nearly straight as in *tundrarum*, but slightly less in depth and heavier horizontally; coronoid processes usually more truncated at tip than in these other races."

Measurements.—From original description: "Tanned skins of type, and no. 3506, adult female, allotype, measure, respectively: Total length, 1,870, 1,562 mm.; tail, 366, 362; hind foot, 261, 235. Field measurements of one male and one female which did not reach the museum are: Total length, 1,625, 1,422; tail, 432, 406; hind foot, 305, 254; height at shoulders, 813, 660; depth of chest, 406, 305; girth, 736, 660." *Skull* (type, from table accompanying original description): Greatest length, 252; condylobasal length, 233; zygomatic breadth, 136; maxillary tooth row, 107; upper carnassial, crown length, 28, crown width, 16; first upper molar, anteroposterior diameter, 18, transverse diameter, 25; lower carnassial, crown length, 31. Average of 3 adult males and 2 adult females (same table), respectively, from type locality: Greatest length,

245.3, 238.8; condylobasal length, 232, 219; zygomatic breadth, 129.3, 120; maxillary tooth row, 106, 101.4; upper carnassial, crown length, 27.4, 26, crown width, 16.6, 15.4; first upper molar, antero-posterior diameter, 17.6, 17.4, transverse diameter, 24.2, 27; lower carnassial, crown length, 29.7, 29.6.

Remarks.—No specimens of this race have been examined by me. It was based by the describer on 6 skins and 8 skulls from the type locality.

In the table of cranial measurements given by Anderson (*op. cit.*) the name *banksianus* appears for specimens from Banks Island. The name was evidently used inadvertently for *bernardi,* of which it is, therefore, a synonym.

CANIS LUPUS MACKENZII Anderson
Mackenzie Tundra Wolf

Canis lupus mackenzii Anderson, Journ. Mamm. 24 (3): 388, August 17, 1943.

Type locality.—Imnanuit, west of Kater Point, Bathurst Inlet, District of Mackenzie, Northwest Territories, lat. 67° 44′ 20″ N., long. 109° 04′ 03″ W., Canada.

Type specimen.—No. 2792, ♂ adult, skin and skull, National Museum of Canada; collected by R. M. Anderson, May 14, 1916. Original number 658.

Distribution.—Arctic coast and tundra region from west side of Mackenzie River delta, east to undetermined limits beyond Bathurst Inlet, south to the northern side of Great Bear Lake.

General characters.—From original description: "Color variable, adults more frequently white, but adult specimens are often buffy with dorsal band of black-tipped hairs; some specimens are almost black. Considerably smaller than *occidentalis,* slightly smaller than *hudsonicus, tundrarum* and *bernardi,* and considerably larger than *manningi.*"

Color.—From original description: "The type specimen is entirely yellowish white with exception of brownish black spot on dorsal side of tail; claws pale horn color. . . . An adult male, N. M. C. No. 2791, taken at Port Epworth, Coronation Gulf, July 20, 1915, is yellowish white, with top of head tawny brown, mixed with black-tipped hairs; neck sparsely black-tipped, and dorsal region with most of hairs black-tipped; legs buffy brown anteriorly, white posteriorly. An adult female, N. M. C. No. 4868, taken on Kogaryuak River, Coronation Gulf, June 10, 1917, by Jos. F. Bernard, is mostly slaty gray, with hairs on back having paler brownish tips; legs and under parts mostly plumbeous or dusky."

Skull.—From original description: "Much larger than in *manningi* of Baffin Island, smaller than in *hudsonicus* from west of Hudson Bay, and *tundrarum* from northern Alaska, with teeth about the same size as in the last two forms but larger than in *manningi.* Compared with *bernardi* from Banks Islands, the teeth of *mackenzii* are much smaller, particularly the upper and lower carnassials. Ramus of mandible short and heavy, with lower edge of ramus much more convex than in *tundrarum;* coronoid processes lower than in *tundrarum* and with tips slightly recurved posteriorly."

Measurements. — From original description: "Approximated from tanned skin of male: Total length, 1,676 mm.; tail vertebrae, 361; hind foot, 247. Specimens of this race measured in the flesh by the writer are as follows: No. 2789, Rae River, west of Coronation Gulf: Total length, 1,570; tail vertebrae, 385; hind foot, 281; weight, 78 pounds. No. 2551, ♀ adult and one other ♀ taken the same month on lower Coppermine River measured, respectively: Total length, 1,565, 1,460; tail vertebrae, 425, 470; hind foot, 285, 295." *Skull* (type, from original description): Greatest length, 248; condylobasal length, 226; zygomatic breadth, 131.8; maxillary tooth row, 102; upper carnassial, crown length, 26.2, crown width, 14; first upper molar, antero-posterior diameter, 17, transverse diameter, 22; lower carnassial, crown length, 30. Average of 3 adult males and 2 adult females (original description), respectively, from Bathurst Inlet, Coronation Gulf: Greatest length, 251, 241; condylobasal length, 228.8, 223.5; zygomatic breadth, 132.8, 129.8; maxillary tooth row, 102.6, 101.5; upper carnassial, crown length, 26.7, 25.4, crown width, 13.9, 13.5; first upper molar, antero-posterior diameter, 17.3, 17, transverse diameter, 22.3, 21.8; lower carnassial, crown length, 29, 28.

Remarks.—The description of *mackenzii,* recently published, was received too late for detailed consideration of the status of the race in relation to neighboring forms. The new race appears to be smaller than the other continental forms with which it must intergrade. The specimens examined are in part the same as those listed by Anderson.

Specimens examined. — Total number, 8, all from Mackenzie District as follows: Coronation Gulf (south side), 1; Dease River, 1 (skull only);[1] Fort Anderson, 1 (skull only); Fort Good Hope, 1; Great Bear Lake, 1 (skull only);[1] Langton Bay, 1 (skull only);[1] Peel River, 1 (skull only), Reliance, Great Slave Lake, 1 (skull only).[1]

CANIS LUPUS MANNINGI Anderson
Baffin Island Tundra Wolf

Canis lupus manningi Anderson, Jour. Mamm. 24 (3): 392, August 17, 1943.

Type locality.—Hantzsch River, east side of Foxe Basin, west side of Baffin Island, District of Franklin, Northwest Territories, lat. about 67° N., long. 24° W., Canada.

Type specimen.—No. 17236, ♀ young adult, skin and skull, National Museum of Canada; collected by Tom H. Manning, December 7, 1938. Original number 70.

Distribution.—Baffin Island, and probably smaller neighboring islands.

General characters.—From original description: "Considerably smaller than any of the other Arctic wolves, but with somewhat larger skull and teeth than in *Canis lupus labradorius*, from south of Hudson Strait. Color somewhat variable, but adults are generally white, and juveniles and subadults have more or less buffy, often with black-tipped hairs along median dorsal line."

Color.—From original description: "The type specimen has hair mostly pure white, with very faint tint of buffy on nose; ears pale buffy at tips; dorsal region with faint buffy tint; feet and tail white; tail with black spot on top but with no black at tip. Two subadult females (nos. 65 and 69, Manning collection) caught at the same place and supposed to belong to the same family group as the type specimen, have top of head faintly tinged with reddish buff, ears similar; a narrow black edging around lower lip and posterior portion of upper lip; back with longitudinal wash of yellowish buff in-

[1]Amer. Mus. Nat. Hist.

clined to reddish, with a few dorsal hairs blackish at tip; black spot on top of tail and tip of tail blackish. No. 68, also a young female, has more grayish on head, with a narrow dorsal band intermixed with blackish-tipped hairs; sides buffy; under parts and tail pure white."

Skull.—From original description: "Much smaller and less massive than in *arctos* in all respects, with rostrum more slender and zygomata proportionately much smaller; bullae much smaller; carnassials much shorter and less massive; tooth-row shorter and all teeth smaller. Compared with *mackenzii*, *manningi* has much smaller skull and teeth, palate more narrow and with posterior end of nasals projecting less far behind maxillaries; bullae smaller, more elongated and subtriangular. Compared with *tundrarum*, from which it is still farther separated geographically, *manningi* shows even greater difference in size; coronoid process much lower than in *tundrarum* and sloping backward, rounded at tip."

Measurements.—From original description: "Type: Total length, 1,003 mm.; tail vertebrae, 389; hind foot, 262. Adult male, no. 94, N.M.C., Ashe Inlet (from tanned skin) and one female adult from Foxe Basin (from tanned skin), respectively: Total length, 1,588, 1,524; tail, 387, 368; hind foot, 191, 191." *Skull* (type, from original description): Greatest length, 231; condylobasal length, 214; zygomatic breadth, 121; maxillary tooth row, 94; upper carnassial, crown length, 22, crown width, 11.8; first upper molar, antero-posterior diameter, 16.6, transverse diameter, 19.8; lower carnassial, crown length, 27.6. Average of 2 adult males and 3 adult females (original description), respectively, from Baffin Island: Greatest length, 253.5, 247.8; condylobasal length, 227.5, 224.3; zygomatic breadth, 137.5, 129.5; maxillary tooth row, 103.4, 101.7; upper carnassial, crown length, 24.3, 24.3, crown width, 13.9, 13.5; first upper molar, antero-posterior diameter, 16, 16.1, transverse diameter, 20.3, 21.6; lower carnassial, crown length, 27.9, 27.3.

Remarks.—No specimens of *manningi* have been examined by me. The subspecies was based on 13 specimens from various localities on Baffin Island. Owing to isolation of habitat and other geographic considerations, the name may be expected to represent a well-marked race.

XVI

CANIS NIGER AND SUBSPECIES

CANIS NIGER Bartram
[Synonymy under subspecies]

Distribution.—Formerly Mississippi River Valley and affluents, north at least to Warsaw, Ill., and Wabash, Ind., south through southern Missouri, eastern Oklahoma, Arkansas, and doubtless western Kentucky and western Tennessee to the Gulf Coast in Louisiana and Mississippi; west from the coastal region to the Pecos River Valley in Texas, and east through Alabama to the Atlantic Coast in Georgia and Florida; exact limits undetermined. Now restricted mainly to the Ozark Mountain region in Missouri, Arkansas, and southeastern Oklahoma and a few outlying sections in Louisiana and Texas.

General characters.—Size rather small; form slender; color inclining toward tawny, especially on muzzle, ears, and outer surfaces of limbs; skull slender; first upper molar with a distinct cingulum on outer side. In typical form, *niger*, resembling *Canis latrans* externally, but larger, more robust; pelage usually somewhat coarser; rhinarium and feet larger; tawny element in coloration more predominant; cranial characters very similar in general but differing in detail. Differs from *Canis lupus* in smaller size and much slenderer

Figure 15. Distribution of subspecies of *Canis niger*

1. *Canis niger niger*
2. *C. n. gregoryi*
3. *C. n. rufus*

proportions, as a rule (*C. n. niger* and *C. n. gregoryi*, large subspecies of *niger*, are similar in size to *C. l. lycaon* and *C. l. baileyi*, small subspecies of *lupus*); rhinarium and foot pads smaller; general coloration more tawny; cranial features usually quite distinctive.

Color.—Normal phase: Upper parts in general a varying mixture of "cinnamon-buff," "cinnamon," or "tawny" with gray and black; dorsal area more or less heavily overlaid with black, and black is conspicuously massed over the tail gland; muzzle, ears, and outer surfaces of limbs usually distinctly tawny; light post-humeral and nuchal bands varying in distinctness about as in the true wolves and coyotes; forearm with a narrow, more or less conspicuous, black line on anterior surface (present also in true wolf and coyote); under parts varying from whitish to "pinkish buff"; tail tipped with black. *Black phase:* Upper parts, limbs, and tail above black or brownish black, thinly and inconspicuously mixed with all white or white-banded hairs; light post-humeral and nuchal bands faintly indicated; under side of neck and pectoral region similar to back, except for a small, nearly pure white median pectoral spot sometimes present; inguinal area, inner sides of thighs, and under side of tail near base more extensively mixed with white. *Young (in first pelage)*: Near "wood brown" above and below, somewhat lighter on inguinal region, darkened over back by brownish black-tipped hairs; ears and forearms tinged with "cinnamon."

Skull.—Size comparatively small and form slender. Closely approaches that of *C. latrans* in form, but is usually larger and differs in combination of details; cranium higher; rostrum deeper; zygomata more widely spreading; supraoccipital shield tending to project farther posteriorly; jugal heavier, more deeply inserted in maxilla, the orbital border more distinctly thickened and tending to bow outward; occipital condyles usually extending farther transversely; auditory bullae usually larger; dentition very similar, but first upper molar with postero-external cusp more nearly equaling antero-external cusp. Comparison with *C. lupus:* Size usually much smaller, but large individuals may exceed small ones of *lupus;* form more slender; large molariform teeth with crowns more deeply cleft, the cusps more compressed laterally, and points and shearing edges more trenchant; upper carnassial with protocone, or antero-internal cusp, usually more prominent, but in some specimens absent; first upper molar with a more prominent cingulum and with postero-external cusp more distinctly smaller as compared with antero-external cusp, also inner lobe bearing more prominent cusplets and enamel ridges; second upper molar variable, but usually larger.

Remarks.—The species is subdivisible into three subspecies: *niger*, *gregoryi*, and *rufus*. Of these, the larger subspecies, *gregoryi* and *niger*, exhibit a remarkable approach in size and general proportions to the small eastern gray wolf, *C. l. lycaon*. They differ externally, however, in shorter pelage and more rufescent instead of predominantly grayish coloration, and internally in combination of cranial details as already pointed out. Perhaps the most reliable distinguishing characters are the more prominent cingulum on the outer side of the first upper molar, and the more deeply cleft crowns and laterally compressed cusps of the large molariform teeth. Subspecies *rufus* in central Texas and Oklahoma, on the other hand, is so small and in general characters agrees so closely with *C. latrans*, which it overlaps in geographic range, that some specimens are difficult to determine. Representatives of the two species occur at the same localities but typical specimens are easily recognized by the contrast in size and the differing combinations of cranial details. Owing to wide range of individual variation, however, some of the smaller specimens of subspecies *rufus* may be confused with large examples of *latrans*. Specimens collected in the vicinity of Llano, Tex., include typical examples of both species and individuals not sharply distinctive of either. Close approach in essential details and the apparent absence of any invariable unit character suggests the possibility of hybridism in some localities in Texas.

CANIS NIGER NIGER Bartram

Florida Red Wolf (Pl. 129)

Lupus niger Bartram, Travels, p. 199, 1791.

Canis floridanus Miller, Proc. Biol. Soc. Wash. 25: 95, May 4, 1912. From Horse Landing, St. Johns River, about 12 miles south of Palatka, Putnam County, Fla.

Canis rufus floridanus Goldman, Jour. Mamm. 18 (1): 45, Feb. 14, 1937.

Canis niger niger Harper, Jour. Mamm. 23 (3): 339, Aug. 14, 1942.

Type locality.—Alachua Savanna (now Payne's Prairie), Alachua County, Fla.

Type specimen.—Not designated.

Distribution.—Formerly Florida, Georgia, and Alabama; limits of range undetermined, but probably included South Carolina; believed to be extinct.

General characters.—Size largest of the subspecies of *rufus.* Similar in color to *gregoryi,* but size apparently somewhat larger; proportions more robust as indicated by skulls examined.

Color.—Type of *floridanus* (= *niger*): Upper parts in general (worn pelage) a coarsely grizzled light buff and gray mixture; muzzle "cinnamon" above, becoming dull white on sides; outer surfaces of limbs near "tawny" or "ochraceous tawny," becoming paler and near "cinnamon-buff" on feet; forearms with a narrow blackish line anteriorly as usual in the group; chin and throat dull white; under side of neck and chest pale buff, tinged with black; abdominal and inguinal areas and inner sides of limbs pinkish buff; ears "cinnamon" mixed with black to near base where the black is thinned out, leaving the cinnamon brighter in tone; tail (much worn) light buffy with a blackish patch over gland. The name, *niger,* was evidently based by Bartram on a specimen in the black phase. No specimens of the Florida wolf in this phase have been examined by me. A skin in winter pelage (March) from 12 miles south of Cherokee, Ala., referred to *niger* is similar to the type and lighter in general color than average specimens of *gregoryi.* The lighter tone is noticeable on the limbs and on the back where the overlying black, as seen in *gregoryi,* is somewhat reduced.

Skull.—Similar in general to that of *gregoryi,* but somewhat larger, more massive; frontal region and rostrum broader; zygomata heavier; dentition heavier. Size and general form much as in *C. l. lycaon,* but frontal region less highly arched; nasals with a more evenly U-shaped, instead of deeply V-shaped, space between the anterior ends; molariform teeth with crowns more deeply cleft, the cusps more compressed laterally and points and shearing edges more tranchant; first upper molar with more prominent cingulum along outer side, and postero-external cusp more distinctly smaller as compared with antero-external cusp, also inner lobe bearing more prominent cusplets and enamel ridges.

Measurements.—An adult male from 12 miles south of Cherokee, Alabama: Total length, 1650; tail vertebrae, 410. *Skull:* Type (♀) from Florida: Zygomatic breadth, 122.2; squamosal constriction, 67.2; width of rostrum, 36.1; interorbital breadth, 43.2; postorbital constriction, 38.9; length of mandible, 158.9; height of coronoid process, 65.5; upper carnassial, crown length (outer side), 23.2, crown width, 12.8; first upper molar, antero-posterior diameter, 15.8, transverse diameter, 21.7; lower carnassial, crown length, 25.6. An adult male from 12 miles south of Cherokee, Alabama: Greatest length, 236; condylobasal length, 219; zygomatic breadth, 125.9; squamosal constriction, 72.3; width of rostrum, 39.7; interorbital breadth, 39.7; postorbital constriction, 37.6; length of mandible, 170; height of coronoid process, 70.7; maxillary tooth row, 98.5; upper carnassial, crown length (outer side), 24.1, crown width, 14.1; first upper molar, antero-posterior diameter, 22; transverse diameter, 21; lower carnassial, crown length, 27.3.

Remarks.—A specimen from 12 miles south of Cherokee, Ala., may be grading toward *gregoryi*, but owing to heavy cranial proportions and large teeth, seems referable to the present subspecies. In rather light coloration also this specimen is not very unlike the type of *floridanus* (= *niger*). The subspecies *niger* rather closely approaches *lycaon* in size and general appearance, but the resemblance is probably superficial, and the two are regarded as specifically distinct.

Specimens examined.—Total number, 2, as follows:
Alabama: Cherokee (12 miles south), 1.
Florida: Horse Landing, 12 miles south of Palatka, 1.

CANIS NIGER GREGORYI Goldman

Mississippi Valley Red Wolf (Pls. 127-128)

Canis rufus gregoryi Goldman, Jour. Mamm. 18 (1): 44, Feb. 14, 1937.

Canis niger gregoryi Harper, Jour. Mamm. 23 (3): 339, Aug. 14, 1942.

Type locality.—Mack's Bayou, 3 miles east of Tensas River, 18 miles southwest of Tallulah, Madison Parish, La.

Type specimen.—No. 136731, ♂ adult, skin and skull, U. S. National Museum (Biological Surveys collection); collected by B. V. Lilly, April 25, 1905. X-catalog number 5338.

Distribution.—Formerly the Mississippi River Valley, north at least to Warsaw, Ill., and Wabash, northern Indiana; probably western Kentucky and western Tennessee; west throughout the Ozark Mountain region in southern Missouri, Arkansas, except northwestern part, to southeastern Oklahoma, and from the lowlands of Louisiana west to eastern Texas; east to southeastern Mississippi. Intergradation with *rufus* on the west and with *niger* on the east is evident.

General characters.—Similar to *rufus* of Texas but much larger, and color averaging less vividly rufescent. Size somewhat smaller, but color similar to *niger* of Florida.

Color.—About as given for the species, but averaging less tawny than *rufus.*

Skull.—Closely resembling that of *rufus,* but decidedly larger and of heavier proportions, with notably broader rostrum. Usually smaller, less massive than that of *niger;* frontal region narrower; dentition lighter.

Measurements.—Two adult males from Barren, Missouri, respectively: Total length, 1650, 1473; tail vertebrae, 393, 362; hind foot, 254, 235. Weight of an adult male from same locality: 67 lbs. Two adult females from Barren, Missouri, respectively: Total length, 1448, 1422; tail vertebrae, 355, 343; hind foot, 216, 222. Weight of an adult female from same locality: 50 lbs. *Skull:* Type (♂) and an adult male from 15 miles northwest of Tallulah, Louisiana, respectively: Greatest length, 250, 249.5; condylobasal length, 228, 230.7; zygomatic breadth, 126, 124.7; squamosal constriction, 73.2, 75.4; width of rostrum, 34.7, 35.9; interorbital breadth, 40.6, 42.6; postorbital constriction, 32.4, 36.7; length of mandible, 173, 176; height of coronoid process, 68.6, 67.8; maxillary tooth row, crown length, 103.8, 104; upper carnassial, crown length (outer side), 23.5, 24.9; crown width, 12, 12; first upper molar, anteroposterior diameter, 15.9, 16.1, transverse diameter, 20.6, 22.6;

lower carnassial, crown length, 26.5, 26.8. An adult female from type locality and one from Sikes, Louisiana, respectively: Greatest length, 222.7, 218.5; condylobasal length, 202.5, 207.7; zygomatic breadth, 114.2, 114.5; squamosal constriction, 67.9, 68.7; width of rostrum, 38, 32.6; interorbital breadth, 35.6, 40.2; postorbital constriction, 31, 37.5; length of mandible, 156.7, 157.7; height of coronoid process, 68.6, 66.8; maxillary tooth row, crown length, 91.2, 93.1; upper carnassial, crown length (outer side), 22.6, 20.1, crown width, 11.7, 11; first upper molar, 15.1, 14.8, transverse diameter, 20, 19; lower carnassial, 24.7, 23.4.

Remarks.—*C. n. gregoryi* is somewhat intermediate in characters, as well as geographic position, between *rufus* and *niger*. The combination of characters presented over a wide range appear, however, to warrant the recognition of the Mississippi River Valley animal as a separate race. Red wolves remained until recently fairly numerous west of the Mississippi River, but of the occurrence of *gregoryi* in the more densely settled country to the eastward, little is known. An interesting early record is that of a specimen from the Maximilian collection in the American Museum of Natural History, Museum Number 112. Translation of the German script on the tag is as follows: "Skull of the bitch wolf in the exhibition gallery from Wabash [Indiana] 1832. Weight of bitch wolf 60 pounds." This skull exhibits the light cranial structure and narrow, compressed dental cusps characterizing the red wolves. The skin and skull of a young male in the same museum, received from C. K. Worthen, is labeled Warsaw, Ill., February 7, 1893. A more recent record of a specimen, also in the American Museum of Natural History, is Biloxi, Miss., collected in November 1931 by Frank Parker.

Specimens examined.—Total number, 247, as follows:

Arkansas: Almond, 1; Aly (8 miles northwest), 1; Aplin, 1; Ava, 3; Bergman, 2; Blue Ball (3 miles south), 4; Cardiff, 1; Carthage (5 miles west), 1; Cedar, 2; Crystal Springs, 1; Delaplaine (3 miles east), 1; Egger (radius of 12 miles), 7; Fallsville, 9; Ferndale, 8; Fifty-Six, 4; Forrest City, 1; Gladstone, 1; Graysonia (5 miles southeast), 1; Hartley, 1; Hollis, 1 (skull only); Hot Springs (9 miles east), 1; Isaac, 6; Lead Hill, 1; Lonsdale (6 miles west), 4; Lurton, 2; Maumelle Creek, Pulaski County, 1; Mena, 1; Mill Creek, 3; Mull, 4; Onyx,

11; Parkdale (12 miles east), 1; Parks (4 miles east), 1; Pinnacle, 6; Potter, 1; Rush, 2; Shady, 3; Signal Hill, Stone County, 1; Simpson, 6; Solo, 1; Stillwater, 8; Thornburg, 1; Wye (8 miles west), 2.

Illinois: Warsaw, Hancock County, 1.[1]

Indiana: Wabash, Wabash County, 1 (skull only).[1]

Louisiana: Avery Island (12 miles north), 1 (skull only); Floyd (10 miles southwest), 1; Indian Lake (23 miles southwest of Tallulah), 1; Jackson Parish, 1(skull only); Little River, La Salle Parish, 1 (skull only)[2]; Mack's Bayou (3 miles east of Tensas River, 18 miles southwest of Tallulah), 1; Madison Parish, 1 (skull only); Mer Rouge, 1; Sabine River, Beauregard Parish, 2 (skulls only); Sikes, 2; Tallulah, 4 (3 skulls only); Vidalia (20 miles southwest), 1 (skull only); Winn Parish, 2.

Missouri, Arcadia, 2; Barren, 7; Cooks Station, 7; Gatewood, 3; Reeds Spring, 2; Sabula (4 miles south), 1 (skull only); Stone County, 3; Tyrone, 2; Upalika, 1; Westover, 5: West Plains, 2.

Oklahoma: Bethel, 5; Big Cedar, 1; Broken Bow (15 miles north), 20; Cedar Creek, Pushmataha County, 2; Fewell, 2; Nashoba (Garland Creek), 1; Octavia (10 miles northeast), 3; Page, 9; Sherwood, 4; Smithville, 12; Talahina, 1 (skull only); Zafra, 1 (skull only).

Texas: Hardin County, 1; Kountze, 2 (1 skull without skin); Mont Belvieu, Chambers County, 1 (skull only); Newton County, 1 (skull only); Polk County, 2 (skulls only); Rock Creek, Newton County, 1 (skull only); Segno, 1; Wakefield, 2 (skulls only).

CANIS NIGER RUFUS Audubon and Bachman
Texas Red Wolf (Pls. 125-126)

Canis lupus var. *rufus* Audubon and Bachman, Quadr. North Amer. 2: 240, 1851.

Canis rufus Bailey, North Amer. Fauna 25: 174, Oct. 24, 1905.

Canis rufus rufus Goldman, Jour. Mamm. 18 (1): 45, Feb. 14, 1937.

---

[1]Amer. Mus. Nat. Hist.
[2]La. State Univ.

Canis niger rufus Harper, Jour. Mamm. 23 (3): Aug. 14, 1942.

Type locality.—Name restricted by Goldman (1937, p. 38) to subspecies occurring 15 miles west of Austin, Tex.

Type specimen.—Not designated.

Distribution.—Formerly northwestern Arkansas, eastern Oklahoma, except Ozark Mountains in southeastern corner, and south through central Texas to the Gulf Coast near Aransas Bay; west to the Pecos River Valley. Now believed to be restricted to parts of central and southern Texas, intergrading with *gregoryi* in the eastern part of the State.

General characters.—Very similar to *gregoryi* of the Mississippi Valley, but smaller, and color averaging more vividly rufescent.

Color.—About as given for the species, but tawny element usually more predominant than in the other subspecies.

Skull.—Closely resembling that of *gregoryi*, but decidedly smaller and of lighter proportions, with notably slenderer rostrum.

Measurements.—Two adult males from Redfork, Oklahoma, respectively: Total length, 1403, 1454; tail vertebrae, 381, 420; hind foot, 210, 221. An adult male from Noble, Cleveland County, Oklahoma: Weight, 55 lbs. *Skull:* Two adult males from vicinity of Llano, Texas, respectively: Greatest length, 225, 226.9; condylobasal length, 207.8, 209; zygomatic breadth, 117.5, 112.3; squamosal constriction, 68.7, 66; width of rostrum, 34.6, 33.3; interorbital breadth, 39.7, 35; postorbital constriction, 36, 34.8; length of mandible, 161, 160.7; height of coronoid process, 61.1, 62.8; maxillary tooth row, 98.2, 94.6; upper carnassial, crown length (outer side), 22.4, 21.3; upper carnassial, crown width, 11.6, 11.6; first upper molar, antero-posterior diameter, 14.3, 14.2, transverse diameter, 19.8, 18.7; lower carnassial, crown length, 24.6, 23.1. Two adult females from vicinity of Llano, Texas, respectively: Greatest length, 200.9, 207.3; condylobasal length, 194, 191.6; zygomatic breadth, 106, 110.2; squamosal constriction, 64.3, 63.1; width of rostrum, 29.8, 31.7; interorbital breadth, 39.7, 33.9; postorbital constriction, 40, 39.1; length of mandible, 149, 151.2; height of coronoid process, 61.1, 60.6; maxillary tooth row, 87.7, 89; upper carnassial, crown length (outer side), 19.4, 21.6, crown width, 9.8, 10.6; first upper molar, antero-posterior diameter, 12.7, 14.7, transverse diameter, 17.3, 18.7; lower carnassial, crown length, 20, 23.2.

Remarks.—The description of *rufus* by Audubon and Bachman clearly refers to the red wolf of Texas. No local habitat was formally designated. However, reference was made (1.c. 242) to the occurrence of the animal 15 miles west of Austin, and that place has been selected as the type locality.

The small size of *rufus* is the principal character distinguishing it from the decidedly larger subspecies inhabiting territory to the eastward. The intergradation of *rufus* with *gregoryi* is clearly shown by specimens from eastern Texas, southeastern Oklahoma, and northwestern Arkansas. In these regions the transition from one subspecies to the other is rather abrupt. As already pointed out in remarks on the species, there appear to be no very tranchant or entirely dependable characters distinguishing in all cases small specimens of *rufus* from large ones of the coyote, *Canis latrans;* and the status of typical *rufus* in relation to the latter is, therefore, not entirely clear. However, as most specimens of the two species are readily recognizable, even where they occur at the same locality, possible hybridism, rather than regular intergradation, is indicated.

Specimens examined.—Total number, 94, as follows:

Arkansas: Boxley, Newton County, 2; Frederick, 1; Hector, 1; Raspberry, 3 (1 skull without skin); Redstar, 1; Summers (5-12 miles north), 7 (3 skulls without skins).

Oklahoma: Atoka, 2; Ridden, 1 (skull only); Red Fork, 2; Tahlequah, 1 (skull only); Wedington, 3 (skins only); Wichita Mountains Refuge, 1.

Texas: Angleon, 4 (2 skulls without skins); Aransas Migratory Waterfowl Refuge, near Austwell, 1 (skull only); Bloomington (5 miles south), Calhoun County, 3; Brady, 3 (1 skull without skin); Bryan (15 miles south), Brazos County, 1; Burnet, 1; Burnet County, 2 (skulls only); Cantey Ranch, near Mineral Wells, Palo Pinto County, 1; Cisco, Hill Brothers Ranch, 12 miles northeast, 1; Cleveland, Liberty County, 1;[1] Click, Llano County, 1; Columbus, 1; Dayton, (6 miles north), 2 (skulls only); Doole (5 miles southeast), 1; Droyet Ranch (6 miles south of Marble Falls), 1; Fairland (5 miles east), 1 (skull only); Frelsburg, 1 (skull only); Kerrville, 2 (1 skull without skin); Kerr County, 1 (skull only); Llano (radius of 22 miles), 14 (1 skin without skull); Loving (Ferguson Ranch, 6 miles northeast), 1; Llano County, 1 (skull only); Magnolia, Montgomery County, 1; Marble Falls, Burnet County, 2; Menard (35 miles west), 3; Murray (Graham Ranch, 6 miles northeast), 1; New Chaney, Montgomery County, 1; New Waverly, Montgomery County, 1 (skull only); Nueces River, Edwards County, 1 (skull only); Parker County, 2 (skeletons with skulls); Port Lavaca (7 miles southwest), 2 (skulls only); Port O'Connor, 4 (skulls onyy); Porters, Montgomery County, 2 (1 skull without skin); Security, Montgomery County, 3;[2] Sheffield (22 miles north), Pecos County, 1; Valley Spring (5 miles north), Llano County, 1 (skull only).

[1]Stanley P. Young Collection.
[2]One in Stanley P. Young Collection.

TABLE 4.—CRANIAL MEASUREMENTS OF ADULT MALES IN U. S. NATIONAL MUSEUM, UNLESS OTHERWISE INDICATED, OF *Canis lupus* GROUP

Species and locality	Number	Greatest length	Condylobasal length	Zygomatic breadth	Squamosal constriction	Width of rostrum	Interorbital breadth	Postorbital constriction	Length of mandible	Height of coronoid process	Maxillary tooth row, crown length	Upper carnassial, crown length (outer side)	Upper carnassial, crown width	First upper molar, antero-posterior diameter	First upper molar, transverse diameter	Lower carnassial, crown length
C. l. tundrarum:																
Alaska—																
Noatak River[1]	264415	282.0	256.3	143.4	82.4	46.8	55.0	47.8	195.5	79.4	115.1	28.8	15.8	20.1	25.4	33.2
Point Barrow[2]	4053	267.5	248.0	143.7	81.4	47.1	46.9	43.7	199.4	84.0	112.9	27.2	16.3	18.0	25.3	30.9
	Average	274.8	252.2	143.6	81.9	47.0	51.0	45.8	197.5	81.7	114.0	28.0	16.1	19.1	25.4	32.1
C. l. pambasileus:																
Alaska—																
Big Delta	265100	280.0	261.2	151.8	84.2	52.6	59.8	47.6	205.5	88.2	118.5	....	....	....	....	33.0
Big Delta	265576	286.4	263.5	150.0	86.8	50.0	55.8	47.2	206.7	87.5	118.5	29.6	16.3	18.6	25.6	33.1
Chicken	203895	286.8	258.9	141.5	82.2	47.3	54.7	45.2	205.9	88.8	114.7	26.4	14.6	17.4	23.8	30.1
Dry Creek (N. of McKinley Park)	266409	275.2	253.7	149.6	81.7	44.9	48.1	43.6	198.9	86.1	114.7	26.2	14.9	17.5	23.8	31.6
Farewell Mountain	242704	288.2	266.0	148.4	87.7	51.2	52.8	47.8	208.7	86.4	121.5	27.6	15.6	18.6	24.0	30.0
Gold Creek	264226	281.4	261.4	147.3	85.5	48.6	47.3	45.8	203.7	85.3	120.4	29.5	14.7	19.2	25.2	33.8
Savage River	264227	277.3	251.5	153.7	84.4	45.6	50.3	45.9	199.3	89.5	112.2	26.9	14.5	17.2	24.2	31.5
Seventy Mile	265982	285.0	265.3	153.0	86.6	49.5	55.6	43.6	208.5	88.3	119.6	29.6	15.9	18.5	26.1	33.4
Sushana River	266406	286.9	268.4	151.6	82.8	46.4	47.4	42.8	210.3	89.1	119.0	27.1	13.6	17.8	24.1	29.4
Tanana	218341	282.0	258.7	145.7	87.2	54.3	54.4	46.5	202.5	84.0	114.4	25.2	14.1	16.7	22.6	28.7
Tanana River	265577	271.3	250.7	151.4	78.7	48.2	51.6	44.7	196.5	84.4	112.2	27.5	14.8	18.8	23.8	31.0
Teklanika River	266407	277.2	257.5	152.5	84.8	46.8	47.1	40.6	201.3	88.5	114.1	26.8	13.5	18.0	24.0	29.9
Yukon—																
White River[3]	33-9-20-5	293.7	269.3	151.5	87.0	49.4	50.3	43.0	208.0	92.9	118.1	26.6	13.7	17.3	24.3	29.8
White River[3]	31-2-16-2	292.8	263.9	149.0	84.2	47.0	49.6	43.5	207.0	84.2	118.5	27.6	15.6	17.7	24.6	30.2
White River[3]	33-9-20-8	282.0	252.7	144.0	83.1	45.5	49.3	49.2	202.4	80.6	114.3	25.4	13.1	17.1	22.7	29.3
	Average	283.1	260.2	149.4	84.5	48.5	51.6	45.1	204.3	86.9	116.7	27.3	14.6	17.9	24.2	31.0
C. l. alces:																
Alaska—																
Kachemak Bay[4]	147470	263.0	245.0	133.8	80.7	44.7	43.9	42.4	185.0	76.5	108.6	26.0	14.4	16.8	23.3	28.9
Kachemak Bay[4]	136743	262.8	250.0	130.5	82.3	45.7	42.5	40.9	190.0	74.0	113.2	27.5	15.4	17.3	23.3	31.1
	Average	262.9	247.5	132.2	81.5	45.2	43.2	41.7	187.5	75.3	110.9	26.8	14.9	17.1	23.3	30.0

C. l. occidentalis:																
Alberta—																
Edmonton	242907	276.7	248.1	144.3	81.0	45.8	50.8	44.8	194.6	79.0	111.3	27.6	13.9	18.3	23.9	30.3
Smith Landing	177370	274.0	250.0	148.8	82.5	50.2	51.5	41.9	196.5	85.1	110.7	25.5	15.3	16.4	21.8	28.5
Wood Buffalo Park[5]	98230	278.2	262.5	145.5	90.5	47.2	46.2	44.6	197.6	80.8	114.1	27.2	14.4	17.6	24.2	30.8
Wood Buffalo Park[5]	98226	274.2	258.8	144.0	84.9	50.7	46.1	43.2	199.0	82.8	115.4	28.5	15.6	18.0	25.2	33.6
British Columbia—																
Cache Creek, Peace River District[6]	4698	283.0	255.2	152.7	86.6	51.3	51.4	46.8	204.7	83.6	114.5	26.9	15.9	16.9	24.4	31.2
Mackenzie—																
Artillery Lake	262688	281.0	258.0	149.8	82.3	44.4	50.0	43.8	.....	....	120.4	28.6	15.9	18.9	25.5	....
Aylmer Lake[5]	29040	272.0	245.3	143.4	81.7	43.3	50.7	45.6	191.7	83.0	100.8	27.2	14.1	17.9	24.2	30.0
Coronation Gulf	236104	278.5	256.0	142.5	83.3	45.6	49.0	46.1	198.3	81.0	118.7	27.7	14.7	19.2	24.7	31.0
Dease River[5]	34446	265.3	240.8	146.2	85.2	43.0	51.4	44.1	186.5	84.3	108.7	25.3	13.4	16.3	24.0	29.9
Fort Simpson[7]	9001	292.8	266.0	156.5	85.4	50.1	53.2	44.9	204.8	85.3	116.4	30.6	17.1	18.8	24.8	33.8
Fort Simpson[7]	9003	270.3	245.0	147.8	84.4	49.6	49.9	41.0	190.9	82.5	111.1	27.9	15.2	16.8	22.4	30.0
Fort Simpson[4]	134131	272.0	253.5	132.7	84.1	48.0	41.8	41.8	193.2	78.2	112.6	27.0	15.0	17.7	24.6	29.7
Yukon—																
Macmillan River (north fork)	134496	283.3	255.7	148.0	87.2	47.5	49.0	42.8	204.0	87.2	111.0	26.5	14.5	17.2	24.6	31.0
Pelly Lakes	214478	276.5	253.6	152.3	83.5	51.3	53.4	46.1	200.5	86.1	110.0	27.0	14.5	17.8	24.2	31.0
Pelly Lakes	214479	275.0	256.9	150.2	85.4	47.5	52.0	47.1	202.7	92.9	112.1	28.2	15.8	17.7	24.0	31.7
Pelly Lakes	214477	270.9	247.7	143.7	83.1	46.2	47.8	44.3	195.4	84.2	111.6	26.4	14.6	16.7	23.0	29.1
Pelly Lakes	214481	277.3	256.3	145.2	82.2	49.1	46.4	40.7	202.7	87.2	116.7	26.8	14.8	18.1	24.4	30.2
	Average	276.5	253.5	146.7	84.3	47.7	49.4	44.1	197.7	84.0	112.7	27.3	15.0	17.7	24.1	30.7
C. l. hudsonicus:																
Keewatin—																
Cape Fullerton[5]	19493	260.0	240.7	146.1	80.5	46.7	46.0	38.8	.....	....	111.0	27.3	16.0	18.7	25.9	....
Hudson Bay[5]	19348	254.0	233.2	137.0	78.1	46.2	46.1	37.3	183.1	73.7	107.8	26.9	14.6	18.5	24.2	30.0
Schultz Lake	180281	258.3	241.0	146.4	83.9	46.0	47.2	41.8	190.3	84.6	110.1	26.8	14.2	17.4	24.2	32.6
Schultz Lake	180282	262.1	237.7	145.5	80.2	44.2	47.6	38.8	186.3	75.1	107.2	25.5	14.5	17.6	22.1	28.8
Wager River[5]	22940	263.3	240.8	137.2	80.1	43.2	47.0	41.2	187.3	73.7	109.7	25.6	14.0	17.5	23.5	29.1
	Average	259.5	238.7	142.4	80.0	45.3	46.8	39.6	186.8	76.8	109.2	26.4	14.7	17.9	24.0	30.1
C. l. arctos:																
Arctic America—																
Ellesmere Islands[5]	42119	264.7	236.9	138.7	79.4	46.0	45.6	40.4	186.8	76.1	108.6	26.4	15.3	17.6	23.0	30.1
C. l. labradorius:																
Labrador—																
Hopedale[8]	7409	262.2	243.5	141.5	78.8	49.5	46.6	46.9	189.6	81.8	110.1	25.7	13.7	17.1	23.3	29.4
Porcupine	210059	266.2	240.0	143.5	79.4	45.8	46.6	43.8	188.0	74.7	113.1	25.9	14.4	16.1	23.1	30.6
Quebec—																
Fort Chimo (near)[9]	23138	244.5	227.5	125.0	74.9	42.2	39.6	44.5	173.4	69.3	102.9	25.0	13.1	16.7	22.5	27.4
	Average	257.6	237.0	136.7	77.7	45.8	44.3	45.1	183.7	75.3	108.7	25.5	13.7	16.6	23.0	29.1
C. l. beothucus:																
Newfoundland	264482	254.0	230.0	138.7	78.2	44.1	46.7	45.4	182.7	78.6	104.0	26.2	14.7	17.5	23.0	29.0

FOOTNOTES [1] Subadult. [2] Type locality, Colo. Mus. Nat. Hist. [3] Roy. Ont. Mus. Zool. [4] Type locality. Young. [5] Amer. Mus. Nat. Hist. [6] Prov. Mus. [7] Type locality. [8] Mus. Comp. Zool. [9] Type locality. Subadult.

TABLE 4.—CRANIAL MEASUREMENTS OF ADULT MALES IN U. S. NATIONAL MUSEUM, UNLESS OTHERWISE INDICATED, OF *Canis lupus* GROUP—(Continued)

Species and locality	Number	Greatest length	Condylobasal length	Zygomatic breadth	Squamosal constriction	Width of rostrum	Interorbital breadth	Postorbital constriction	Length of mandible	Height of coronoid process	Maxillary tooth row, crown length	Upper carnassial, crown length (outer side)	Upper carnassial, crown width	First upper molar, antero-posterior diameter	First upper molar, transverse diameter	Lower carnassial, crown length
C. l. lycaon:																
Florida[1]	11179	250.2	224.5	128.2	75.4	38.9	43.8	43.7	172.1	73.5	100.1	25.0	12.7	16.3	20.9	27.4
Michigan—																
Calderwood	168820	259.3	237.8	132.5	75.7	41.4	44.9	41.4	183.5	69.7	105.3	25.0	14.0	16.3	22.4	27.3
Cusino	170692	244.2	230.4	128.0	76.4	40.1	43.8	40.2	176.2	76.1	96.5	24.1	14.1	15.8	21.3	27.4
Escanaba River	265071	248.5	234.0	139.3	74.6	43.2	50.0	44.2	179.5	69.9	104.5	26.0	13.4	16.9	23.4	29.3
Escanaba River	265072	249.2	.....	134.9	77.4	41.3	50.6	41.7	177.2	76.5	104.6	24.1	12.4	16.9	22.9	28.7
Kenton	243395	239.5	225.0	134.1	75.9	41.3	41.6	42.6	175.0	66.6	99.8	25.1	13.4	16.6	21.8	27.7
Minnesota—																
Elk River	45561	257.3	236.5	136.5	78.6	41.6	46.8	42.6	180.3	74.9	106.6	24.3	12.9	15.7	21.7	27.7
Gunflint Lake[2]	1221	251.5	241.0	138.2	77.5	42.9	46.4	42.7	178.7	72.7	107.8	27.1	15.2	17.7	24.2	30.5
Gunflint Lake[2]	1349	256.8	236.0	136.0	78.2	44.5	46.0	41.0	183.0	75.7	109.3	25.4	13.0	17.3	22.8	29.5
New York—																
Adirondack Mts.	1804	233.0	219.3	127.9	76.9	36.7	43.0	41.8	168.6	69.0	95.6	24.0	13.0	16.9	22.3	27.1
Ontario—																
Brent, Algonquin National Park[3]	24-11-19-1	245.3	229.4	136.3	77.0	41.1	44.0	41.5	175.7	69.6	104.7	23.8	13.2	16.3	20.2	28.0
Mattawa (40 mi. NE)	140562	238.0	233.5	127.3	77.4	38.0	42.6	38.4	172.5	68.0	101.5	25.1	13.6	16.2	21.5	29.3
Mattawa (40 mi. NE)	140561	237.7	222.0	136.8	76.0	40.1	47.1	42.2	171.3	69.0	99.5	22.5	12.8	16.4	21.2	26.0
Whitney[4]	77344	246.0	231.3	138.0	75.4	41.1	48.7	41.2	181.2	71.3	106.3	23.9	12.7	16.7	21.5	26.6
Pennsylvania[5]	2261	234.2	221.0	122.4	73.5	35.7	43.5	41.2	165.5	65.2	101.0	24.2	12.9	16.8	21.6	28.8
Quebec—																
Lucerne[4]	77343	243.9	228.9	129.3	71.8	40.5	38.6	36.0	174.5	68.1	103.3	23.9	12.8	17.1	21.6	28.8
Montebello[6]	32-2-1-1	253.0	233.0	140.3	76.2	41.4	45.3	38.1	181.7	75.0	104.8	23.7	13.7	16.3	21.3	27.9
Montebello[6]	31-12-29-2	250.5	236.0	136.0	78.8	41.5	43.9	37.6	178.5	71.0	106.6	23.4	12.5	17.7	21.9	28.2
Wisconsin—																
Vilas Co. (near Mich. line)[7]	51772	267.3	247.7	140.7	79.6	43.4	48.4	45.5	194.4	76.5	113.1	26.0	15.2	18.2	23.4	30.3
	Average	247.7	231.5	133.8	76.4	40.8	45.2	41.2	177.3	71.5	103.7	24.6	13.3	16.7	22.0	28.2
C. l. nubilus:																
Colorado—																
Bent County	51434	261.5	239.8	133.2	82.3	43.9	46.5	42.2	179.3	75.9	106.2	25.4	13.5	16.0	23.4	29.4
Kansas—																
Gove County	139156	254.4	232.5	135.7	74.6	43.5	45.7	39.3	177.5	74.5	105.6	26.1	13.8	16.3	22.5	29.2

Montana—																
Kinsey	232866	264.5	244.5	145.1	80.2	48.8	50.2	43.9	189.5	76.1	112.1	25.4	14.1	....	....	27.4
Miles City	228133	258.2	244.2	142.0	80.7	46.7	47.6	36.7	188.8	81.1	110.0	25.2	13.4	15.9	22.5	28.9
Miles City	211143	254.4	238.9	139.5	78.0	46.2	45.6	39.2	183.2	78.8	107.5	25.2	13.2	16.2	21.7	28.3
Nebraska—																
Kearney	884	258.4	228.9	137.7	80.4	44.3	46.6	35.7	180.3	81.0	102.8	26.1	13.1	15.9	22.6	29.2
Kearney	1308	253.5	232.3	135.2	75.7	42.2	48.1	40.3	183.5	81.2	106.3	25.2	12.4	17.2	22.7	28.9
Kearney	1315	253.2	230.8	133.7	76.8	43.6	47.2	41.8	181.8	74.6	106.0	26.0	14.9	16.7	23.6	29.2
Kearney	1312	243.7	228.5	134.7	76.7	45.7	46.9	42.0	181.0	78.1	108.6	25.0	13.2	18.4	24.2	31.0
Kearney	1314	244.2	223.8	133.7	77.7	45.5	45.1	39.5	173.0	72.3	102.8	25.5	14.4	16.9	21.8	30.8
Platte River	2568	253.0	231.7	137.7	78.3	43.3	52.2	39.6	178.8	75.2	104.0	25.0	14.6	15.5	22.7	28.4
Platte River	3686	250.9	228.4	140.9	76.3	47.7	46.8	36.7	178.0	75.8	105.0	25.7	14.4	17.6	24.4	29.9
New Mexico—																
Santa Rosa (18 mi. south)	168344	259.1	240.5	139.5	80.2	46.1	51.4	41.4	186.1	76.1	112.1	25.9	16.1	....	23.1	29.2
North Dakota—																
Medora (20 mi. south)	69486	255.6	235.8	134.9	76.0	44.0	48.0	42.7	183.4	77.3	109.0	25.4	13.9	15.8	21.9	29.4
Oklahoma—																
Wichita Mountains	147703	256.4	233.4	132.4	75.8	42.2	44.8	35.0	175.7	75.7	108.7	26.7	15.1	17.1	24.8	30.4
South Dakota—																
Faith	227682	254.8	234.0	133.1	75.3	47.8	46.6	40.9	182.5	76.3	105.4	24.5	13.6	17.4	22.3	28.4
Folsom	223729	264.4	237.2	141.6	80.4	47.7	49.5	40.1	181.0	79.5	105.9	24.8	13.7	16.8	21.9	28.5
Wyoming—																
Douglas	227679	250.7	239.8	144.0	78.7	48.0	49.6	41.5	186.5	77.7	107.6	24.9	14.7	16.1	23.0	28.7
Douglas	227673	249.3	229.5	136.0	74.2	41.7	43.3	31.5	181.0	71.7	107.7	25.9	13.9	18.1	23.6	29.3
	Average	254.7	234.4	137.4	77.8	45.2	47.5	39.5	181.6	76.8	107.0	25.5	14.0	16.7	22.9	29.2
C. l. irremotus:																
Alberta—																
Lethbridge (25 mi. southeast)	78120	265.9	249.2	144.0	80.7	44.9	46.4	39.6	189.8	73.6	109.7	26.2	13.7	17.0	23.0	28.9
Idaho—																
Argora, Clark Co.	227084	259.1	241.5	137.1	79.2	42.8	44.9	37.5	182.0	75.3	108.8	26.2	15.5	17.5	23.9	32.0
Leadore (10 mi. south)	215803	258.9	236.8	143.8	76.5	42.0	43.8	38.1	183.8	77.0	106.4	24.8	13.5	16.7	23.3	29.0
Soda Springs	233721	257.0	235.2	144.0	76.7	46.7	51.2	38.7	184.7	79.0	105.7	24.5	13.1	15.4	22.0	27.9
Soda Springs	234400	249.3	234.0	133.8	75.4	46.2	46.7	35.4	180.2	76.5	104.0	25.2	12.9	15.4	21.3	27.0
Tyhee, Bannock Co.	216405	251.7	234.8	136.4	77.4	44.2	45.2	34.4	182.0	72.9	106.2	25.0	13.7	16.7	23.0	28.5
Montana—																
Lame Deer	203802	253.4	236.5	141.6	84.6	44.8	43.9	39.6	183.5	75.4	106.0	26.2	14.1	16.6	23.1	30.1
Little Belt	156824	275.8	254.3	146.6	85.0	50.0	52.4	43.6	193.2	83.9	116.6	27.7	15.1	18.4	25.3	31.4
Powderville	58409	255.3	235.0	139.4	81.6	47.0	43.0	40.3	178.5	76.2	105.5	26.4	15.0	16.7	24.0	29.7
Powderville	58289	257.8	240.5	132.8	82.9	47.2	41.7	35.8	179.2	77.7	109.4	26.0	14.3	17.5	22.9	29.6
Powderville	57821	258.4	238.1	130.6	79.2	44.2	40.3	32.2	178.7	74.7	109.0	26.6	15.0	16.7	23.3	29.5
Red Lodge[8]	214869	259.2	237.0	144.9	81.1	47.7	44.6	34.7	186.0	74.4	105.7	25.7	13.9	17.6	20.2	28.8
Red Lodge[9]	214868	262.0	241.0	142.7	81.0	49.5	43.1	35.5	193.5	82.6	106.2	26.1	15.3	18.4	24.1	29.5
Three Forks[10]	271651	285.3	258.4	149.5	87.8	48.7	52.9	40.1	201.5	80.9	116.5	27.6	14.7	17.3	23.8	30.4
South Dakota—																
Belle Fourche	265070	260.0	240.0	145.0	83.0	46.4	46.9	38.4	184.7	77.3	107.3	25.2	13.8	17.7	23.2	29.7

FOOTNOTES: [1] Mus. Comp. Zool. [2] Minn. Mus. Nat. Hist. [3] Roy. Ont. Mus. Zool. [4] Mus. Vert. Zool. [5] Acad. Nat. Sci. Phila. [6] Roy. Ont. Mus. Zool. [7] Field Mus. Nat. Hist. [8] Type specimen. [9] Type locality. [10] Al Johnston.

TABLE 4.—CRANIAL MEASUREMENTS OF ADULT MALES IN U. S. NATIONAL MUSEUM, UNLESS OTHERWISE INDICATED, OF *Canis lupus* GROUP—(Continued)

Species and locality	Number	Greatest length	Condylobasal length	Zygomatic breadth	Squamosal constriction	Width of rostrum	Interorbital breadth	Postorbital constriction	Length of mandible	Height of coronoid process	Maxillary tooth row, crown length	Upper carnassial, crown length (outer side)	Upper carnassial, crown width	First upper molar, antero-posterior diameter	First upper molar, transverse diameter	Lower carnassial, crown length
C. l. irremotus—continued																
Wyoming—																
Barber, Johnson Co.	242148	264.5	245.6	141.0	78.6	46.5	52.6	42.7	192.2	79.3	110.4	26.5	14.2	17.0	24.7	29.7
Cora	147214	256.0	235.0	138.5	79.1	46.1	46.6	38.9	.....	....	106.5	28.5	15.2	18.4	24.5	31.2
Elk	224475	256.8	239.5	139.2	74.8	45.8	45.7	40.4	181.5	71.8	110.7	26.1	13.7	16.9	23.9	29.8
Elk	227683	256.4	238.3	139.9	78.6	48.8	44.9	36.2	182.4	77.0	106.6	24.4	13.3	17.0	23.1	28.6
Lenore	224463	251.5	235.0	141.2	78.2	43.2	45.7	38.0	181.9	73.2	106.5	25.2	14.1	....	22.8	29.1
Manville	211643	278.5	257.0	142.3	83.2	48.8	47.3	36.5	200.0	83.7	.....	27.2	15.0	16.6	24.3	30.3
Pinedale	148726	258.0	238.0	145.3	79.6	46.4	47.4	40.7	184.8	79.7	107.7	27.5	15.1	17.3	24.1	30.7
	Average	260.5	240.9	140.9	80.2	46.3	46.2	38.1	185.9	77.2	108.2	26.1	14.3	17.1	22.9	29.6
C. l. columbianus:																
British Columbia—																
Iskut Summit (60 mi. south Telegraph Creek)[1]	31043	288.9	268.0	155.0	86.2	50.8	52.3	45.4	206.4	89.5	114.8	28.8	14.1	18.0	23.6	31.4
Pemberton[2]	4656	265.7	249.0	144.1	82.1	46.6	43.9	43.4	199.6	82.5	113.5	27.3	14.2	17.8	24.8	31.2
Wistaria[3]	3559	272.9	260.0	148.4	82.5	46.0	48.8	45.7	196.2	75.0	112.1	27.1	13.8	17.3	24.1	31.1
Wistaria[4]	4264	263.9	244.4	147.7	80.8	45.0	43.1	38.3	193.0	80.9	107.3	26.8	14.0	16.4	22.9	29.5
	Average	272.9	255.4	148.8	82.9	47.1	47.0	43.2	198.8	82.0	111.9	27.5	14.0	17.4	23.9	30.8
C. l. ligoni:																
Alaska—																
Eleanor Cove, Yakutat Bay[5]	36.9.18.246	251.5	236.5	140.5	79.2	44.6	45.4	42.3	184.5	77.9	103.3	24.8	13.4	15.6	21.9	28.0
Kuiu Island	243332	254.0	245.6	143.2	78.4	45.6	47.0	42.6	193.3	70.9	111.9	24.8	13.6	17.9	24.1	30.2
Kupreanof Island[6]	243323	262.1	251.0	145.3	80.0	43.4	49.1	43.4	197.0	72.9	112.8	25.2	13.9	17.7	24.5	30.4
Kupreanof Island	244207	270.8	254.8	141.5	80.6	44.1	46.0	43.6	197.0	72.4	114.7	26.0	14.4	18.9	24.5	31.0
Prince of Wales Island	243574	262.5	239.9	142.2	81.4	44.1	48.0	45.1	191.4	74.1	108.7	24.6	13.3	15.4	21.1	28.0
Wrangell	244206	262.0	239.4	146.4	84.4	47.9	47.0	41.5	184.5	73.3	110.3	25.0	14.2	16.3	23.3	28.3
Zarembo Island	243329	261.5	241.2	144.0	80.5	42.6	43.7	43.3	183.7	74.0	107.5	25.0	14.5	16.2	23.9	28.4
Zarembo	243328	259.5	242.8	141.0	79.8	41.7	42.2	42.2	191.0	72.2	111.7	24.4	14.2	16.8	24.1	28.3
Zarembo	243333	255.8	235.0	140.4	78.9	44.8	45.7	40.6	190.5	75.4	106.9	24.9	13.7	16.2	23.9	30.0
	Average	260.0	242.9	142.7	80.4	44.3	46.0	42.7	190.3	73.7	109.8	25.0	13.9	16.8	23.5	29.2

C. l. fuscus:																
California—																
Litchfield[1]	34228	247.8	232.3	135.2	79.1	47.0	45.9	38.6	178.9	72.9	105.5	26.3	13.7	15.5	23.4	30.2
Oregon—																
Cascadia	235530	256.5	235.5	137.0	78.8	45.0	47.8	44.3	187.0	85.0	109.1	25.6	14.2	16.8	22.0	30.1
Cascadia	243984	256.0	238.3	141.1	75.6	44.3	50.3	44.0	187.2	83.3	107.6	25.5	12.3	16.9	23.1	28.4
Clackamas River[7]	427	251.0	236.0	137.0	79.3	44.2	50.3	46.2	185.8	77.1	.....	24.9	14.8	16.3	22.2	29.1
Estacada	228800	259.5	244.3	143.4	81.1	44.9	49.8	43.7	190.3	83.4	107.0	....	13.6	....	....	29.4
Glide (20 mi. NE)[7]	438	254.4	233.0	134.7	81.8	44.2	47.8	42.5	187.3	82.9	102.3	24.0	14.4	16.4	22.2	28.6
Molalla River[7]	422	255.2	237.8	141.0	79.9	45.0	56.0	49.5	188.3	85.0	105.7	24.2	13.8	15.6	21.7	27.0
Rogue River	243985	259.4	235.3	135.2	78.6	45.6	49.2	41.5	184.2	83.6	107.1	26.5	14.8	17.8	23.7	30.2
Silver Lake (30 mi. south)	247357	264.9	244.8	140.8	77.8	43.7	49.6	38.5	184.2	74.8	107.4	25.8	13.0	17.2	23.3	28.7
Tiller	223817	258.3	242.0	136.5	77.4	44.5	48.0	42.5	186.5	84.4	107.6	25.7	15.0	17.4	22.9	29.9
Washington—																
Puget Sound	3438	267.0	249.1	142.0	81.2	48.5	52.6	47.6	.....	....	109.1	27.3	14.9	17.2	24.1	....
	Average	257.3	238.9	138.5	79.1	45.2	49.8	43.5	186.0	81.2	106.8	25.6	14.0	16.7	22.9	29.2
C. l. crassodon:																
British Columbia—																
Vancouver Island[8]	137805	244.3	232.2	126.3	77.7	41.8	43.0	47.9	177.8	63.7	105.7	27.1	16.6	17.8	24.6	31.3
Vancouver Island[1]	12457	256.2	239.6	143.4	80.1	44.8	50.1	45.6	183.5	72.1	107.5	26.2	15.9	17.6	23.1	30.4
Vancouver Island[3]	3339	251.6	234.2	138.0	76.8	42.9	47.8	42.3	184.9	74.4	105.0	25.6	13.9	16.5	22.2	28.9
	Average	250.7	235.3	135.9	78.2	43.2	47.0	45.3	182.1	70.1	106.6	26.3	15.5	17.3	23.3	30.2
C. l. youngi:																
California—																
Providence Mts.[1]	33389	252.1	232.3	150.0	80.0	44.9	49.0	44.9	186.2	82.6	107.4	25.9	15.1	17.1	22.7	30.1
Colorado—																
Salt Creek, Garfield County	210742	265.0	248.5	148.0	82.5	48.2	51.5	45.4	193.4	82.1	110.3	25.2	13.4	17.1	24.8	29.1
Sulphur, Rio Blanco County	224975	254.5	242.7	139.8	78.3	46.8	50.7	42.6	189.2	78.6	109.9	25.2	13.2	16.9	23.5	28.3
West Creek, Garfield County	224525	260.5	242.9	142.4	84.0	47.1	46.1	37.7	188.6	76.6	110.9	26.9	14.3	17.1	23.7	29.6
New Mexico—																
Abiquiu	223512	251.5	236.8	139.8	77.3	49.4	49.1	40.6	181.0	79.2	107.9	24.7	14.0	17.0	22.4	30.0
Utah—																
Duchesne	224457	260.4	248.5	142.7	82.6	48.0	47.9	41.7	194.5	83.2	111.7	25.8	14.2	16.4	22.5	29.4
Grouse Creek, Box Elder County	221961	265.4	242.2	144.7	81.8	49.7	47.8	43.6	190.5	78.9	112.3	25.2	14.0	16.7	22.1	29.9
Heart Draw, San Juan County[6]	224001	258.5	243.5	136.7	82.8	47.7	44.3	40.6	187.7	77.1	107.8	26.5	14.1	17.3	23.7	30.0
Heart Draw, San Juan County[9]	224000	254.0	235.9	136.6	80.2	44.4	44.1	39.3	186.0	76.1	108.4	26.4	14.1	16.9	23.8	30.2
La Sal (10 mi. SE)	221829	260.4	245.6	145.8	83.8	46.2	48.4	37.6	186.7	76.3	107.4	25.7	13.9	15.9	20.1	28.9
Wyoming—																
Federal	227684	252.0	231.7	137.1	77.2	46.6	46.7	42.2	178.4	75.2	103.6	25.0	13.7	17.3	22.8	29.2
Laramie	208508	262.0	246.6	147.2	79.9	45.8	46.2	39.0	191.3	77.2	110.6	26.1	14.9	17.2	22.7	29.5
Rock Springs	214813	260.0	240.5	148.7	79.1	48.8	50.5	41.2	187.4	77.8	108.2	25.7	14.9	16.2	23.2	29.4
	Average	258.2	241.4	143.0	80.7	47.2	47.9	41.3	187.8	78.5	109.0	25.7	14.1	16.9	22.9	29.5

FOOTNOTES: [1] Mus. Vert. Zool. [2] B. C. Prov. Mus. [3] B. C. Prov. Mus. Type specimen. [4] B. C. Prov. Mus. Type locality. [5] Roy. Ont. Mus. Zool. [6] Type specimen. [7] Ore. Agric. College. [8] Subadult. [9] Type locality.

TABLE 4.—CRANIAL MEASUREMENTS OF ADULT MALES IN U. S. NATIONAL MUSEUM, UNLESS OTHERWISE INDICATED, OF *Canis lupus* GROUP—(Continued)

Species and locality	Number	Greatest length	Condylobasal length	Zygomatic breadth	Squamosal constriction	Width of rostrum	Interorbital breadth	Postorbital constriction	Length of mandible	Height of coronoid process	Maxillary tooth row, crown length	Upper carnassial, crown length (outer side)	Upper carnassial, crown width	First upper molar, antero-posterior diameter	First upper molar, transverse diameter	Lower carnassial, crown length
C. l. mogollonensis:																
New Mexico—																
Chloride	232445	258.4	235.0	142.1	79.7	44.2	47.3	38.9	184.8	80.5	104.1	24.9	13.9	16.1	22.7	28.8
Chloride	216250	257.4	235.4	136.9	79.5	45.1	47.6	38.0	182.9	75.6	99.7	25.6	14.9	18.2	23.4	30.8
Chloride	216249	259.8	236.1	142.6	81.7	42.8	47.6	45.6	184.0	81.5	106.5	26.0	13.1	16.5	23.0	29.6
Chloride	224516	255.0	237.5	137.4	79.7	46.4	44.2	39.6	181.0	77.3	107.0	25.2	14.9	15.4	22.5	28.1
Fairview	232451	253.5	231.5	144.6	83.4	46.1	45.7	42.2	179.6	79.4	102.0	24.3	13.9	15.8	21.3	26.8
Fairview	235088	252.0	229.8	142.5	80.6	43.6	45.7	41.4	182.5	80.9	107.1	24.2	13.5	16.4	22.4	27.0
Gila Nat. Forest	148976	257.5	234.8	141.8	82.1	45.9	51.0	42.2	183.2	73.0	105.7	27.7	15.0	17.4	23.9	31.5
Gila Nat. Forest	148971	255.0	231.9	133.7	82.9	46.8	46.0	38.9	181.0	76.9	105.2	26.8	14.9	17.9	23.2	31.1
Luna (10 mi. NW)[1]	224548	253.5	236.3	142.1	80.8	43.7	46.1	36.8	184.7	78.4	107.0	25.1	13.9	16.7	22.9	30.0
Magdalena	221655	253.2	228.0	133.8	80.3	44.7	43.4	39.4	177.9	77.3	104.5	25.3	14.6	16.0	22.6	28.6
Monticello	228264	258.5	234.0	149.5	83.2	47.8	46.1	40.7	184.4	81.8	106.5	25.6	16.0	15.6	22.7	28.5
	Average	255.8	233.7	140.6	81.3	45.2	46.4	40.3	182.4	78.4	105.0	25.5	14.4	16.5	22.8	29.2
C. l. monstrabilis:																
New Mexico—																
Sacramento Mts.	159016	245.9	227.4	135.0	77.2	45.1	46.0	37.7	175.0	73.8	103.7	25.6	14.3	17.5	22.3	30.0
Sacramento Mts.	159020	255.3	.....	131.2	....	44.6	42.9	38.3	177.8	73.4	102.6	24.1	12.3	15.7	21.1	27.3
Sacramento Mts.	159022	257.9	232.5	134.4	78.4	45.1	42.6	35.8	174.0	74.2	104.6	26.2	13.7	16.4	23.6	30.4
Texas—																
Guadalupe Mts.	110046	263.0	243.8	141.0	82.2	46.8	44.5	40.5	183.3	78.6	108.6	26.8	15.0	17.9	24.0	29.8
Ozona	227902	257.5	233.0	140.0	77.7	46.0	47.0	43.2	179.2	77.5	108.9	26.1	14.3	15.4	21.9	28.8
Ozona	227885	251.0	232.0	139.0	77.5	45.6	46.9	39.9	178.8	77.5	104.7	25.6	15.0	16.5	22.7	29.2
Rankin (10 mi. south)[1]	209497	260.0	236.8	137.5	80.4	43.7	45.4	39.5	184.4	83.9	103.8	24.7	14.3	15.1	22.5	28.0
Rankin (10 mi. south)	222090	255.5	237.8	131.5	74.7	46.2	46.9	40.7	178.2	79.1	106.7	25.8	14.8	17.1	24.2	30.0
	Average	255.8	234.8	136.2	78.3	45.4	45.3	39.5	178.8	77.3	105.5	25.6	14.2	16.5	22.8	29.2

C. l. baileyi:																
Arizona—																
Helvetia	226435	240.1	213.5	129.7	74.1	38.5	43.7	39.7	168.0	71.2	96.9	22.6	11.7	14.8	18.8	24.9
Santa Rita Mts.	251525	235.0	216.2	135.6	74.5	42.7	41.6	37.3	171.0	77.4	96.0	23.4	12.8	15.9	19.7	26.2
Chihuahua—																
Colonia Garcia[1]	98312	232.1	221.4	129.7	74.8	39.5	44.5	38.9	171.0	70.4	100.2	24.7	12.0	15.8	21.5	27.2
Colonia Garcia[2]	117059	246.5	231.5	144.7	82.8	43.4	46.2	44.8	183.0	77.8	104.2	25.1	14.6	15.9	22.2	27.0
Colonia Garcia[2]	98307	241.0	222.4	129.7	74.3	39.7	40.1	38.2	169.0	76.0	99.7	25.3	12.8	16.3	21.1	26.1
Colonia Juarez	98313	247.5	225.0	132.4	74.4	41.5	43.3	38.3	172.3	75.9	101.4	24.1	13.4	15.9	19.7	26.8
Gallego	170556	245.2	225.9	138.0	77.2	40.7	40.9	31.4	172.1	73.9	101.3	25.0	13.5	15.7	20.1	28.0
New Mexico—																
Animas (35 mi. SE)	234499	237.3	221.3	131.4	75.2	43.3	42.1	37.9	161.9	70.8	100.0	27.7	14.4	16.9	22.9	29.1
Animas Mts.	262129	249.8	226.0	140.1	82.6	41.8	45.8	41.7	176.3	74.8	100.2	25.3	13.4	15.3	22.0	27.7
Hachita	231324	240.2	224.8	132.3	76.2	42.1	42.5	36.3	173.1	77.5	103.3	25.4	13.7	16.1	21.4	27.6
Hachita	231320	236.8	217.5	136.4	78.7	38.9	43.0	36.4	166.4	74.6	96.0	24.7	13.0	15.3	20.7	26.8
	Average	241.0	222.3	134.5	76.8	41.1	43.1	38.3	171.3	74.6	99.9	24.8	13.2	15.8	20.9	27.0

FOOTNOTES: [1] Type specimen. [2] Type locality.

TABLE 5.—CRANIAL MEASUREMENTS OF ADULT MALES IN U. S. NATIONAL MUSEUM, UNLESS OTHERWISE INDICATED, OF *Canis niger* GROUP

Species and locality	Number	Greatest length	Condylobasal length	Zygomatic breadth	Squamosal constriction	Width of rostrum	Interorbital breadth	Postorbital constriction	Length of mandible	Height of coronoid process	Maxillary tooth row, crown length	Upper carnassial, crown length (outer side)	Upper carnassial, crown width	First upper molar, antero-posterior diameter	First upper molar, transverse diameter	Lower carnassial, crown length
C. n. rufus:																
Arkansas—																
Boxley	243312	221.4	208.8	121.0	67.8	35.7	36.5	36.1	162.2	67.6	96.6	21.8	11.8	14.4	20.0	24.1
Oklahoma—																
Atoka	243317	218.2	202.3	118.7	65.7	35.0	41.1	37.0	156.0	66.5	93.6	20.1	10.5	13.9	19.3	23.4
Redfork	133233	228.5	212.4	120.0	67.2	32.4	39.3	36.1	161.3	64.4	97.8	21.8	11.6	15.3	19.4	24.5
Redfork	135748	217.2	204.0	111.1	63.0	31.1	34.9	36.2	156.5	60.5	92.1	20.3	11.3	13.8	18.1	22.5
Texas—																
Angleton	261753	218.7	202.5	114.5	63.6	32.3	33.7	31.9	155.5	62.8	93.4	21.3	10.0	14.3	18.4	24.6
Aransas Migratory Waterfowl Refuge, Aransas County	265645	220.3	205.8	111.3	67.6	32.7	34.9	36.3	156.4	60.8	90.6	20.9	10.1	13.7	19.2	23.2
Burnet	224531	221.6	208.0	109.5	67.4	33.2	36.3	36.8	155.5	66.2	92.8	21.9	11.7	15.0	19.4	24.1
Doole	224972	216.4	204.1	106.5	64.3	33.5	35.7	36.4	152.3	59.0	91.0	21.4	10.2	13.6	17.6	23.5
Edwards County	108680	216.9	204.7	113.2	63.9	32.6	36.5	33.7	160.2	63.2	91.2	21.8	10.8	14.4	18.9	25.3
Kerr County	146744	218.0	210.0	111.2	67.5	32.9	36.4	33.8	159.5	60.3	91.0	21.7	10.6	15.2	19.7	24.0
Llano	224003	225.0	207.8	117.5	68.7	34.6	39.7	36.0	161.0	61.1	98.2	22.4	11.6	14.3	19.8	24.6
Llano	224530	226.9	209.0	112.3	66.0	33.3	35.0	34.8	160.7	62.8	94.6	21.3	11.6	14.2	18.7	23.1
Llano	223589	210.0	201.6	108.0	65.4	31.6	38.9	34.5	148.1	60.5	91.3	20.8	10.1	13.7	18.0	22.5
Llano	214853	209.4	196.0	111.5	63.2	31.6	35.8	38.5	148.7	59.7	92.3	20.1	10.9	13.2	17.7	22.4
Llano	225366	209.5	196.5	105.5	60.7	32.8	36.9	34.2	157.2	59.5	92.3	21.2	10.6	13.0	17.7	22.3
Llano	224185	214.2	199.4	109.3	65.0	32.2	33.9	33.4	151.0	61.1	91.7	21.0	10.9	14.5	19.0	24.4
Llano	224529	222.0	206.7	114.0	65.7	32.5	37.1	39.9	160.0	69.2	94.4	21.0	11.0	14.7	18.7	23.3
Marble Falls	228239	222.5	207.0	103.2	68.8	30.0	36.7	37.3	157.8	57.6	96.9	22.5	11.0	14.8	19.9	24.2
Marble Falls	228069	214.5	202.3	105.9	63.3	31.8	32.3	31.4	155.0	57.6	93.7	22.5	10.7	13.9	18.3	24.9
Marble Falls	228517	208.0	197.7	111.4	63.2	34.6	36.5	38.6	150.7	60.3	91.0	21.7	10.6	15.2	19.7	24.0
Menard	213288	218.7	201.3	110.5	62.5	33.8	33.8	33.7	155.0	61.7	90.5	21.3	10.5	14.6	18.3	23.0
Port O'Connor	99719	235.0	221.5	121.9	70.1	34.7	40.3	33.7	167.0	69.0	96.0	22.7	12.3	14.9	20.2	24.6
Port O'Connor	99718	220.8	201.4	112.9	66.2	32.5	41.5	37.7	156.3	65.6	90.0	20.8	10.9	13.7	18.4	23.0
Sheffield	227900	208.3	200.8	107.5	62.3	33.2	35.8	33.2	150.7	63.2	91.2	21.8	10.8	14.4	18.9	25.3
	Average	218.4	204.7	112.0	65.3	32.9	36.6	35.5	156.4	62.6	93.5	21.5	11.0	14.3	19.0	23.8
C. n. gregoryi:																
Arkansas—																
Blue Ball	243432	219.5	206.4	119.5	67.3	36.8	37.9	38.9	156.7	63.3	96.0	24.6	13.5	16.1	21.0	26.5
Blue Ball	243434	223.0	198.5	122.5	70.4	36.4	41.5	38.7	153.5	65.9	91.0	23.2	11.7	14.7	19.7	26.2

Arkansas—*continued*																
Egger	242586	244.6	221.8	120.5	68.8	36.7	40.1	36.3	169.0	64.7	100.9	24.0	11.7	15.9	21.2	25.8
Ferndale	243308	231.2	215.3	123.5	68.0	38.1	37.3	34.6	161.5	64.1	95.4	22.9	13.1	15.1	20.3	25.5
Ferndale	242576	229.5	217.5	125.8	68.8	37.5	41.6	37.2	163.5	64.2	95.3	22.8	13.0	15.1	20.2	25.4
Hollis	248720	242.8	223.3	126.7	75.4	39.4	43.5	39.0	171.3	66.9	98.5	23.7	12.5	15.8	22.2	25.8
Hot Springs	243430	236.3	221.2	130.0	71.2	39.9	47.9	39.9	171.7	68.1	102.7	23.6	13.1	15.4	20.8	26.8
Isaac	242583	240.4	221.4	131.3	74.7	41.6	42.2	40.6	173.4	74.0	101.5	25.2	13.4	16.5	22.2	27.9
Pinnacle	243593	248.0	225.4	137.7	72.9	41.5	46.2	42.1	174.8	73.8	99.9	24.2	13.0	15.3	21.1	26.5
Tallsville	236550	245.3	231.0	124.5	71.9	37.8	39.8	33.4	174.9	64.7	100.9	24.0	11.7	15.9	21.2	25.8
Illinois—																
Warsaw[1]	4609	220.5	208.4	115.5	68.3	34.3	38.2	36.5	158.4	64.3	92.0	22.4	10.4	14.6	19.0	24.2
Louisiana—																
Mer Rouge	132229	245.2	225.5	121.0	70.8	38.7	38.6	35.5	171.4	70.0	101.7	24.9	13.2	16.6	21.6	27.0
Tallulah (vicinity)[2]	136731	250.0	228.0	126.0	73.2	34.7	40.6	32.4	173.0	68.6	103.8	23.5	12.0	15.9	20.6	26.5
Tallulah (vicinity)	133687	249.5	230.7	124.7	75.4	35.9	42.6	36.7	176.0	67.8	104.0	24.9	12.0	16.1	22.6	26.8
Winn Parish	265475	242.4	221.0	126.7	69.8	35.7	37.0	34.5	170.7	74.0	101.2	22.1	12.7	14.9	20.2	25.1
Mississippi—																
Biloxi[3]	100225	234.5	219.9	122.0	70.6	33.6	38.9	35.5	168.0	68.9	98.0	23.2	12.0	15.2	20.7	24.9
Missouri—																
Barren	244246	245.3	233.7	130.4	72.5	37.5	44.2	40.5	180.0	72.2	103.9	24.5	11.6	15.5	21.0	27.3
Barren	244247	234.5	221.7	122.3	69.2	37.3	39.1	37.6	169.2	67.7	102.8	23.8	13.6	14.7	20.7	27.3
Barren	244523	226.0	215.8	124.8	69.3	35.7	39.2	40.2	162.0	67.6	98.7	22.8	12.0	15.2	19.8	26.1
Barren	244299	218.5	207.4	123.9	67.8	34.2	36.1	35.4	154.0	68.0	91.1	23.0	11.9	14.5	20.0	25.5
Cook's Station	244301	226.4	208.2	119.1	67.3	32.9	40.4	36.4	160.0	67.3	96.1	21.8	11.7	15.2	19.9	25.3
Cook's Station	244424	242.8	225.0	124.4	71.3	36.1	40.7	41.0	169.8	64.8	98.8	22.5	11.6	16.2	21.6	26.4
Gatewood	244212	247.2	227.6	121.0	66.8	35.3	37.8	38.3	169.4	71.4	103.0	24.3	12.5	15.1	20.1	26.2
Gatewood	244213	238.8	226.2	115.2	67.7	32.9	38.5	36.6	169.9	69.2	103.1	23.2	12.0	15.2	20.7	26.5
West Plains	235435	235.8	219.0	121.4	67.6	39.2	40.0	35.0	166.4	70.7	99.1	24.1	11.5	15.5	20.8	27.5
West Plains	235436	233.8	215.0	125.3	72.2	36.1	38.3	34.9	169.8	62.3	97.4	22.0	12.8	14.8	19.2	24.8
Oklahoma—																
Broken Bow	234436	247.9	231.0	126.5	71.7	40.3	43.7	39.6	178.5	73.9	103.2	23.8	13.6	15.9	21.5	25.8
Broken Bow	234434	233.7	217.4	122.5	68.0	38.9	41.8	39.6	168.4	70.6	100.3	23.7	12.1	15.4	21.2	25.3
Broken Bow	232436	230.5	216.5	123.9	67.1	34.8	39.0	37.7	165.4	66.5	102.1	23.4	12.5	15.2	21.0	26.0
Broken Bow	232423	233.0	215.3	130.5	70.9	39.4	43.7	40.6	165.4	65.0	99.5	24.4	13.1	15.8	21.1	25.2
Page	234451	237.7	209.8	120.0	68.7	37.6	42.7	40.6	169.4	64.0	96.9	25.2	12.3	16.7	21.6	26.7
Sherwood	234427	236.0	219.5	121.2	68.0	38.8	37.1	37.8	169.5	67.8	99.8	24.9	12.6	15.7	21.9	26.9
Smithville	234437	239.0	224.4	120.5	67.9	37.0	41.0	39.7	176.0	71.5	101.9	23.4	12.8	15.4	21.3	26.7
Smithville	231538	222.0	208.0	116.5	67.2	35.5	34.2	32.3	156.7	64.0	90.0	24.1	10.7	15.3	21.8	27.3
Smithville	235499	228.0	209.4	122.5	71.8	39.2	42.2	39.3	163.2	73.4	93.3	23.0	11.3	16.4	21.8	25.2
Smithville	235497	232.0	222.0	115.5	67.9	35.9	36.1	33.1	165.0	68.4	98.2	24.6	12.1	15.2	21.4	26.3
Texas—																
Hardin County	262473	246.7	228.0	119.5	74.1	37.9	40.5	39.4	175.9	73.4	102.1	23.4	12.5	15.5	20.1	25.2
Polk County	250679	241.0	222.3	120.3	70.3	34.9	40.3	37.2	170.0	74.0	98.8	21.4	11.0	15.3	20.2	24.5
Polk County	250678	228.2	214.1	107.8	66.4	35.8	36.1	36.5	165.0	69.7	97.2	24.2	12.6	16.2	21.5	26.0
	Average	236.1	219.3	122.9	70.0	37.0	40.2	37.5	167.9	68.5	99.2	23.6	12.4	15.5	20.9	26.1
C. n. niger:																
Alabama—																
Cherokee	223936	236.0	219.0	125.9	72.3	39.7	39.7	37.6	170.0	70.7	98.5	24.1	14.1	22.0	21.6	27.3

FOOTNOTES: [1] Subadult. Amer. Mus. Nat. Hist. [2] Type specimen. [3] Amer. Mus. Nat. Hist.

TABLE 6.—CRANIAL MEASUREMENTS OF ADULT FEMALES IN U. S. NATIONAL MUSEUM, UNLESS OTHERWISE INDICATED, OF *Canis lupus* GROUP

Species and locality	Number	Greatest length	Condylobasal length	Zygomatic breadth	Squamosal constriction	Width of rostrum	Interorbital breadth	Postorbital constriction	Length of mandible	Height of coronoid process	Maxillary tooth row, crown length	Upper carnassial, crown length (outer side)	Upper carnassial, crown width	First upper molar, antero-posterior diameter	First upper molar, transverse diameter	Lower carnassial, crown length
C. l. tundrarum:																
Alaska—																
Point Barrow[1]	4054	270.5	244.2	140.5	77.2	47.0	50.5	46.2	195.5	80.0	112.6	24.5	13.4	15.9	21.1	28.4
Point Barrow[3]	16748	258.7	242.2	138.5	76.1	43.2	47.3	41.9	188.1	74.7	110.6	25.9	15.0	17.7	24.7	30.5
	Average	264.6	243.2	139.5	76.7	45.1	48.9	44.1	191.8	77.4	111.6	25.2	14.2	16.8	22.9	29.5
C. l. pambasileus:																
Alaska—																
Eagle	265983	254.8	243.2	134.4	79.0	43.5	46.4	42.8	181.5	72.9	105.7	26.5	14.4	17.1	23.6	29.1
Fairbanks	264420	265.9	245.5	133.0	74.9	44.6	44.3	40.7	191.3	71.6	111.9	25.4	14.8	17.1	22.8	28.7
Little Delta River	266121	260.0	240.1	142.8	75.7	44.9	47.2	43.1	190.5	79.0	110.1	25.3	13.5	16.5	23.5	29.8
Tanana	218342	269.0	246.8	129.4	79.8	41.1	46.1	40.5	191.1	74.6	111.0	25.7	14.5	17.0	23.2	27.7
Yukon—																
White River[3]	33-9-20-4	261.7	245.8	131.7	78.0	41.8	39.5	37.0	189.0	73.5	109.8	25.6	14.8	16.7	23.7	30.6
	Average	262.3	244.3	134.3	77.5	43.2	44.7	40.8	188.6	74.3	109.7	25.7	14.4	16.9	23.4	29.2
C. l. alces:																
Alaska—																
Kachemak Bay[3]	147471	280.5	263.5	141.3	82.2	47.4	49.0	44.3	201.3	79.1	118.5	25.5	12.8	17.1	22.3	30.3
Kachemak Bay[4]	147472	272.0	253.2	141.4	81.8	46.6	45.9	42.1	194.3	82.0	112.3	24.5	13.0	17.1	22.3	29.1
	Average	276.3	258.4	141.4	82.0	47.0	47.5	43.2	197.8	80.6	115.4	25.0	12.9	17.1	22.3	29.7
C. l. occidentalis:																
Alberta—																
Wood Buffalo Park[5]	130266	257.3	237.5	143.0	83.1	44.6	42.3	45.0	185.5	76.4	104.8	25.8	14.2	17.0	23.4	29.7
Wood Buffalo Park[5]	92227	265.8	244.7	140.5	84.3	44.9	42.5	38.8	188.7	75.2	110.1	25.0	13.9	16.3	23.4	29.2
Wood Buffalo Park[5]	98232	256.0	245.5	134.0	81.8	44.4	41.7	42.6	184.4	76.3	107.6	26.3	13.1	16.9	23.4	28.7
Wood Buffalo Park[5]	130170	256.5	243.5	131.4	80.5	44.9	41.9	41.5	185.5	76.6	106.7	25.2	13.4	16.3	21.9	29.7

Mackenzie—																
Fort Anderson	6508	257.8	241.9	139.5	81.3	45.9	44.6	39.5	.....	....	110.0	26.1	15.1	17.8	23.5	....
Fort Smith	134781	249.5	233.2	133.0	79.7	40.5	40.0	37.2	183.2	74.0	102.7	24.4	13.4	16.1	21.8	26.9
Great Bear Lake[5]	34447	249.5	233.0	130.0	75.5	42.7	42.3	36.0	176.7	70.1	106.6	26.5	14.2	18.0	24.1	29.0
Great Slave Lake[5]	121469	255.5	239.0	135.4	79.8	41.0	44.5	40.0	182.4	77.0	105.9	24.6	13.3	15.7	22.8	27.8
Yukon—																
Macmillan River (north fork)	134497	254.0	233.7	137.4	77.7	42.7	42.8	42.8	180.8	78.9	102.0	23.9	13.8	15.4	22.2	27.4
	Average	255.8	239.1	136.0	80.4	43.5	42.5	40.4	183.4	75.6	106.3	25.3	13.8	16.6	22.9	28.6
C. l. hudsonicus:																
Keewatin—																
Schultz Lake[3]	180283	251.0	228.8	134.8	77.4	42.4	44.4	43.2	181.9	75.4	104.1	24.5	13.8	17.4	22.6	27.6
C. l. orion:																
Arctic America—																
Greenland[5]	42084	242.4	227.5	132.8	74.7	39.6	42.1	35.8	173.4	71.0	102.6	24.5	13.8	16.2	22.0	28.0
C. l. labradorius:																
Labrador—																
Hopedale[6]	3020	237.8	223.8	130.4	71.4	39.7	....	44.0	173.4	68.7	101.9	25.0	13.2	17.5	23.4	28.5
Quebec—																
Fort Chimo (near)	23136	247.1	222.7	132.7	73.0	41.7	43.5	46.9	175.5	73.8	98.4	25.0	12.4	15.3	21.3	28.1
	Average	242.5	223.3	131.6	72.2	40.7	43.5	45.5	174.5	71.3	100.2	25.0	12.8	16.4	22.4	28.3
C. l. lycaon:																
Michigan—																
Marquette (30 mi. NW)	242289	234.4	217.6	121.2	69.1	38.4	43.4	42.5	167.7	64.3	98.2	22.5	11.8	15.0	21.0	26.1
Marquette (30 mi. NW)	242290	233.7	217.2	125.3	72.2	36.9	43.6	37.9	169.3	66.9	96.8	22.5	11.7	16.3	20.9	26.0
Marquette County[7]	21207	250.8	232.3	129.5	75.1	40.2	48.9	41.7	177.7	68.7	104.2	23.5	13.1	16.5	22.0	25.7
Randville	168349	244.0	226.4	129.7	76.5	41.2	43.3	39.5	173.8	72.0	99.2	23.1	12.7	14.6	19.5	26.1
Walsh[8]	......	267.0	248.8	142.0	79.4	42.5	43.0	39.9	190.8	79.4	110.0	24.7	14.1	16.8	22.3	27.2
Ontario—																
Algonquin Nat. Park	178452	230.3	208.5	116.3	71.9	35.9	38.5	36.8	157.7	61.0	94.4	22.6	11.4	16.0	19.4	26.0
Silver Islet, Thunder Bay[3]	11281	230.3	221.8	126.7	74.5	39.8	35.5	35.2	165.5	71.1	98.9	24.0	12.7	16.3	23.2	27.6
Pennsylvania—[9]	2262	234.8	215.8	.....	75.7	37.1	41.6	35.9	167.2	67.9	98.1	23.7	12.5	15.3	20.8	26.4
Quebec—																
Lucerne[10]	77342	234.7	222.6	131.2	71.7	39.5	40.8	34.6	169.0	72.2	98.1	22.9	11.7	15.6	20.6	27.1
Lucerne[3]	31-3-13-2	226.9	.....	118.7	70.2	35.0	37.2	34.0	.....	....	94.0	21.9	12.3	16.1	20.8	....
Montebello[3]	31-12-29-1	213.6	203.3	118.2	69.6	34.4	35.8	30.4	155.0	62.5	91.0	22.5	12.0	16.0	19.5	25.8
Montebello[3]	31-12-29-4	224.7	211.4	117.9	70.2	35.3	37.2	33.8	157.7	65.8	94.5	21.8	12.4	15.8	21.0	25.9
Montebello[3]	31-12-29-3	225.2	.....	122.5	69.3	37.1	42.4	35.0	163.8	65.8	96.2	21.8	11.8	15.1	20.6	25.9
Wisconsin—																
Eagle River	150421	254.0	.....	130.8	74.7	41.8	45.3	42.7	178.0	71.0	103.2	24.2	13.6	15.6	21.7	28.3
Vilas County (near Michigan line)[7]	51773	258.7	242.3	134.0	79.5	40.5	47.8	41.2	189.5	78.8	108.4	23.5	14.2	16.9	22.1	28.5
	Average	237.5	222.3	126.0	73.3	38.4	41.6	37.4	170.2	69.1	99.0	23.0	12.5	15.9	21.0	26.6

FOOTNOTES: [1] Type locality. Colo. Mus. Nat. Hist. [2] Type specimen. [3] Roy. Ont. Mus. Zool. [4] Type locality. [5] Amer. Mus. Nat. Hist. [6] Mus. Comp. Zool. [7] Field Mus. Nat. Hist. [8] Stanley P. Young. [9] Acad. Nat. Sci. Phila. [10] Mus. Vert. Zool.

TABLE 6.—CRANIAL MEASUREMENTS OF ADULT FEMALES IN U. S. NATIONAL MUSEUM, UNLESS OTHERWISE INDICATED, OF *Canis lupus* GROUP—(Continued)

Species and locality	Number	Greatest length	Condylobasal length	Zygomatic breadth	Squamosal constriction	Width of rostrum	Interorbital breadth	Postorbital constriction	Length of mandible	Height of coronoid process	Maxillary tooth row, crown length	Upper carnassial, crown length (outer side)	Upper carnassial, crown width	First upper molar, antero-posterior diameter	First upper molar, transverse diameter	Lower carnassial, crown length
C. l. nubilus:																
Colorado—																
Bent County	51435	225.8	213.0	124.6	72.0	43.4	40.0	39.5	162.5	68.8	97.0	24.3	13.3	17.0	22.1	28.3
Montana—																
Meredith	222040	245.8	228.0	128.4	78.0	42.3	41.8	41.6	178.8	74.2	104.5	24.4	13.5	16.4	21.8	27.6
Miles City	224443	241.9	226.8	130.0	75.2	46.2	49.6	41.6	172.5	69.9	103.8	24.6	13.8	16.8	22.0	27.3
Miles City	224442	244.0	223.4	131.1	74.3	43.7	43.7	38.2	172.5	66.9	102.1	25.0	13.1	17.3	23.1	28.3
Mizpah	223691	222.0	212.8	129.2	72.3	42.4	46.9	42.4	168.7	65.9	101.0	23.3	13.3	15.5	21.3	27.0
Nebraska—																
Kearney	3343	228.7	210.7	119.4	70.6	38.7	38.9	34.8	161.7	66.5	99.5	24.1	12.8	16.9	23.2	27.8
Platte River	3575	231.0	212.5	130.5	71.4	40.9	40.3	38.0	165.5	71.4	96.2	24.2	14.1	15.5	20.2	28.0
Platte River	2611	233.5	212.9	126.2	73.0	38.1	37.3	35.3	167.0	66.3	.....	23.4	11.6	14.8	20.0	25.6
New Mexico—																
Santa Rosa (18 mi. south)	168345	250.5	230.8	135.1	74.5	42.0	44.9	37.8	180.7	75.7	106.1	26.1	14.3	16.3	22.3	27.9
South Dakota—																
Dewey	221852	241.3	223.8	134.6	72.9	43.3	43.6	38.6	171.4	73.7	103.9	26.1	13.5	17.2	21.9	29.5
Fort Randall, Gregory County	12907/11268	228.3	210.5	123.7	71.0	41.6	42.8	38.2	164.0	65.7	94.3	23.0	13.2	15.5	20.0	24.9
Imlay	210683	249.3	229.0	131.1	75.9	45.5	43.8	37.3	179.7	78.5	103.8	25.1	13.2	17.1	22.3	29.6
Wyoming—																
Douglas	212919	226.7	218.5	129.1	73.4	39.2	41.6	37.7	165.0	66.0	99.2	24.2	13.7	15.9	22.7	28.5
	Average	236.1	219.4	128.7	73.4	42.1	42.7	37.0	170.0	70.0	101.0	24.4	13.3	16.3	21.8	27.7
C. l. irremotus:																
Alberta—																
Gleichen[1]	7657	238.7	222.0	124.5	71.6	41.4	38.5	35.9	169.9	66.8	101.4	25.0	14.0	17.1	23.5	29.5
Idaho—																
Alridge	215247	242.3	224.9	128.8	74.4	42.6	43.5	34.9	174.9	73.0	99.5	24.9	14.3	17.7	23.7	29.8
Alridge	214904	242.5	225.9	128.0	73.8	41.3	38.9	33.5	175.0	74.6	102.9	23.9	12.8	17.0	22.7	27.4
Leadore	236102	233.4	219.0	120.5	70.3	40.3	41.6	39.1	167.5	67.8	99.6	23.9	13.3	16.4	21.4	28.2
Pocatello (10 mi. east)	234228	235.2	221.5	121.6	68.8	38.5	39.3	36.9	167.5	67.6	100.2	24.6	12.7	16.5	22.7	27.5
Soda Springs	234700	233.3	216.2	124.4	71.2	40.7	44.9	36.0	165.8	67.8	98.9	22.6	11.9	14.7	21.0	25.6
Soda Springs	231437	232.8	219.3	127.7	74.4	42.0	76.7	40.2	165.4	69.9	97.7	23.0	12.2	15.2	20.6	26.1
Soda Springs	234701	241.3	221.9	119.7	73.2	42.7	40.2	36.7	170.4	71.3	101.3	24.1	13.4	15.9	20.9	27.0
Soda Springs (20 mi. NE)	227671	237.5	219.8	127.0	70.6	41.7	42.9	36.6	169.5	67.7	100.7	23.0	12.2	15.4	21.3	26.7
Tyhee, Bannock Co.	214893	237.4	222.9	126.7	71.1	41.5	43.9	38.1	166.0	68.7	99.4	23.9	13.0	15.1	21.8	28.3

Montana—																	
Beaverhead Mts.	228351	239.0	225.0	126.2	71.3	39.3	43.0	39.0	172.4	68.3	102.0	23.8	14.4	16.4	22.7	28.5
Beaverhead Mts.	228518	241.4	226.2	124.1	73.5	39.6	41.5	34.7	173.2	69.7	102.3	24.2	14.7	17.6	22.6	27.8
Belt	223432	248.0	230.0	131.2	76.5	40.2	45.0	42.3	174.7	70.3	103.4	24.9	13.3	16.5	22.3	28.0
Dillon	222667	254.5	237.7	127.0	76.8	42.8	45.7	39.7	179.4	73.5	109.2	26.0	13.4	16.8	22.9	30.3
Dillon	225227	244.5	225.5	123.3	69.1	40.8	41.7	36.9	173.0	70.6	102.3	25.2	14.8	16.4	23.7	28.0
Ingomar	224164	242.3	225.0	125.1	74.5	39.8	42.0	36.4	175.0	73.0	105.3	24.0	12.9	16.9	21.3	28.0
Kruger	228135	242.5	221.4	131.5	74.5	40.6	39.5	37.8	169.7	68.4	101.6	23.4	13.4	15.0	21.3	27.0
Little Belt **Mts.**	156827	237.5	219.3	125.1	70.4	38.5	42.0	37.8	168.0	70.5	101.5	24.0	12.6	16.2	21.5	27.3
Powderville	57723	238.5	223.0	121.5	72.9	41.7	41.7	40.1	170.5	69.6	103.4	24.0	12.7	16.9	21.4	27.6
Riceville	228132	241.8	223.4	131.1	75.0	40.0	40.1	39.1	171.0	70.3	102.7	24.8	12.1	16.0	21.8	27.7
Wyoming—																	
Arvada	223595	241.5	225.8	131.8	75.7	42.1	41.1	35.9	173.0	66.2	103.9	22.6	12.2	15.1	20.4	25.3
Barber, Johnson Co.	242147	248.0	231.0	139.4	75.9	46.8	49.1	43.0	179.5	73.0	105.7	24.7	13.4	16.8	23.1	28.0
Cokeville	178738	239.5	225.4	126.7	77.0	40.5	40.8	36.8	168.0	70.5	100.7	23.8	12.7	17.0	23.2	27.0
Kelly	230790	238.2	220.5	133.6	72.7	41.0	41.7	34.3	172.2	70.5	99.7	22.4	13.0	15.5	21.2	26.5
Lost Springs	227675	244.5	230.0	132.0	72.5	39.9	42.9	36.7	170.8	67.3	103.0	24.4	11.4	16.5	21.7	27.2
Split Rock	234729	247.7	234.5	134.0	77.8	43.1	44.3	36.9	181.2	73.5	108.2	25.8	12.9	17.1	24.6	28.9
Split Rock	212926	246.3	230.4	129.0	74.6	43.9	45.4	40.8	180.0	73.4	104.4	25.2	13.1	16.5	23.6	29.4
	Average	241.1	224.7	127.5	73.3	41.2	42.5	37.6	172.0	70.1	102.3	24.2	13.1	16.3	22.2	27.7
C. l. columbianus:																	
British Columbia—																	
Chezacut[2]	4672	254.8	235.4	135.4	77.7	43.1	45.7	39.7	184.1	69.5	108.1	24.7	13.0	16.7	22.0	28.4
Iskut Summit, six mi. south of Telegraph Creek[3]	31042	259.0	242.5	140.0	79.5	41.2	42.2	39.7	193.3	78.6	110.5	25.7	12.7	17.2	23.8	30.9
Wistaria[4]	4262	262.2	235.8	140.0	79.3	45.4	46.8	44.6	185.3	73.6	105.8	25.6	12.9	16.7	22.0	29.0
Wistaria[4]	4263	266.5	246.4	133.8	79.5	43.1	42.7	37.0	188.7	73.0	108.4	24.7	13.4	17.1	21.8	28.2
	Average	260.6	240.0	137.3	79.0	43.2	44.4	40.3	187.6	73.7	108.2	25.2	13.0	16.9	22.4	29.1
C. l. ligoni:																	
Alaska—																	
Baker Island	243334	246.7	227.3	141.8	79.1	41.8	47.6	46.3	182.5	73.8	103.3	23.3	13.7	15.1	21.9	28.0
Baker Island	243335	258.0	233.0	141.8	79.2	43.0	45.7	43.0	186.8	81.2	105.1	24.3	14.1	16.1	22.5	28.7
Dry Bay, Alsek River[5]	36–9–18–280	249.0	232.5	131.5	78.5	41.5	46.5	40.1	177.7	75.4	101.8	23.3	13.5	14.8	21.0	27.0
Ketchikan	264991	249.5	233.5	134.7	76.9	43.2	41.9	41.5	183.0	74.4	106.1	23.0	14.0	15.7	22.0	27.8
Ketchikan	264990	251.7	231.0	135.5	76.2	43.8	44.3	41.4	186.3	71.9	108.3	24.6	14.2	16.1	22.5	29.1
Kuiu Island	243331	244.0	229.0	132.2	77.4	43.4	43.9	41.6	178.5	66.7	104.6	22.8	12.8	16.3	21.6	27.5
Kuiu Island	264195	250.0	233.4	130.2	74.5	40.6	41.9	39.8	182.2	70.6	107.9	23.8	12.8	16.1	23.5	28.0
Kuiu Island	264193	251.2	234.2	134.3	75.8	40.3	40.7	40.0	183.8	74.1	104.8	26.0	14.3	17.1	24.3	29.5
Kupreanof Island	243324	250.0	232.8	135.5	76.1	42.4	41.2	36.4	185.3	73.4	106.1	23.9	12.9	16.4	22.9	28.7
Prince of Wales Island	243576	240.8	227.2	133.5	76.7	40.5	40.9	42.7	178.8	71.3	104.3	23.0	13.6	15.4	21.2	27.6
Prince of Wales Island	243573	240.0	222.4	135.0	76.2	39.4	39.5	40.1	175.0	68.5	100.1	23.1	12.7	14.3	20.8	26.3
Zarembo Island	243330	237.0	223.9	130.0	73.6	41.3	40.9	41.3	178.0	69.6	102.1	22.2	13.8	....	....	....
Zarembo Island	243326	243.4	229.2	132.4	74.8	40.1	42.9	42.4	181.4	69.0	106.5	23.2	13.4	14.6	21.1	26.5
	Average	247.0	230.0	134.5	76.5	41.6	42.9	41.3	181.5	72.3	104.7	23.4	13.5	15.7	22.1	27.9

FOOTNOTES: [1] **Field Mus. Nat. Hist.** [2] B. C. Prov. Mus. [3] Mus. Vert. Zool. [4] B. C. Prov. Mus. Type locality. [5] Roy. Ont. Mus. Zool.

Table 6.—Cranial measurements of adult females in U. S. National Museum, unless otherwise indicated, of *Canis lupus* group—(Continued)

Species and locality	Number	Greatest length	Condylobasal length	Zygomatic breadth	Squamosal constriction	Width of rostrum	Interorbital breadth	Postorbital constriction	Length of mandible	Height of coronoid process	Maxillary tooth row, crown length	Upper carnassial, crown length (outer side)	Upper carnassial, crown width	First upper molar, antero-posterior diameter	First upper molar, transverse diameter	Lower carnassial, crown length
C. l. fuscus:																
Oregon—																
Cascadia	235515	239.8	218.5	128.3	75.4	44.0	45.0	41.7	170.5	72.8	98.6	21.9	12.9	15.1	21.3	26.3
Cascadia	236528	237.5	222.8	131.8	72.0	40.6	46.8	43.0	172.4	71.8	101.4	22.8	12.5	15.0	20.8	26.4
Estacada	227740	245.0	220.7	130.4	75.8	44.0	43.3	42.3	175.3	76.1	101.6	23.3	13.1	14.3	20.3	26.6
Glide (40 mi. E)	226432	240.2	223.	123.2	75.1	39.5	41.6	38.2	173.7	73.6	99.9	23.1	14.1	15.3	20.9	27.8
Glide (15 mi. NE)	224002	240.8	.....	127.4	75.6	42.9	44.9	39.4	178.0	74.2	103.4	23.3	13.3	15.9	21.1	26.9
Rogue River	243986	250.4	229.8	128.7	74.8	42.8	48.2	42.4	180.5	77.2	103.1	24.4	12.9	16.7	22.0	27.2
Washington—																
Ashland (25 mi. NE)	233248	253.5	235.3	137.0	78.7	43.3	46.8	40.9	184.7	80.6	103.1	24.5	13.0	16.0	22.0	26.8
	Average	243.9	192.9	129.5	75.3	42.4	44.7	41.1	176.4	75.2	101.6	23.3	13.1	15.5	21.2	26.9
C. l. crassodon:																
British Columbia—																
Alberni[1]	1862	249.5	231.0	135.4	75.5	44.3	47.0	42.3	182.0	70.0	105.7	25.2	14.5	15.9	22.2	28.0
Vancouver Island	135451	241.9	222.1	132.0	79.0	40.8	43.4	43.0	170.8	70.1	101.8	24.9	14.6	17.2	21.7	28.8
Vancouver Island	137806	247.8	230.5	134.0	76.4	41.0	46.8	44.4	178.4	66.3	106.4	25.1	14.9	17.2	23.5	28.7
	Average	246.4	227.9	133.8	77.0	42.0	45.7	43.2	177.1	68.8	104.6	25.1	14.7	16.8	22.5	28.5
C. l. youngi:																
Colorado—																
Glade Park, Mesa County	223710	238.2	223.5	127.2	77.0	40.8	42.0	38.9	169.7	69.4	101.1	24.7	13.1	16.2	21.7	27.6
Piceance	210906	244.5	228.7	130.9	73.2	42.7	43.2	39.0	175.8	70.6	106.7	24.6	12.7	16.1	22.0	28.0
Piceance	216355	242.8	226.5	128.8	72.5	40.0	44.1	39.9	172.2	70.4	104.0	24.5	13.4	15.3	22.1	27.8
Turman's Creek, Rio Blanco Co.	216354	234.5	218.5	131.4	74.3	40.3	39.7	36.0	171.6	73.1	99.9	23.1	12.0	15.1	21.0	26.8
West Creek, Garfield County	224526	242.8	231.4	131.7	74.3	42.9	49.7	39.1	180.5	75.3	106.4	25.1	13.8	16.6	22.9	28.9
New Mexico—																
Canjilon	231344	240.0	222.5	125.0	75.9	44.0	40.3	36.7	167.2	73.7	102.2	24.4	14.1	16.0	21.7	28.9
Wyoming—																
Federal	221850	237.1	211.3	128.0	77.7	43.6	37.8	37.8	162.2	73.1	99.5	23.1	12.3	15.8	21.3	27.6
Laramie	235504	233.7	224.4	131.8	72.1	43.5	43.0	37.7	171.3	69.9	102.5	....	13.0	....	....	....
	Average	239.2	223.4	129.4	74.5	42.2	42.5	38.1	171.3	71.9	102.8	24.2	13.1	15.9	21.8	27.9

C. l. mogollonensis:																
Arizona—																
Escudilla Mts.	157627	238.3	219.0	129.7	73.5	42.1	41.1	39.8	168.7	68.0	96.1	23.9	13.5	16.0	21.6	27.4
Escudilla Mts.	205745	232.7	213.7	122.5	74.8	38.1	39.8	37.1	165.5	69.2	98.2	24.0	13.7	16.1	21.3	26.5
Heber	224173	247.3	224.4	144.4	81.1	44.0	44.2	37.4	175.3	76.5	102.7	25.0	14.7	16.8	22.3	29.2
New Mexico—																
Chloride	224167	245.5	222.8	129.4	76.1	41.5	47.4	41.8	173.2	72.6	102.8	23.9	13.5	16.4	21.5	27.4
Chloride	224584	236.8	218.0	130.7	76.6	45.2	44.9	43.3	169.6	73.7	98.9	24.8	14.5	15.6	21.8	28.2
Fairview	235087	242.5	225.5	138.6	80.1	43.6	41.3	39.1	178.0	79.0	103.0	24.6	13.9	15.7	21.8	27.5
Gila Nat. Forest	148979	240.2	222.3	125.2	75.6	41.5	39.2	38.5	167.0	67.4	102.2	24.1	14.3	16.5	22.4	28.3
Luna	226434	240.2	222.4	133.5	75.2	44.1	46.0	42.3	174.0	78.7	101.3	24.7	14.3	16.4	22.0	27.8
Magdalena	221656	241.2	221.6	126.4	77.8	44.7	40.0	38.6	173.0	73.0	99.8	22.9	12.7	14.5	20.2	26.3
	Average	240.5	221.1	131.2	76.8	42.8	42.7	39.8	171.6	73.1	100.6	24.2	13.9	16.0	21.7	27.6
C. l. monstrabilis:																
New Mexico—																
Elk	223503	236.4	212.3	126.2	69.2	39.3	40.5	39.1	168.4	68.4	96.5	23.7	12.9	14.8	21.1	27.3
Sacramento Mts.	159021	233.8	217.0	126.0	73.1	39.3	43.3	42.1	166.8	67.4	96.0	21.0	11.9	15.1	20.9	25.4
Texas—																
Big Lake	224165	252.3	228.8	126.3	74.0	40.6	43.3	38.4	173.3	73.5	102.2	23.6	13.3	15.4	21.1	27.4
Monahans	118990	242.5	225.3	125.8	75.3	42.3	44.5	42.3	172.0	67.8	103.9	24.5	13.5	16.5	22.4	27.8
Rankin	209498	250.4	231.3	138.5	78.1	45.3	45.2	40.3	178.8	73.5	103.3	24.8	13.8	17.1	22.1	28.0
Rankin	215361	232.3	216.9	128.9	75.2	39.6	45.0	42.2	166.2	68.3	95.9	24.8	12.9	14.8	20.9	27.(
Rankin	211242	251.7	228.1	126.0	74.3	39.3	45.1	40.3	171.3	69.2	104.2	24.2	13.8	17.0	22.5	27.7
Rankin	215360	246.8	226.0	124.1	75.3	38.7	42.4	39.4	170.5	73.3	99.3	23.7	13.8	15.2	20.9	26.4
	Average	243.3	223.8	127.7	74.3	40.6	43.7	40.5	170.9	70.2	100.2	23.8	13.2	15.7	21.5	27.1
C. l. baileyi:																
Arizona—																
Santa Rita Mts.	251526	231.2	211.8	124.7	75.6	39.4	42.2	38.3	160.9	67.8	97.9	23.4	12.9	16.3	19.8	25.3
Chihuahua—																
Colonia Garcia[2]	99668	224.4	209.5	126.1	74.1	37.9	43.1	42.8	165.0	69.0	95.4	24.5	12.2	15.1	20.4	26.3
Colonia Garcia[2]	98311	234.2	215.9	130.9	74.6	38.1	40.0	40.3	168.0	69.0	99.3	23.4	12.1	15.5	19.5	24.9
Durango—																
El Salto	94728	231.5	210.0	124.6	70.3	38.8	42.8	39.7	159.7	66.2	98.3	25.2	13.0	16.0	20.5	27.7
New Mexico—																
Hachita	231536	232.9	209.9	128.8	73.0	40.1	43.8	42.7	163.0	69.8	93.2	22.8	12.0	14.4	19.5	25.4
Hachita	231323	233.3	217.0	131.6	75.9	41.7	45.4	41.2	163.8	73.8	95.7	24.0	12.3	15.5	21.0	26.4
Texas—																
Fort Davis (16 mi. NW)	266568	231.0	212.5	127.5	74.9	37.8	42.7	42.1	162.5	67.5	96.7	23.9	12.7	15.1	19.1	25.4
	Average	231.2	212.4	127.7	74.1	39.1	42.9	41.0	163.3	69.0	96.6	23.9	12.5	15.4	20.0	25.9

FOOTNOTES: [1] B. C. Prov. Mus. [2] Type locality

TABLE 7.—CRANIAL MEASUREMENTS OF ADULT FEMALES IN U. S. NATIONAL MUSEUM, UNLESS OTHERWISE INDICATED, OF *Canis niger* GROUP

Species and locality	Number	Greatest length	Condylobasal length	Zygomatic breadth	Squamosal constriction	Width of rostrum	Interorbital breadth	Postorbital constriction	Length of mandible	Height of coronoid process	Maxillary tooth row, crown length	Upper carnassial, crown length (outer side)	Upper carnassial, crown width	First upper molar, antero-posterior diameter	First upper molar, transverse diameter	Lower carnassial, crown length
C. n. rufus:																
Arkansas—																
Boxley	243321	202.5	190.9	111.0	64.1	31.2	34.3	35.5	146.0	60.7	88.5	21.1	10.6	13.8	19.4	23.5
Hector	266420	202.7	191.3	108.5	63.1	32.2	36.9	36.8	144.3	57.3	86.9	21.0	9.6	13.4	18.4	23.5
Oklahoma—																
Redden	261766	209.5	201.5	106.4	64.7	32.4	37.3	39.3	155.0	59.8	93.4	21.8	10.9	14.9	18.0	24.1
Tahlequah	251059	210.5	196.4	105.0	62.8	32.8	34.7	36.0	151.6	56.8	89.9	20.5	10.0	13.5	18.6	23.7
Texas—																
Click	228089	210.4	195.0	110.5	64.6	32.6	35.8	35.2	146.2	60.3	88.6	21.5	9.5	14.5	17.8	23.8
Llano	214852	207.3	191.6	110.2	63.1	31.7	33.9	39.1	151.2	60.6	89.0	21.6	10.6	14.7	18.7	23.2
Llano	223713	200.9	193.7	106.0	64.3	29.8	39.7	40.0	149.0	61.1	87.7	19.4	9.8	12.7	17.3	20.0
Llano	223649	198.5	190.6	100.3	63.0	29.9	34.7	32.2	143.0	57.1	87.1	19.1	9.3	12.4	17.7	21.8
Llano	224580	212.0	197.2	103.2	63.6	28.6	32.1	33.2	152.5	57.9	91.8	20.9	10.4	13.8	19.4	22.8
Port O'Connor	99720	203.2	187.5	105.4	62.0	31.3	33.0	35.9	141.6	55.4	82.4	20.0	9.3	13.8	18.8	21.5
	Average	205.8	193.6	105.7	63.5	31.3	35.2	36.3	148.0	58.7	88.5	20.7	10.0	13.8	18.4	22.8
C. n. gregoryi:																
Arkansas—																
Blue Ball	243433	222.8	206.8	112.3	65.7	34.9	35.5	33.2	159.5	65.4	95.7	21.3	11.8	14.8	19.1	24.0
Blue Ball	243431	218.5	204.0	108.0	64.9	32.7	36.1	37.1	156.0	58.9	90.2	20.7	9.8	13.9	18.1	22.8
Ferndale	242574	222.9	120.2	120.2	67.4	35.5	40.8	37.5	158.9	63.7	96.9	22.7	11.7	15.2	20.5	25.0
Isaac	242584	213.5	202.0	116.0	67.0	36.5	37.3	35.9	154.0	61.3	90.6	21.6	10.1	14.5	19.2	23.8
Isaac	242582	216.2	206.0	119.2	65.3	37.2	36.2	36.1	159.0	60.6	94.3	24.7	13.0	16.3	22.5	26.7
Isaac	242580	209.3	195.5	100.6	62.2	33.5	33.4	34.5	148.6	56.1	90.9	21.8	11.4	14.4	19.4	24.1
Pinnacle	243594	221.5	205.3	117.0	69.1	34.7	38.7	39.6	157.3	62.2	93.6	23.7	12.0	15.8	21.0	25.8
Solo	243306	224.6	211.3	112.5	64.8	33.8	41.5	40.7	159.9	64.4	95.9	22.6	12.7	15.7	20.5	25.4
Stillwater	244226	228.2	215.8	125.5	70.4	36.2	39.4	39.0	166.0	65.3	99.6	24.7	12.1	16.0	21.8	27.8
Wye	224228	204.9	190.5	114.4	65.2	35.5	35.0	33.4	147.9	63.8	87.2	22.4	11.2	15.2	19.8	25.1
Indiana—																
Wabash[1]	112	232.0	.....	117.0	70.2	34.3	35.4	39.6	161.8	66.1	94.0	22.0	12.1	14.6	20.6	25.1
Louisiana—																
Sabine River	248333	216.8	198.5	113.6	68.4	33.9	37.3	35.9	151.9	64.2	90.7	21.5	11.1	15.2	19.9	24.8
Sikes	265134	218.5	207.7	114.5	68.7	32.6	40.2	37.5	157.7	66.8	93.1	20.1	11.0	14.8	19.0	23.4
Tallulah (vicinity)	136105	222.7	202.5	114.2	67.9	38.0	35.6	31.0	156.7	68.6	91.2	22.6	11.7	15.1	20.0	24.7

Missouri—																
Arcadia	245738	226.4	213.5	117.3	66.2	35.6	37.5	38.7	162.2	67.2	97.0	22.0	11.8	15.5	20.2	25.6
Barren	244298	225.8	210.4	112.2	66.8	33.5	36.7	34.8	168.2	69.1	98.1	22.1	12.8	15.5	20.1	25.4
Cook's Station	244300	225.6	212.1	120.5	70.0	33.8	38.5	38.7	139.4	65.0	94.8	21.9	11.6	14.7	19.6	25.8
Cook's Station	244490	219.5	206.5	115.5	70.0	30.7	35.0	36.0	156.5	66.0	91.1	22.0	10.8	14.9	19.5	25.4
Cook's Station	244302	220.5	207.8	113.4	68.9	31.4	33.4	32.0	159.4	65.0	94.3	22.8	10.7	15.3	19.3	24.6
Gatewood	244214	230.7	214.9	118.4	64.0	37.3	35.6	36.8	161.1	66.3	96.8	23.0	12.6	14.5	19.3	25.3
Stone County	244224	222.5	206.3	115.0	65.1	30.0	38.1	35.9	158.1	65.6	94.5	21.4	9.5	13.2	18.3	24.3
Stone County	244215	221.7	203.8	114.0	67.0	34.0	32.2	34.5	154.2	62.8	91.0	22.0	11.0	14.3	18.8	24.7
Tyrone	244526	222.3	208.5	118.5	69.0	35.0	35.4	39.8	156.4	64.0	93.6	22.1	11.6	15.0	19.0	25.1
Upalika	244528	220.5	212.5	121.0	66.7	35.4	37.2	36.9	163.5	63.6	95.6	28.8	12.1	15.8	20.1	26.6
Oklahoma—																
Broken Bow	234431	225.0	212.8	120.0	70.4	38.1	37.3	35.8	162.8	66.4	94.9	23.9	11.8	16.5	20.7	26.6
Broken Bow	232422	216.5	202.4	119.0	66.5	36.4	44.9	36.3	156.0	67.8	89.8	23.4	11.0	15.4	20.1	25.5
Broken Bow	233433	214.5	201.2	113.0	67.3	31.3	34.0	35.0	157.0	64.1	93.0	21.6	10.4	15.0	18.8	23.7
Page	234450	222.1	204.5	114.2	65.9	34.4	36.2	38.8	156.7	65.4	91.9	23.6	11.1	15.2	19.3	25.0
Sherwood	234426	230.0	215.2	118.5	66.8	36.2	37.4	36.0	165.5	66.5	100.3	23.2	12.2	16.2	21.1	25.5
Sherwood	234429	217.0	203.5	116.3	66.1	34.1	34.7	36.1	157.0	63.3	92.1	22.7	11.7	14.8	19.4	23.6
Sherwood	234428	212.4	197.6	111.9	67.3	31.8	37.2	39.6	151.0	62.3	90.9	20.1	11.3	13.9	18.4	22.7
Smithville	231540	219.4	206.0	118.5	68.1	33.9	44.4	33.5	155.5	64.5	94.1	24.3	12.5	15.9	21.5	25.4
Smithville	234416	217.4	205.5	115.0	66.0	35.3	35.3	36.4	156.0	65.8	92.9	22.3	12.2	15.0	19.9	23.8
Smithville	232416	213.0	198.9	114.4	67.1	32.4	35.7	41.5	154.5	63.5	87.7	22.0	11.0	15.2	20.0	23.8
Texas—																
Kountze	147701	222.3	208.4	115.0	67.5	34.4	37.6	37.2	158.4	60.3	96.9	22.3	12.7	15.8	20.4	24.9
	Average	220.5	209.4	115.6	67.1	34.4	37.0	36.6	157.3	64.3	93.6	22.6	11.5	15.1	19.9	24.9
C. n. niger:																
Florida—																
St. Johns River	38488 / 19376	.....	.....	122.2	67.2	36.1	43.2	38.9	158.9	65.5	.....	23.2	12.8	15.8	21.7	25.6

FOOTNOTE: [1] Subadult. Amer. Mus. Nat. Hist.

XVII

REFERENCES AND SELECTED BIBLIOGRAPHY

ABERNATHY, JOHN R.

1936. Catch 'em alive Jack. Reissue with extensive variations in text of the author's In Camp with Theodore Roosevelt. 224 pp. New York Association Press. 1933.

ABERT, J. W. (LT.)

1848. Report of Lt. J. W. Abert of his examination of New Mexico in the years 1846-1847. U. S. House Executive Documents No. 41, 30th Cong., 1st sess., 1847-1848, pp. 417-548, with map; also as Senate Doc. No. 23, 30th Cong., 1st sess., pp. 1-132.

ADAMS, A. LEITH

1873. Field and Forest rambles, with notes and observations on the natural history of eastern Canada. 333 pp., illus. London.

ALASKA GAME COMMISSION

1938. Game and fur conditions [in Alaska]. Fourteenth Ann. Rept. to the Secretary of Agriculture, 1937-38. 25 pp. mimeog.

ALBERT, G. D.

1882. History of the county of Westmoreland. 727 pp. L. H. Everts & Co., Philadelphia.

ALDOUS, CLARENCE M.

1939. Coyotes in Maine. Jour. Mamm. 20 (1): 104-106. February.

ALLEN, GLOVER M.

1920. Dogs of the American Aborigines. Bull. Mus. Comp. Zool. 63 (9): 431-517, illus. March. Cambridge, Mass.

1942. Extinct and vanishing mammals of the Western Hemisphere . . . Amer. Comm. for International Wildlife Prot., Special Publication No. 11, pp. XV plus 620, illus. December 11.

—————, and BARBOUR, THOMAS

1937. The Newfoundland wolf. Jour. Mamm. 18 (2): 229-234, illus. May. New: *Canis lupus beothucus.*

ALLEN, HENRY T.

1895. Hunting in Many Lands. Wolf hunting in Russia. A book of the Boone and Crockett Club. 447 pp., illus. New York.

ALLEN, J. A.

1869. Catalogue of the mammals of Massachusetts; with a critical revision of the species. Bull. Mus. Comp. Zool. 1 (8): 143-252.

1871a. Notes on the mammals of Iowa. Proc. Boston Soc. Nat. Hist. 13: 178-194. December 15, 1869. (Also published separately, 18 pp.)

1871b. On the mammals and winter birds of east Florida . . . . Bull. Mus. Comp. Zool. 2 (3): 161-450. April. Cambridge, Mass.

1874a. Notes on the mammals of portions of Kansas, Colorado, Wyoming, and Utah. Bull. Essex Inst. 6 (3): 43-52; 6 (4): 53-66. March and April. Salem, Mass.

1874b. Notes on the natural history of portions of Montana and Dakota . . . . Proc. Boston Soc. Nat. Hist. 17: 33-91.

1876a. Description of some remains of an extinct species of wolf and extinct species of deer from the lead region of the Upper Mississippi. Amer. Jour. Sci. (3d ser.) 11: 47-51.

1876b. Former range of some New England carnivorous mammals. Amer. Nat. 10: 708-715.

1876c. Geographical variations among North American mammals. . . . Bull. U. S. Geol. and Geog. Survey Terr. 2 (4): 309-344. July 1. Washington, D. C. Amer. Nat. 10: 625-627, October.

1876d. The extirpation of the larger indigenous mammals of the United States. The Penn Monthly 7 (82): 794-806.

1876e. The American bisons living and extinct. Memoirs Geol. Survey Kentucky 1 (pt. 2): 1-246, with 12 pls. and map. Cambridge, Mass.; also Mem. Mus. Comp. Zool. 4 (10): 1-246.

1877. History of the American bison, Bison americanus. *In* Hayden, 9th Ann. Report U. S. Geol. & Geog. Survey Terr. 1875, pp. 443-587.

1895a. List of mammals collected in the Black Hills region of South Dakota and in western Kansas by Mr. Walter W. Granger, with field notes by the collector. Bull. Amer. Mus. Nat. Hist. 7 (art. 7): 259-274. August 21.

1895b. On collection of mammals from Arizona and Mexico made by Mr. W. W. Price, with field notes by the collector. Bull. Amer. Mus. Nat. Hist. 7 (art. 6): 193-258. June 29.

ALLEN, LEWIS F.

1868. American cattle: Their history, breeding, and management. 528 pp. New York.

ALLEN, PAUL

1814. History of the expedition under command of Captains Lewis and Clark to the sources of the Missouri; thence across the Rocky Mountains and down the river Columbia to the Pacific Ocean. Performed during the years 1804-5-6. By order of the Government of the United States. 2 vols., illus., Phila., Bradford and Inskeep; and A.B.M.H. Inskeep, New York. J. Maxwell, Printer, Vol. 2, pp. 114, 122.

ALMIRALL, LEON V.

1926. Coyote coursing. 64 pp., illus. December 12. Denver, Colo.

1941. Canines and coyotes. 150 pp., illus. Caldwell, Idaho.

ALTSHELER, BRENT
1936. Natural history index-guide, sec. 2, div. 1, 311 pp. Nat. Hist. Pub. Co., Louisville, Ky.

AMES, A. E.
1874. Mammalia of Minnesota. Bull. Minn. Acad. Nat. Sci. 1: 68-71.

ANDERSON, R. M.
1934. Mammals of eastern Arctic and Hudson Bay. Pp. 67-108. Canada's Eastern Arctic, Dept. Interior, Ottawa.
1938. Mammals of the province of Quebec. Pp. 68-69. Prepared for the Provancher Soc. of Nat. Hist. of Canada, Quebec.
1943. Summary of the large wolves of Canada, with description of three new Arctic races. Journ. Mamm. 24 (3): 386-393. August.

ANGELL, HOMER D.
1940. Champoeg—Oregon's shrine to civil government. Extension of remarks in the House of Representatives, Monday, May 27. Cong. Record Appendix 86 (105): 10, 740.

ANONYMOUS
1800. A brief state of the Province of Quebec . . . written in the year 1787. Mass. Hist. Soc. Coll. for 1799, vol. 6, pp. 48-63.
1852. Children suckled by wolves. Chamber's Journal, 17 (n.s.): 122-123.
1853. The wolf as an object of superstition. Chamber's Edinburgh Journal (n.s.) 20: 27-30.
1854. Wolf nurses in India. Harper's New Monthly Magazine, 9 (50): 199. July.
1856a. Fur hunting in Oregon. Harper's New Monthly Magazine 12 (69): 340-346. February.
1856b. Israel Putnam. Harper's New Monthly Magazine 12 (71): 579-580. April.
1869. Wolf-hunting in Chicago. Appleton's Journal 2: 230-231.
1871. A full-page illustration, engraved from a sketch by artist W. M. Gray, showing buffalo bulls guarding a herd against a wolf pack. Harper's Weekly 15: 724-725.

1875. Some wild animals of Newfoundland. Forest and Stream 4 (25): 390. July 29.

1882. Wolf children. Chamber's Journal, 59: 597-599.

1885a. History of Crawford County, Pa. Warner, Bears & Co., Chicago. P. 529.

1885b. Wolf hunting with the Sibley hounds. American Field 24 (23): 535. December 5.

1885c. Wolves in Maine. Forest and Stream 24: 429. June 25. Timber wolf said to have attacked a man at Pittston, Maine.

1886. An Adirondack wolf. Rome (New York) Sentinel. February 10. Also Forest and Stream 26: 71. February 18.

1887. The gray wolf eating watermelons. Forest and Stream 29: 403. December 15.

1888a. Texas wolves. Forest and Stream 29: 504. January 19.

1888b. Wolves in France. The Field, the Farm, the Garden, 71 (1): 14. January. London.

1897. History of Tioga County, Pa. P. 44, illus. R. C. Brown & Co., Harrisburg, Pa.

1908. The wolf hunter. Rod and Gun and Motor Sports in Canada 10 (7): 603. December.

1910a. Wolf bounty frauds (Ontario). Rod and Gun in Canada 11 (12): 1218. May.

1910b. A relation of Maryland. Ann. Dom. 1635. Narratives of Early Maryland, 1633-1684: 63-112. New York.

1910c. A Parry Sound wolf hunt. Forest and Stream 74: 338, February 26.

1911. Wolves and big game. Rod and Gun in Canada 12 (10): 1352. March.

1913a. The cunning of the wolf. Outdoor World and Recreation 48 (6): 342. May.

1913b. Wolves in Ontario-Canada. Forest and Stream 80: 142, February 1.

1914a. The timber wolf in Oregon. Forest and Stream 82: 54-55.

1914b. The wolf in Maine. Forest and Stream 82 (16): 514. April.

1915. White wolf killed. Forest and Stream 84: 101, February.
1926. Wild animals that think. Literary Digest 88 (10): 71-75. March 6.
1927. Combatting the wolves in northern Canada. Natural Resources Canada, Canadian Dept. of the Interior 6 (3): 3. Ottawa. March.
1927a. Wolf children of India. Living Age, 332 (4307): 1021-1022. June 1.
1927b. India's wolf children found in caves. Literary Digest, 95: 54-56. October 8.
1934. Treatment of rabies is preventive rather than cure. Hygeia 12 (8): 765. August.
1939a. Trained timber wolves. Outdoor Life 83 (7): 65.
1939b. The Oregon trail. P. 63. Compiled and written by the Federal Writers' Project of WPA. Sponsored by Oregon Trail Memorial Association, Inc. American Guide Series. New York.
1940a. From Ketchikan to Barrow. Alaska Sportsman 6 (7): 21. July. Comment re wolf depredations on reindeer.
1940b. The animal kingdom. The Pierpont Morgan Library, New York. P. 70.
1943. Indiana fur value shown in invoice left by Vigo [Francis] of Vincennes three lifetimes ago. Outdoor Indiana 10 (10): 3, 15. November.

ANTHONY, H. E.
1928. Field book of North American mammals. G. P. Putnam's Sons, New York, p. 254.

ARNOLD, BRIDGEWATER
1927. A dictionary of fur names. Nat. Assoc. Fur Industry, New York: 22.

ARNOLD, SAMUEL GREENE
1859. History of the state of Rhode Island. 2 vols. New York.

ARTHUR, STANLEY C.
1928. The fur animals of Louisiana. State of Louisiana Department of Conservation, Bull. No. 18, pp. 1-433.

ASH, EDWARD C.
1927. Dogs, their history and development. 2 vols. London.

AUBREY, CHARLES
1908. Memoirs of an old buffalo hunter. Forest and Stream 71: 133-134, 172, 216-217.
AUDUBON, JOHN JAMES, and BACHMAN, JOHN
1851-54. The quadrupeds of North America. 3 vols. New York. New: *Canis lupus* var. *rufus* (= *C. niger rufus*).
AUGHEY, SAMUEL
1880. Sketches of the physical geography and geology of Nebraska. 326 pp. Omaha.
B., F. M.
1899. A Pennsylvania Putnam and a wolf. Forest and Stream 52: 405. May 27.
B., J. A.
1884. A hunt with the Comanches. Forest and Stream 23: 163-164.
BACK, GEORGE (CAPTAIN)
1936. Narrative of the Arctic land expedition to the mouth of the Great Fish River, and along the shores of the Arctic Ocean in the years 1833, 1834, 1835. Zool. App. by John Richardson. 663 pp. London, Paris, Brussels, Leipzig, Frankfort, Philadelphia.
BAILEY, VERNON
1905. Biological survey of Texas. U. S. Dept. Agr., Bur. Biol. Survey. North Amer. Fauna 25: 1-222, illus. October 24.
1907a. Directions for the destruction of wolves and coyotes. U. S. Dept. Agr., Bur. Biol. Surv. Circ. 55: 1-6.
1907b. Destruction of deer by the northern timber wolf. U. S. Dept. Agr., Bur. Biol. Surv. Circ. 58: 1-2, illus. May 4.
1907c. Wolves in relation to stock, game, and the national forest reserves. U. S. Dept. Agr., Forest Serv. Bull. 72: 1-31, illus.
1908. Destruction of wolves and coyotes—results obtained during 1907. U. S. Dept. Agr., Bur. Biol. Surv. Circ. 63: 1-11, illus.
1909. Key to animals on which wolf and coyote bounties are often paid. U. S. Dept. Agr., Bur. Biol. Surv. Circ. 69: 1-3, illus. May.

1918. Wild animals of Glacier National Park. U. S. Dept. of the Interior, Natl. Park Service, 210 pp. Mammals, pp. 1-102.

1926. A biological survey of North Dakota. U. S. Dept. Agr., Bur. Biol. Survey. North Amer. Fauna 49: 1-226.

1928. Animal life of the Carlsbad Cavern. Monograph Amer. Soc. Mammalogists 3: 1-195, illus. Baltimore.

1930. Animal life of Yellowstone National Park. 241 pp. Springfield, Ill.

1931. Mammals of New Mexico. U. S. Dept. Agr., Bur. Biol. Survey. North Amer. Fauna 53: 1-412.

1936. The mammals and life zones of Oregon. U. S. Dept. Agr., Bur. Biol. Survey. North Amer. Fauna 55: 1-416, illus.

1940. The home life of the big wolves. Natural History 46 (2): 120-122, illus. September.

BAIN, JAMES

1901. Travels and adventures in Canada and the Indian territories between the years 1760-1776 by Alexander Henry, fur trader. 347 pp. Boston.

BAIRD, SPENCER F.

1857-59. The mammals of North America. General report on North American mammals. 764 pp. Philadelphia.

1859. Mammals of the U. S. and Mexican boundary survey 2 (pt. 2): 1-62, illus.

Refers to *Canis torquatus*, a manuscript name of Berlandier's which can not be satisfactorily assigned.

BALL, V.

1873. Notes on children found living with wolves in the northwestern provinces and Oudh. Proc. Asiatic Soc. Bengal: 8, 128-129. January-December.

BALLANTYNE, ROBERT MICHAEL

1859. Hudson Bay, or everyday life in the wilds of North America. 322 pp., 3rd Ed. London and New York.

BANCROFT, HUBERT HOWE

1882-90. The works of Hubert Howe Bancroft. 39 vols. Vol. 29, History of Oregon, 1834-1848. 1886. San Francisco.

BANGS, OUTRAM
1898a. The land mammals of peninsular Florida and the coast region of Georgia. Proc. Boston Soc. Nat. Hist. 28 (7): 157-235.
1898b. A list of the mammals of Labrador. Amer. Nat. 32: 489-507. July.
BANNISTER, H. M.
1869. The Esquimaux dog. Amer. Nat. 3 (10): 522-530. December.
BARNES, CLAUDE T.
1927. Utah mammals. Univ. of Utah Bull. 17 (12): 1-183. Salt Lake City.
BARNES, WILL C.
1915. Fighting predatory animals on the western ranges. Breeders' Gazette 67: 705-706, illus.
1921. How a den of wolves was exterminated. Breeders' Gazette 80: 923-924, 956-957, illus.
BARROWS, WILLARD
1863. History of Scott County, Iowa. Annals Iowa State Hist. Soc. (1st ser.) 1: 11-176.
BARTLETT, G. W.
1909. How shall we destroy the wolves? Rod and Gun and Motor in Canada 11 (3): 240-242. August.
BARTLETT, JOHN RUSSELL
1856-65. Records of the colony of Rhode Island and Providence plantations in New England. 10 vols. Vol. 1. Printed by order of Legislature, 1636 to 1663. Providence, Rhode Island.
BARTON, BENJAMIN SMITH
1803. On Indian dogs. Alexander Tillock's Philosophical Magazine 15: 1-9, 136-142. London.
1805. Some accounts of the different species and varieties of native American or Indian dogs. Phila. Medical and Physical Journal 1 (pt. 2, sec. 1): 3-31.
BARTRAM, WILLIAM
1928. The travels of William Bartram. 414 pp. Edited by Mark Van Doren. New York.

BATTY, JOSEPH H.
1874. Notes from the plains. The American Sportsman 5 (1): 1.
1882. How to hunt and trap. 226 pp. New York.
1884. A hunt with the Comanches. Forest and Stream 23: 163-164. Sept. 25.
BAYNES, ERNEST HAROLD
1923. Timber wolves—wild and tame. Nature Magazine 2 (6): 333-338, 356.
BEALS, CHARLES EDWARD
1916. Passaconaway in the White Mountains. 343 pp. Boston.
BEARD, D., CAHALANE, V. H., JACKSON, H. H. T., LINCOLN, F. C., and THOMPSON, BEN.
1942. Fading trails. A story of endangered wildlife. Pp. XV plus 279. The Macmillan Co., New York.
BEATTY, RICHARD CROOM
1932. William Byrd of Westover. 233 pp. Boston and New York.
BEDDARD, FRANK EVERS
1902. Mammalia. 605 pp. London and New York. Also The Cambridge Nat. Hist., vol. 10.
BEEBE, VICTOR L.
1934. History of Potter County, Pennsylvania. 280 pp. Potter County Hist. Soc., Coudersport.
BEEBE, WILLIAM
1943. Our zoo's former inhabitants. Four mammals and a bird that were driven from our grounds long before the Zoological Society took possession. Animal Kingdom, 46 (5): 111-116, illus. September-October. N. Y. Zool. Soc.
BEECHEY, F. W. (CAPTAIN)
1839. The zoology of Capt. Beechey's voyage . . . . 1825-28. Mammalia by J. Richardson. Pp. VIII plus 180. London.
New: *Canis lupus* var. *fusca* (= *Canis lupus fuscus*).
BELL, HERBERT CHAS., Ed.
1890. History of Venango County, Pennsylvania. 1164 pp. Brown, Runk & Co., Chicago.

BELL, WILLIAM BONAR
1920. Hunting down stock killers. U. S. Dept. Agr. Yearbook, pp. 289-300, illus. Also Separate No. 845. Washington, D. C.
1926. Wolf and coyote control. The Producer 7 (9): 3-4; 7 (10): 6-8. February and March. Denver, Colo.

BENNITT, RUDOLF, and NAGEL, WERNER O.
1937. A survey of the resident game and fur-bearers of Missouri. Univ. of Missouri Studies 12 (2): 1-215, illus. April 1. Columbia, Mo.

BENSON, ADOLPH B.
1937. The America of 1750—Peter Kalm's travels in North America. 2 vols., illus. Vol. 1, pp. 1-380; vol. 2, pp. 1-797. The English version of 1770 revised from the original Swedish.

BENT-PROWERS COUNTY CATTLE AND HORSE GROWERS' ASSOCIATION
1938. Minutes of annual meetings, 1870-1938. 386 pp. Las Animas, Colo.

BERLANDIER, L.
1851. On the species of Mexican wolves; with preliminary remarks by a committee of the Academy of Natural Sciences of Philadelphia. Proc. Acad. Nat. Sci. Phila. 5: 156-157. February.

BERNARD, WILLIAM
1906. Westport and the Santa Fe trade. Kansas Hist. Collections 1905-1906 9: 552-565. Topeka.

BEVERLY, ROBERT
1705. The history and present state of Virginia. In four parts, illus. 104, 40, 64, 83 pp.
1707. Histoire de la Virginie. 433 pp., illus. French translation. Publ. Thomas Lombrail, Amsterdam.

BEWICK, THOMAS
1804. A general history of quadrupeds. 531 pp. First American edition. New York.

BIBLE, HOLY
Old Testament, II Samuel, Ch. 23, vs. 20.

BILLINGS, E.
1856. The natural history of the wolf (*Canis lupus*), and its varieties. The Canad. Nat. and Geol. 1 (3): 209-215. Montreal.

BLACK, J. D.
1936. Mammals of northwestern Arkansas. Jour. Mamm. 17 (1): 29-34. February.
1937. Mammals of Kansas. 30th Biennial Rept. Kansas State Bd. Agr. 1935-36, pp. 116-217, illus.

BLACKMAN, EMILY C.
1873. History of Susquehanna County, Pennsylvania, 640 pp. Clayton, Remsen, and Hoffelfinger, Philadelphia.

BLISS, ISLEY, and RICHARDS, W. M.
1936. Four centuries in Kansas. P. 18. Wichita.

BOLE, B. P., JR., and MOULTHROP, PHILIP NELSON
1942. The Ohio recent mammal collection in the Cleveland Museum of Natural History. Cleveland Mus. Nat. Hist. Sci. Pub. 5 (6): 83-181. September 11.

BONNYCASTLE, SIR RICHARD HENRY
1842. Newfoundland in 1842. 2 vols. A sequel to The Canadas in 1841. London.

BOWLEGS, BILLY
1923. Coursing in the good old days. Outdoor Life 52 (2): 93-98, illus. August.

BRACKENRIDGE, H. M.
1904. Journal of a voyage up the river Missouri in 1811. Early Western Travels 6: 21-166. Edited by Reuben Gold Thwaites. Cleveland.

BRADBURY, JOHN
1904. Travels in the interior of America in the years 1809, 1810, and 1811. . . . Early Western Travels, vol. 5, p. 118. Edited by Reuben Gold Thwaites. Cleveland.

BRADSBY, H. C.
1891. History of Bradford County, Pennsylvania. 1320 pp. S. B. Nelson & Co., Chicago.

BRAINARD, DAVID L.
1940. Six came back—the Arctic adventure of David L. Brainard. 305 pp. Edited by Bessie Rowland James. Indianapolis and New York.

BRANCH, EDWARD DOUGLAS
1929. The hunting of the buffalo. 240 pp. D. Appleton & Co., New York and London; pp. 7-8, 11, 16, 107.

BRECK, LLOYD
1908. In wild Wisconsin. Forest and Stream 71: 297. August 22.

BREHAUT, ERNEST
1912. An encyclopedist of the Dark Ages, Isidore of Seville. 274 pp. Also Studies in History, Economics, and Public Law 48 (1): 225. Edited by the faculty of Political Science, Columbia Univ. Whole No. 120. New York.

BREWER, WILLIAM H.
1930. Up and down California in 1860-1864. 601 pp. New Haven, Connecticut.

BRIGHAM, JOHN B.
1859. Louisa [County]. 5th Ann. Rept. Iowa State Agr. Soc., 1858. Pp. 364-373.

BRISTOW, ARCH, and DUTTON, CHARLES J.
1939. Last stand of the lobo. Hunter-Trader-Trapper Outdoorsman 79 (2): 23-24, illus. August.

BRITISH COLUMBIA, PROVINCE OF
1895. Animal pests. Fourth report of the Dept. of Agr. of the Province of British Columbia, 1894. Pp. 1126-1131. Victoria.
1897. Noxious animals and animal pests. Fifth report of the Dept. of Agr. of the Province of British Columbia, 1895-96. Pp. 1167-1177. Victoria.
1910. Game animals, birds, and fishes of British Columbia. Bureau of Provincial Information Bull. 17: 27. 6th edition.

BROOKS, ALLAN
1926. Past and present big-game conditions in British Columbia and the predatory animal question. Jour. Mamm. 7: 37-40.
1944. Do predators eradicate disease? Rod & Gun, 45 (8): 13, 29; illus. January.

BROOKS, FRED ERNEST
1911. The mammals of West Virginia. Report of West Va. State Board of Agr. 20: 9-30. (For quarter ended Dec. 30, 1910.)
BROWN, C. EMERSON
1936. Rearing wild animals in captivity, and gestation periods. Jour. Mamm. 17 (1): 10-13. February.
BROWN, R. C., Ed.
1895. History of Butler County, Pennsylvania. R. C. Brown Co. 1360 pp. Harrisburg.
BROWN, THOMAS POLLOK
1934. California names. An alphabetical list of geographical place names in California. A pamphlet of 28 unnumbered pages issued by the American Trust Company, San Francisco.
BROWNING, MESHACH
1928. Forty-four years of the life of a hunter. 400 pp. Philadelphia.
BRYANT, EDWIN
1885. Rocky Mountain adventures. 452 pp. New York.
BUCHANAN, ANGUS
1920. Wild life in Canada. John Murray, Pub. London, 264 pp., illus.
BUCK, S. J. and E. H.
1939. The planting of civilization in western Pennsylvania. 565 pp. Univ. Pittsburgh Press, Pittsburgh.
BUDD, THOMAS
1902. Pennsylvania and New Jersey. Burrows Brothers Co., Cleveland, p. 73.
BUFFON, GEORGES LOUIS LECLERC
1750-1804. Histoire naturelle, generale, et particuliere, avec la description du cabinet du roy, 44 vols. Vol. 9, 375 pp., illus. Paris, 1761. Description of the "loup noir," pp. 362-370, and plate 41. The plate was copied and reproduced as plate 89 of Schreber (1775) over the name *Canis lycaon* (= *C. l. lycaon*).
BULLOCK-WEBSTER, FRANK
1909. Wolves in British Columbia. Rod and Gun in Canada 11 (7): 611. December.

BURT, WILLIAM HENRY
1938. Faunal relationships and geographic distribution of mammals in Sonora, Mexico. Univ. Mich., Mus. of Zool. Misc. Publ. 39: 1-77, 26 maps.

BUSHNELL, DAVID I., JR.
1938. Drawings by George Gibbs in Far Northwest, 1849-1851. Smithsn. Misc. Coll. 97 (8): 1-28, illus.

BYERS, O. P.
1912. Personal recollections of the terrible blizzard of 1886. Kansas Historical Collections 1911-1912 12: 99-117.

BYRD, COL. WM.
1901. The writings of Colonel William Byrd, of Westover in Virginia, 1728. 461 pp. Edited by John Spencer Bassett, New York.

CABOT, WILLIAM B.
1920. Labrador. 354 pp., illus. Boston.

CAGE, DUNCAN S.
1890. The big-game of North America. Coursing the gray wolf. 581 pp., illus. Ed. by G. O. Stiles, Chicago and New York.

CAHN, ALVIN R.
1937. The mammals of the Quetico Provincial Park of Ontario. Jour. Mamm. 18 (1): 19-30.

CAMERON, JENKS
1929. The Bureau of Biological Survey—its history, activities, and organization. Service Monograph of the U. S. Government 54: 46. Brookings Institution, Washington, D. C.

CAMPANIUS, HOLM TOMAS
1834. A short description of the province of New Sweden. Now called, by the English, Pennsylvania in America. Memoirs Pa. Hist. Soc. v. 3 (pt. 1), 166 pp. Philadelphia.

CANADA, DEPT. OF THE INTERIOR
1923. Canadian Nat. Parks Branch. J. B. Harkin, Commissioner. Report of the Commissioner of Canadian Nat. Parks, Ottawa, 1922, pp. 41-47. App. 4-5.
1924. Canadian Nat. Parks Branch. J. B. Harkin, Commissioner. Report of the Commissioner of Canadian Nat. Parks, Ottawa, 1923, pp. 1-36.

1927. Combatting the wolves in northern Canada. Natural Resources of Canada 6 (3): 3. Ottawa.
1934. National Parks of Canada. Nat. Parks, Branch, J. B. Harkin, Commissioner. Report of the Commissioner, 1933, pp. 1-51. Ottawa.

CANADA, DEPT. OF MINES AND RESOURCES
1937. Report of lands, parks, and forests. Pp. 56, 63, 86. R. A. Gibson, Director, Ottawa.

CARHART, ARTHUR HAWTHORNE
1939. World champion wolfer. Outdoor Life 84 (3): 22-23, 74-75, illus.

———, and YOUNG, STANLEY P.
1929. The last stand of the pack. 295 pp., illus. New York.

CARL ———
1886. Montana wolves and panthers. Forest and Stream 26: 508-509.

CARL, G. CLIFFORD, and HARDY, GEO. A.
1942. Report on a collecting trip to the Lac La Hache Area, British Columbia. Rept. Prov. Mus. Nat. Hist.; Prov. of British Columbia, Canada. Victoria, pp. 25-49.

CARMAN, EZRA AYERS, and others
1892. Special report on the history and present condition of the sheep industry of the United States. Bur. Anim. Ind., U. S. Dept. Agr. 1,000 pp. Washington, D. C.

CARNEY, EMERSON
1902. The gray wolf. Forest and Stream 58 (5): 84. February 1.

CARSON, LAWRENCE
1939a. Black wolves of Revillagigedo. The Alaska Sportsman 5 (1): 8-9, 25-29, illus. January.
1939b. Some wolves get away. The Alaska Sportsman 5 (10): 18-20, 22-26, illus. October.

CARTER, E. D.
1898. Wolves in Iowa. Forest and Stream 50 (18): 345. April.

CARTWRIGHT, DAVID W.
1875. Natural history of western wild animals and guide for hunters, trappers and sportsmen. 280 pp. Toledo, Ohio.

CARY, MERRITT
1911. A biological survey of Colorado. U. S. Dept. Agr., Bur. Biol. Survey. North Amer. Fauna 33: 1-256, illus.

CASSIN, JOHN
1858. United States exploring expedition during the years 1838, '39, '40, '41, '42 under the command of Charles Wilkes. Ed. 2, Vol. 8, Mammalogy and Ornithology, pp. 1-466, 2 illus. and folio atlas. Philadelphia.

CATESBY, MARK
1743 or 1771. The natural history of Carolina, Florida, and the Bahama Islands. 2 vols. London.

CATLIN, GEORGE
1848. Catlin's notes of eight years' travels and residence in Europe with his North American Indian collection. 2 vols., 3d Ed. London.
1913. North American Indians. Modern edition. 2 vols. Philadelphia.

CHAPMAN, CHARLES H.
1907. Taking of wolves by trap, poison, and dogs. Pp. 1-3. Michigan State Dept. of Fish and Game. Sault Ste. Marie.

CHAPMAN, H. H.
1938. Wolf packs. Journal of Forestry, p. 1158. November.

CHASE, STUART
1936. Rich land, poor land. A study of waste in the natural resources of America. Pp. i-x; 1-361; illus.; Whittlesey Hounse, New York; London, McGraw-Hill Book Co., Inc., pp. 178-191.

CHITTENDEN, HIRAM MARTIN
1935. The American fur trade of the far West. 2vols. New York.

CLAPP, HENRY
1868. Notes of a fur hunter. American Naturalist 1 (12): 652-666. February.

CLARK, AUSTIN H.
1943. Iceland and Greenland. Smithsn. Inst., War background studies No. 15, Pub. 3735, pp. IV plus 103, illus. August 19.

CLARK, WILLIAM, and LEWIS, MERIWETHER
1904-05. Original journals of the Lewis and Clark expedition, 1804-1806. 8 vols. Edited by Reuben Gold Thwaites. New York.

CLARKE, C. H. D.
1940. A biological investigation of the Thelon Game Sanctuary, with remarks on the natural history of the interior barren lands. Canada Dept. of Mines and Resources, Mines and Geology Branch, Nat. Mus. of Canada Bull. 96, Biol. Ser. 25: 1-135. Ottawa.

CLAYTON, JOHN
1844. A letter from Mr. John Clayton rector of Crofton at Wakefield and Yorkshire to the Royal Society May 12, 1688. Tracts and Other Papers Relating to the Colonies of North America, vol. 3, 45 pp. Collected by Peter Force.

CLYMAN, JAMES
1928. The adventures of a trapper and covered wagon emigrant as told in his reminiscences and diaries, 1792-1881. Edited by Charles L. Camp. San Francisco Historical Society.

COCKERELL, T. D. A.
1927. History of Colorado. Natural History, vol. 1, pp. 139-200. Colo. State Hist. and Nat. Hist. Soc. Denver.

COCKING, MATTHEW
1908. Journal of Matthew Cocking from York factory to Blackfeet country, 1772-73. Edited with introduction and notes by Laurence J. Burpee. Trans. Royal Soc. Canada, sec. II, pp. 106-110. Ottawa.

COLBERT, EDWIN H.
1939. Wild dogs and tame—past and present. Natural History 43 (2): 90-95, illus.

COLLINS, GRENOLD
1937a. Excerpt from Alaska Game Commission report. February 26, Juneau, Alaska. In files of Fish and Wildlife Service, Washington, D. C.
1937b. Report of Arctic patrol and inspection trip, pp. 24-26. In files of Fish and Wildlife Service.

COLORADO LIVE STOCK RECORD
1884. April 18. Denver.
COMEAU, NOEL
1940. Notes preliminaires sur la presence du *Canis tundrensis ungavensis*, n. ssp. dans la province de Quebec. Ann l'Acfes, Montreal, 6: 121-122.
CONNELLY, WILLIAM ELSEY
1915. The Lane trail. Kansas Hist. Collections 1913-1914 13: 268-279. Topeka.
COOPER, COURTNEY RYLEY
1926. High country—the Rockies yesterday and today. 294 pp. Boston.
COOPER, J. G., SUCKLEY, G., and GIBBS, G.
1860. The natural history of Washington Territory, with much relating to Minnesota, Nebraska, Kansas, Oregon, and California. . . . 1853-1857, 3 pts. in 1 vol. Pac. R. R. Repts., vol. 12, Book 2, 399 pp.
COOPER, JOHN M.
1938. Snares, deadfalls, and other traps of the northern Algonquins and northern Athabaskans. The Catholic Univ. America Anthropological Series 5, p. 144, illus. Washington, D. C.
COOPER, WILLIAM
1810. A guide in the wilderness—history of the first settlements in the western counties of New York, p. 23. Dublin. 1897 Ed., 41 pp. Rochester.
COOS COUNTY (OREGON)
1887. Coos County Court Journal 4: 1.
COPE, E. D.
1879. On the genera of Felidae and Canidae. Proc. Acad. Nat. Sci. Phila., pp. 168-194.
1880. On the zoological position of Texas. U. S. Natl. Mus. Bull. 17: 1-51.
1883. On the extinct dogs of North America. The Amer. Nat. 17 (3): 235-249, illus. March.
CORBIN, BEN
1900. Corbin's advice, or, the wolf hunter's guide. 76 pp., illus. Bismarck, North Dakota.

CORNEY, PETER
1896. Voyages in the northern Pacific. 138 pp. Honolulu.

CORNISH, CHARLES JOHN
1907. Animal artisans and other studies of birds and beasts. Longmans, Green & Co., London, New York, Bombay, and Calcutta. 274 pp., illus.

CORNISH, CHARLES J., et al
1906. Library of natural history—living animals of the world. 5 vols. New York.

CORY, CHARLES B.
1896. Hunting and fishing in Florida, including a key to the water birds known to occur in the state. 304 pp. Boston.
1912. The mammals of Illinois and Wisconsin. Field Mus. Nat. Hist. Publ. 153, Zool. Ser. 11: 1-505. Chicago.

COUES, ELLIOTT, U. S. A.
1867. The quadrupeds of Arizona. Amer. Nat. 1 (6): 281-292; 1 (7): 351-363; 1 (8): 393-400; 1 (10): 531-541.
1873. The prairie wolf or coyote, *Canis latrans*. Amer. Nat. 7 (7): 384-389. Salem, Mass.
1876. An account of the various publications relating to the travels of Lewis and Clarke, with a commentary on the zoological results of their expedition. U. S. Dept. of the Interior, Geol. and Geog. Survey Terr. Bull. (ser. 2) 1: 417-444. February 8.
1877. Fur-bearing animals. A monograph of the North American Mustelidae. U. S. Dept. of the Interior, Geol. Surv. Terr. Misc. Publ. No. 8, pp. 1-348. Washington, D. C.
1893. History of the Expedition under the Command of Lewis and Clark. 4 vols. F. P. Harper. New York.
1897. Manuscript journals of Alexander Henry and David Thompson, 1799-1814. 3 vols. New York.
See Henry, Alexander, and Thompson, David.

————, and YARROW, H. C.
1875. Report upon the collections of mammals made in portions of Nevada, Utah, California, Colorado, New Mexico, and Arizona, during the years 1871, 1872, 1873, and 1874. Geog. and Geol. Explor. and Surveys west of 100th Mer. 5: 37-129.

COUPIN, HENRI EUGENE VICTOR
1904. Animals that hunt. Smithsn. Inst. Ann. Rept. for 1903, pp. 567-571, August 29. Washington, D. C. A translation from Revue Scientifique (Paris), pp. 274-277.

COWAN, IAN McTAGGART
1939. The vertebrate fauna of the Peace River district of British Columbia. B. C. Prov. Mus., Occas. Papers No. 1, pp. 1-102. Victoria, British Columbia.

COWIE, ISAAC
1913. The company of adventurers; a narrative of seven years of the Hudson's Bay Company during 1867-1874 on the great buffalo plains. . . . 515 pp. Toronto.

COX, ROSS
1831. Adventures on the Columbia River 1811-1817. 2 vols. London.

COYNER, DAVID H.
1847. The lost trappers—a collection of interesting scenes and events in the Rocky Mountains. 255 pp. Cincinnati.

CRABB, E. D.
1924. The gross weight of Woodhouse's wolf. Jour. Mamm. 5 (3): 199-200.

CRANE, JOCELYN
1931. Mammals of Hampshire County, Massachusetts. Jour. Mamm. 12 (3): 267-272.

CRIDDLE, NORMAN
1925. The habits and economic importance of wolves in Canada. Dom. of Canada Dept. of Agr. Bull. (n.s.) 13: 1-24.

CRILE, GEORGE W.
1941. Intelligence, power, and personality. 347 pp., illus. New York and London.

CROOK COUNTY (OREGON)
1885. Crook County Commissioners' Journal 1: 334.

CROSS, E. C.
1940. Arthritis among wolves. The Canad. Field-Nat. 54 (1): 2-4, 4 illus. January. Ottawa.
CROSS, OSBORNE (MAJOR)
1850. A report in the form of a journal to the quartermaster general of the march of the regiment of mounted riflemen to Oregon from May 18 to October 5, 1849. U. S. War Dept. Rept. 1849-50. Printed for Senate 1850, Doc. No. 3, Report Quartermaster General, App. A, pp. 126-244. Washington, D. C.
CUMING, SIR ALEXANDER
1928. Journal of a journey to the Cherokee Mountains. Samuel Cole Williams' Early Travels in the Tennessee Country. 540 pp. Johnson City, Tenn.
CUMING, F.
1904. Sketches of a tour to the western country, 1807-1809. Ed. by Reuben Gold Thwaites in Early Western Travels. Vol. 4, 377 pp. Arthur H. Clark Co., Cleveland.
CUSTER, ELIZABETH B.
1890. Following the Guidon. 341 pp., illus. New York.
DALRYMPLE, BUD
1919. The gray wolf of South Dakota. 31 pp. Altoona, Pa.
1923. The value of the tame wolf as a decoy. Outdoor Life 52 (3): 188.
D'ARTAGUETTE, DIRON
1928. Journal of a journey from New Orleans to the Illinois country, 1722-1723, p. 75. Johnson City, Tenn.
DARWIN, CHARLES
1874. The descent of man, and selection in relation to sex. 797 pp., illus. 2nd Ed.
DAVIS, CLYDE B.
1928. Wolf pursues deer into water. Outdoor Life—Outdoor Recreation 62 (4): 86. October.
DAVIS, DUKE
1939. More on habits of wolves. Field and Stream 44 (2): 12-13. June.

DAVIS, STELLA M.
1929. The last wolf in Portland (Me.). Maine Naturalist 9 (2): 73. June.

DAVIS, WILLIAM B.
1939. The recent mammals of Idaho. 400 pp., 2 pls., 33 figs. The Caxton Printers, Ltd., Caldwell, Idaho. April 5.

DAVIS, WM. W. H.
1876. History of Bucks County, Pennsylvania. 875 pp. Democrat Book and Job Office Print, Doylestown.

DAWKINS, W. BOYD
1874. Cave hunting. Researches on the evidence of caves respecting the early inhabitants of Europe. Pp. i-xxiv; 1-455, illus.; London, Macmillan Company; pp. 76, 79, 81, 131, 146, 400, 401.

DAWSON, W. M.
1937. Heredity in the dog. U. S. Dept. Agr. Yearbook. Pp. 1314-1349. Also Separate No. 1601. Washington, D. C.

DAY, ALBERT M.
1932. Handbook for hunters of predatory animals. U. S. Dept. Agr., Bureau of Biological Survey. Pp. 1-52, illus.

DEARBORN, NED
1919. Trapping on the farm. Yearbook, U. S. Dept. Agric.: 451-484, illus.; 468. Yearbook Separate 823.
1932. Foods of some predatory fur-bearing animals in Michigan. School of Forestry and Conservation, Univ. Mich. Bull. 1: 1-52, illus; 50; Ann Arbor.

DEGERBOL, MAGNUS
1927. Uber prahistorische, dänische Hunde. Vidensk. Medd. Dansk naturh. Foren. Kobenhavn, Bind 84: 17-71, illus.
Includes remarks on wolves of Greenland and Ellesmere Island.

DEKAY, J. E.
1842. The natural history of New York. Zoology, pt. 1, 146 pp., illus. Albany.

DELLINGER, S. C., and BLACK, J. D.
1940. Notes on Arkansas mammals. Jour. Mamm. 21 (2): 187-191. May.

DELMONT, JOSEPH
1931. Catching wild beasts alive. 285 pp. London. Remarks and observations on the dingo as compared to the wolf.
DENNY, CECIL (SIR)
1943. Down the Peace (River) in a dug-out. The Beaver, Outfit 273, pp. 10-13, illus. March. Hudson's Bay Co., Winnipeg, Manitoba, Canada.
DENVER, CITY AND COUNTY
1927. Municipal facts 10 (5 and 6): 14. Publ. by City and County of Denver, Colo. May and June.
DE SMET, P. J. (FATHER)
1847. Oregon missions and travels over the Rocky Mountains in 1845-46. 408 pp. New York.
DE TONTY, HENRY
1917. Memoir on LaSalle's discoveries, sent in 1693 to Count Pontchartrain. P. 302. New York.
DE WITT, LEONARD C.
1940. Vanquishes her foe in battle to the death. Western Sportsman 4 (2): 6, 7, 25, illus. January.
DICE, LEE R.
1927. Manual of recent wild mammals of Michigan. Univ. Mich. Handbook Series, No. 2; pp. 39. Ann Arbor.
DICK, EVERETT
1928. The long drive. Kansas Historical Collections 1926-1928 17: 27-97.
DICKINSON, JOHN P.
1939. Range cattle days in old Colorado. The American Cattle Producer 21 (3): 9-10. August.
DILLIN, JOHN G. W.
1924. The Kentucky rifle. 124 pp. plus index, illus. Publ. National Rifle Association, Washington, D. C.
DIONNE, C. E.
1902. Les mammiferes de la province de Quebec. 285 pp., illus. Quebec.
DIXON, JOSEPH S.
1916. The timber wolf in California. California Fish and Game 2 (3): 125-129.

1934. Mother wolf carries food for twelve miles to her young. Jour. Mamm. 15 (2): 158.

1938. Birds and mammals of Mount McKinley National Park, Alaska. U. S. Dept. Int. Natl. Park Service, Fauna Ser. No. 3: 1-236.

DODDRIDGE, JOSEPH (REV.)

1824. Notes on the settlement and Indian Wars of the western parts of Virginia and Pennsylvania from the year 1763 until the year 1783. 316 pp. Wellsburgh, Va.

1876a. Notes on the settlement and Indian wars of the western parts of Virginia and Pennsylvania from the year 1763 until the year 1783. 331 pp. Albany, N. Y.

1876b. Western Virginia and Pennsylvania. P. 99.

DODGE, RICHARD IRVING

1876. The Black Hills. 151 pp. New York.

1877. The plains of the great West and their inhabitants. . . . 448 pp. New York.

DONALDSON, THOMAS

1887. The George Catlin Indian Gallery in the U. S. National Museum (Smithsonian Institution), with memoirs and statistics. U. S. Government Printing Office, Washington, D. C. Pp. vii plus 939, illus.

DONHAM, C. R., SIMMS, B. T., and MILLER, F. W.

1926. So-called salmon poisoning in dogs (Progress Report). Jour. Veterinary Medical Assoc. (n.s. 21) 68 (6): 701-715, illus.

DONHAM, C. R., and SIMMS, B. T.

1927. Coyote susceptible to salmon poisoning. Jour. Amer. Veterinary Medical Assoc. (n.s. 24) 71 (2): 215-217.

DORR, HENRY C.

1885. The Narragansetts. R. I. Hist. Soc. Coll. 7: 135-237. Providence.

DOUGLAS, DAVID

1914. Journal kept by David Douglas during his travels in North America 1823-27. 364 pp. Publ. under the direction of the Royal Horticultural Society. London.

Describes collecting a "new species" of *Canis* (= *C. l. fuscus*).

DOUGLAS, NORMAN
1938. Old Calabria. 498 pp. Oxford University Press. New York and London.
DUFRESNE, FRANK
1935. Estimated value of Alaska wildlife. The Daily Alaska Empire, Progress ed., 3rd sec., pp. 1-8. March. Juneau, Alaska.
1942. Mammals and birds of Alaska. U. S. Dept. Interior, Fish and Wildlife Service Circ. 3: 1-37, illus. Washington, D. C.
1943. Grizzly fight (Wolves vs. grizzly bears). Field & Stream, 48 (6): 22-23, 64, 1 illus. (drawn). October.
DUIS, E.
1874. The good old times in McLean County, Illinois. 865 pp. Bloomington, Ill.
DUNNE, A. L.
1939. Report on wolves followed during February and March 1939. The Canad. Field-Nat. 53 (8): 117-118. Ottawa.
DU PRATZ, LE PAGE
1774. The history of Louisiana. 387 pp. Transl. from the French ed. publ. in 1758. London.
1928. History of Louisiana. Samuel Cole Williams' Early Travels in the Tennessee Country. P. 110. Johnson City, Tenn.
DURANT, SAMUEL W.
1877a. History of Lawrence County, Pennsylvania. 228 pp. L. H. Everts & Co., Philadelphia.
1877b. History of Mercer County, Pennsylvania. 156 pp. L. H. Everts & Co., Philadelphia.
DUTCHER, WILLIAM
1887. Old-time natural history. Forest and Stream 28 (6): 105-106. March 3.
EASTMAN, CHARLES ALEXANDER
1904. Red Hunters and the animal people. 248 pp. Harper & Bros. New York and London.
ECKELS, RICHARD PRESTON
1937. Greek wolf lore. 88 pp. Univ. of Pennsylvania, Philadelphia.

EDITOR
1938. Trains wolves for sled team. The Outdoorsman 77 (4): 6. October.
EDWARDS, STACY
1922. An unusual timber wolf. Outdoor Life 50 (5): 383-384, illus. November.
ELLIOT, DANIEL GIRAUD
1904. The land and sea mammals of Middle America and the West Indies. Field Columbian Mus., Publ. 95, Zool. Ser. 4 (pt. 2): 441-850. Chicago.
1905. A check list of mammals of the North American continent, the West Indies, and the neighboring seas. Field Columbian Mus., Publ. 105, Zool. Ser. 6: 1-761. Chicago.
ELLIS, FRANKLIN, and EVANS, SAMUEL
1883. History of Lancaster County, Pennsylvania. Everts & Peck, Philadelphia. 1101 pp.
ELTON, CHARLES
1931. Epidemics among sledge dogs in the Canadian Arctic and their relation to disease in the Arctic fox. Canad. Jour. of Research 5 (6): 673-692. December.
ELY, ALFRED, ANTHONY, H. E., and CARPENTER, R. R. M.
1939. North American big game. A Book of the Boone and Crockett Club, New York. 533 pp.
EMMART, EMILY WALCOTT
1940. The Badianus Manuscript. (Codex Barberini, Latin 241.) Vatican Library. An Aztec herbal of 1552. 341 pp., illus., 118 plates reproduced; 2 figs. and 4 pls. Baltimore.
EVANS, ESTWICK
1819. A pedestrious tour of four thousand miles through the western states and territories, during the winter and spring of 1818. 256 pp. Concord, N. H. (Thwaite's Early Western Travels 8: 91-364, 1904.)
FARLEY, FRANK L.
1925. Changes in the status of certain animals and birds during the past fifty years in Central Alberta. Canad. Field Nat. 39 (9): 200-202. December.

FAVOUR, ALPHEUS HOYT
1936. Old Bill Williams—mountain man. 229 pp. Chapel Hill, N. C.
FERRIS, WARREN ANGUS
1940. Life in the Rocky Mountains. Edited by Paul C. Phillips. 365 pp., illus. Denver.
FETTERLY, ROBERT
1943. Frontispiece. Alaska Sportsman, 9 (9). September.
FEUILLEE-BILLOT, MME. A.
1932. Les derniers loups de France. La Nature 60 (2): 551-559.
FISHER, SYDNEY GEORGE
1900. The making of Pennsylvania. J. B. Lippincott & Co., Philadelphia. 364 pp.
FLINT, DR. THOMAS
1924. Diary of Dr. Thomas Flint. California to Maine and return, 1851-55. 78 pp. Los Angeles.
FLOWER, MAJOR STANLEY S.
1929. Mammals. List of the vertebrate animals exhibited in the gardens of the Zool. Soc. of London, 1828-1927 1: 1-419. London.
1931. Contributions to our knowledge of the duration of life in vertebrate animals. Proc. Zool. Soc. London 5 (pt. 1): 145-234.
FLOWER, WILLIAM HENRY, and
LYDEKKER, RICHARD
1891. An introduction to the study of mammals, living and extinct. 763 pp. London.
FORREST, EARLE R.
1926. History of Washington County, Pennsylvania. S. J. Clarke Pub. Co., Chicago. 3 vols.
FOUQUET, L. C.
1925. Buffalo days. Kansas Hist. Collections 1923-1925, vol. 16, pp. 341-352.
FOWLER, JACOB
1898. The journal of Jacob Fowler, narrating an adventure from Arkansas through the Indian Territory, Oklahoma, Kansas, Colorado, and New Mexico, to the sources of Rio Grande del Norte, 1821-22. 183 pp. New York. Edited with notes by Elliott Coues.

FOX, HERBERT
1923. Diseases in captive wild mammals and birds. 665 pp., illus. J. B. Lippincott Company. Philadelphia, London, and Chicago.
FREEMAN, FREDERICK
1858-62. The history of Cape Cod: the annals of Barnstable County including the district of Mashpee. 2 vols. Boston.
FREMONT, JOHN CHARLES
1887. Memoirs of my life. 655 pp., 1 vol. Chicago and New York.
FREUCHEN, PETER
1935a. Arctic adventure—my life in the frozen North. 467 pp. New York and Toronto.
1935b. Report of the fifth Thule expedition, 1921-24, the Danish expedition to Arctic North America in charge of Knud Rasmussen 2 (4 and 5), Mammals, Pt. 2, Field Notes and Biological Observations. Copenhagen.
FRYXELL, F. M.
1926. An observation on the hunting methods of the timber wolf. Jour. Mamm. 7 (3): 226-227. August.
FULLER, A. R.
1885. Dog-wolf hybrid. Forest and Stream 25: 507. July 23.
FUNKHOUSER, WILLIAM DELBERT
1925. Wild life in Kentucky. Ky. Geol. Surv., Frankfort, 385 pp., illus.
GABRIELSON, IRA NOEL
1941. Wildlife conservation. 250 pp., illus. New York.
GARMAN, H.
1894. A preliminary list of the vertebrate animals of Kentucky. Bull. Essex Inst. 26 (1-3): 1-63. January, February, March.
GARRARD, LEWIS H.
1850. Wah-to-yah and the Taos Trail. 349 pp. Cincinnati and New York.
GARRETSON, MARTIN S.
1938. The American bison. 254 pp. New York.

GASS, SERGEANT PATRICK
1904. Gass's Journal of the Lewis and Clark expedition. 298 pp. Reprint of the edition of 1811. Chicago.

GERSTELL, RICHARD
1937. The Pennsylvania bounty system. Research Bull. 1: 3. Harrisburg.

GESELL, ARNOLD
1941. Wolf child and human child. 107 pp. New York.

GIBSON, W. HAMILTON
1881. Camp life in the woods and the tricks of trapping and trap making. 300 pp., illus. New York.

GIDLEY, JAMES W., and GAZIN, C. LEWIS
1938. The Pleistocene vertebrate fauna from Cumberland Cave, Maryland. U. S. Nat. Mus. Bull. 171: 1-99, illus.

GILLMORE, PARKER
1874. Prairie and forest. A description of the game of North America, with personal adventures in their pursuit. Harper Bros., New York. 378 pp., illus.

GILPIN, J. BERNARD
1870. On the mammalia of Nova Scotia. Nova Scotian Inst. Nat. Sci. Proc. and Trans. 2 (4) pt. 2: 58-69.

GLASER, FRANK
1934. Letter to Alaska Game Commission sent from Healy Forks, Alaska, to Juneau, Alaska, dated December 26. In files of Fish and Wildlife Service, Washington, D. C.

GODMAN, JOHN D.
1846. American natural history. 2 vols. in 1. 3d ed. Philadelphia.

GOLDMAN, EDWARD A.
1937. The wolves of North America. Jour. Mamm. 18 (1): 37-45. February 14.
New: *Canis lupus labradorius*, *C. l. ligoni*, *C. l. youngi*, *C. l. irremotus*, *C. l. monstrabilis*, *C. l. mogollonensis*, and *C. rufus gregoryi*.
1941. Three new wolves from North America. Proc. Biol. Soc. Wash. 54: 109-114. September 30.
New: *Canis lupus alces*, *C. l. columbianus*, and *C. l. hudsonicus*.

GOLDSMITH, OLIVER
1818. Natural history. Pp. 76-78. Pub. by Benjamin Warner.

GOODRICH, A. T.
1837. The Territory of Florida: Civil and Natural History. P. 63. New York.

GOODWIN, GEORGE GILBERT
1935. Mammals of Connecticut. Conn. State Geol. & Nat. Hist. Survey Bull. 53: 1-221.
1936. Big game animals in the northeastern United States. Jour. Mamm. 17 (1): 48-50.

GOOLD, WILLIAM
1889. All about wolves. Portland, Maine Daily Press. December 14.

GORDON, W. R.
1942. I tamed a wolf for my dog team. The Alaska Sportsman 8 (10): 10-11, 29-31, illus. October.

GRAHAM, ALBERT ADAMS (COMPILER)
1883. History of Fairfield and Perry counties, Ohio. 1186 pp., 2 maps. Chicago.

GRAHAM, GIDEON
1939. Animal outlaws. 256 pp., illus., 2d edition. Collinsville, Oklahoma.

GRANT, MADISON
1908, 1910. Condition of wild life in Alaska. New York Zool. Soc. 12th Ann. Rept. (1907): 125-134. Or Publ. 1976, Smithsonian Inst. Ann. Report for 1909: 521-529, 1 plate. Washington, D. C.

GRANT, ULYSSES SIMPSON
1885-86. Personal memoirs of U. S. Grant. 2 vols. New York.

GREAT BRITAIN
1749. House of Commons. Report from Committees of the House of Commons. From the Committee on the state of the Hudson's Bay Company 2: 263-266.

GREELEY, HORACE
1860. An overland journey from New York to San Francisco in the summer of 1859, pp. 93-94. New York, San Francisco.

GREELY, ADOLPHUS W.
1888. Report on the proceedings of the United States expedition to Lady Franklin Bay, Grinnell Land. 2 vols., v. 1, 545 pp.; v. 2, 738 pp. Washington, D. C.
GREEN, JACOB
1822. Curious instinct of the common hog (*Sus scrofa* Linn.). American Journal of Science 4 (2): 309-310.
GREEN, R. G., and EVANS, C. A.
1940. A deficiency disease of foxes. Science 92 (2381): 154-155. August 16.
GREGG, JOHN
1943. The strange "dog" of Fort Selkirk. The Beaver, Outfit 273. Hudson's Bay Co., Winnipeg, Manitoba, Canada, p. 31, illus.
GREGG, JOSIAH
1905. Commerce of the prairies; or the journal of a Santa Fe trader 1831-39. Early Western Travels, vols. 19 and 20. Edited by Reuben Gold Thwaites. Cleveland.
GREGORY, TAPPAN
1935. The black wolf of the Tensas. Chicago Acad. Sci. Program Activities 6 (3): 1-68, illus.
1936. Mammals of the Chicago region. Chicago Acad. Sci. Program Activities 7 (2-3): 1-75. July.
1939. Eyes in the night. Timber Wolves. 243 pp., illus. New York.
GREGORY, WILLIAM K.
1933. Nature's wild dog show. Bull. New York Zool. Soc. 36 (4): 83-96, illus.
GRENFELL, WILFRED T., et al
1913. Labrador, the country and the people. 529 pp. New York.
GRINNELL, GEORGE BIRD
1892. Blackfoot lodge tales. 310 pp. New York.
1893. Pawnee stories and folk tales. P. 246. New York.
1896. About wolves and coyotes. Forest and Stream 47: 511-512. December 26.
1897a. Various trapping methods. How wolves were caught. Forest and Stream 49 (20): 382. November 13.

1897b. Trail and Campfire. Wolves and wolf nature. 353 pp. A book of the Boone and Crockett Club. New York.
1904. American big game in its haunts. A book of the Boone and Crockett Club. 497 pp. New York.
1907. Dog-wolf partnership. Forest and Stream 69 (20): 772. November.
1911. When antelope were plenty. Forest and Stream 77 (16): 582-583, 600-601. October.
1914. The wolf hunters. 303 pp. New York.
1924. A letter to Audubon. Jour. Mamm. 5 (4): 223-230.

GRINNELL, J. B.
1863. Sheep on the prairies. Report of the Commissioner of Agr. for the year 1862. 37th Cong., 3d sess., Ex. Doc. No. 78, pp. 300-312.

GRINNELL, JOSEPH
1933. Review of the recent mammal fauna of California. Univ. Calif. Publ. Zool. 40 (2): 71-234, September. Berkeley.

———, DIXON, JOSEPH S., and LINSDALE, JEAN M.
1937. Fur-bearing animals of California. . . . Contributions from Univ. of Calif. Mus. Vert. Zool. 2 vols. Berkeley.

GUBERNATIS, ANGELO DE
1872. Zoological mythology, or the legends of animals. 2 vols. London.

HAFEN, LE ROY R., and YOUNG, FRANCIS MARION
1938. Fort Laramie and the pageant of the West, 1834-1890. 429 pp. Glendale, Calif.

HAHN, WALTER LOUIS
1909. The mammals of Indiana. 33rd Ann. Rept. Indiana Department of Geology and Natural Resources. Pp. 417-663. Indianapolis.

HALL, ARCHIBALD
1861. On the mammals and birds of the District of Montreal. The Canad. Nat. and Geol. 6 (4): 284-309.

HALL, E. RAYMOND
1932. Remarks on the affinities of the mammalian fauna of Vancouver Island, British Columbia, with descrip-

tions of new subspecies. Univ. Calif. Publ. Zool. 38 (12): 415-423. November 8.

New: *Canis occidentalis crassodon* (= *C. lupus crassodon*).

1942. Fur Bearers and the War. Trans. 7th North Amer. Wildlife Conference, Amer. Wildlife Inst., Toronto, Canada. Pp. 472-480.

HALLIDAY, W. E. D.

1940. Predatory animals in the national parks (Canadian). Forest and Outdoors 36 (9): 277-278, 292-293; 36 (10): 317-318, 324-326, 329, illus. Montreal. September and October.

HALLOCK, CHARLES

1880. The sportsman's gazetteer and general guide. 700 pp. and appendix 208 pp., illus. New York.

HAMILTON, W. J.

1939. American mammals, their lives, habits, and economic relations. 434 pp., illus. New York and London.

HARDING, A. R.

1923. Wolves—timber and prairie. Outdoor Life 51 (1): 52. January.

HARGRAVE, JAMES

1938. The Hargrave correspondence, 1821-1843. 472 pp. Publ. by Champlain Society. Toronto.

HARLAN, RICHARD

1825. Fauna Americana, being a description of mammiferous animals inhabiting North America. 318 pp. Philadelphia.

HARMON, DANIEL WILLIAMS

1820. A journal of voyages and travels in the interior of North America between the 47th and 58th degrees of north latitude. 432 pp. Andover, New York. 1903.

HARPER, FRANCIS

1927. The mammals of the Okefenokee Swamp region of Georgia. Proc. Boston Soc. Nat. Hist. 38 (7): 191-396. Also issued as a reprint March 1927.

1932. Mammals of the Athabaska and Great Slave Lakes region. Jour. Mamm. 13 (1): 19-36.

1942. The name of the Florida wolf. Journ. Mamm. 23 (3): 339.

HARPSTER, JOHN W.
1938. Pen pictures of early western Pennsylvania. Univ. Pittsburgh Press. 337 pp.

HARRIS, LEO D.
1940. The unruly gangsters of the Badlands. North Dakota Outdoors 2 (12): 4, illus. June. Bismarck, North Dakota.

HARRY, JOSEPH EDWARD
1936. Dog and dogs. 315 pp. New York and London.

HARTING, JAMES EDMUND
1880. British animals extinct within historic times. 258 pp. Boston.

HARTMANN, GEORGE
1907. Wooed by a sphinx of Azatlan; the romance of a hero of our late Spanish-American War. . . . 125 pp. Prescott, Arizona.

HARTSEL, SAMUEL
1916. Personal narrative. Denver Record-Stockman, p. 6. Historical Review Edition. January.

HARVARD CLASSICS, THE—Elliott
1910. The story of the Volsungs and Niblings 49: 268 (footnote). New York.

HARVEY, OSCAR JEWELL
1927. A history of Wilkes-Barre. 3 vols. Wilkes-Barre, Pa.

HASTINGS, LANSFORD WARREN
1932. The emigrants' guide to Oregon and California. 157 pp. Reproduced in facsimile from the original edition of 1845. Princeton, New Jersey.

HATFIELD, DONALD M.
1940. Animal populations and sunspot cycles. Chicago Nat. 3 (4): 105-110; 107. December.

HATTON, JOHN H.
1939. Livestock albums. American Cattle Producer 21 (6): 5-6, illus. November.

HAWN, LAURENS
1878. Death struggle of a buffalo. Western Homestead. Pp. 190-191. November. Leavenworth, Kansas.

HAYDEN, FERDINAND VANDIVEER
1862. On the ethnography and philology of the Indian tribes of the Missouri Valley. Trans. Amer. Philos. Soc. 12 (n.s.), pt. 2, art. 3; 231-461. Philadelphia.
1863. On the geology and natural history of the Upper Missouri. Trans. Amer. Philos. Soc. 12 (n.s.), pt. 1, art. 1: 1-218, map.
1875. Report of the U. S. Geological Survey. P. 556.
HAYS, W. J.
1871. Notes on the range of some of the animals in America at the time of the arrival of the white men. Amer. Nat. 5: 387-392.
HAZARD, SAMUEL
1828-35. Hazard's register of Pennsylvania. 16 vols. Philadelphia.
1850. Annals of Pennsylvania, 1609-1682. 664 pp. Philadelphia.
HEARNE, SAMUEL
1911. A journey from Prince of Wales's Fort in Hudson's Bay to the northern Ocean in the years 1769-72. 437 pp. Edited by J. B. Tyrrell. Toronto.
HEIN, EDWARD N.
1943. The forest balance. Wisc. Conser. Bull. 7 (9): 10-11. Wisc. Conser. Dept., Madison.
HENDERSON, ARCHIBALD
1920. The conquest of the old Southwest; the romantic story of the early pioneers into Virginia, the Carolinas, Tennessee, and Kentucky, 1740-1790. 395 pp., illus. The Century Company, New York.
HENDERSON, JUNIUS, and CRAIG, ELBERTA L.
1932. Economic mammalogy. 397 pp. Springfield, Ill., and Baltimore, Md.
HENING, WILLIAM WALLER
1810-1823. The statutes at large; being a collection of all the laws of Virginia. 13 vols. Richmond.
HENRY, ALEXANDER
1901. Travels and Adventures in Canada and the Indian Territories—Alexander Henry. Fur Trader, 1760-1776. Pp. 273-274. Boston.

HENRY, ALEXANDER, and THOMPSON, DAVID
1897. New light on the early history of the greater Northwest. Manuscript journals of Alexander Henry and of David Thompson, 1799-1814. 3 vols. Edited by Elliott Coues. New York.

HERNANDEZ, FRANCISCO
1651. Rerum medicarum novae hispaniae thesaurus; sev. plantarum animalium mineralium Mexicanorum historia. 950 pp., illus.
The "Xoloitzcuintli," p. 479, became the basis for *Canis mexicanus* Linnaeus, believed to be a wolf until shown by Allen (1920, p. 478) to apply to Mexican "hairless' dog.

HERRICK, C. L.
1892. Mammals of Minnesota. Geol. and Nat. Hist. Survey of Minn. Bull. 7: 1-299, illus. Minneapolis.

HEVERLY, C. F.
1885. History of Monroe Township and Borough, 1779-1885. 209 pp. Reporter-Journal Printing Co., Towanda, Pennsylvania.
1926. History and geography of Bradford County, 1615-1924. Bradford Co. Hist. Soc. Towanda, Pennsylvania.

HEWITT, C. GORDON
1916. The conservation of our northern mammals. Seventh annual report of Commission of Conservation, Ottawa, Canada. 283 pp., illus. Montreal.
1921. The conservation of the wild life of Canada. XX plus 344 pp., illus.

HICHENS, WILLIAM (CAPTAIN)
1930. Unwanted animals—a world problem. Discovery, Monthly Jour. Knowl. 2 (124): 133-136. April. London.

HILL, N. N., JR. (COMPILER)
1881. History of Licking County, Ohio. 822 pp., also numerous figs. Newark, Ohio.

HILTON, WILLIAM
1911. Narratives of Early Carolina, 1650-1708. A relation of a discovery lately made on the coast of Florida—1664. 388 pp. New York.

HOARE, W. H. B.
1930. Conserving Canada's musk-oxen. 53 pp. North West Terr. and Yukon Branch, Dept. of Interior, Ottawa, Canada.
1939. Sanctuary. The Beaver, a magazine of the North, Outfit 270 (1): 38-41, illus. June. Winnipeg.
HOCHMEYER, ERNEST
1885. Were-wolves and wolf-children. American Field 24 (1): 8. July 4.
HOFFMAN, CHARLES FENNO
1835. A winter in the West. 2 vols. New York.
HOFFMAN, W. J.
1878. List of mammals found in the vicinity of Grand River, D. T. Proc. Boston Soc. Nat. Hist. 19: 95-102. March.
HOLLIS, BURR
1885. Hybrid wolves. Forest and Stream 25: 467. July 9.
HOLLISTER, H.
1869. History of Lackawanna Valley [Pennsylvania]. 442 pp., 2d Ed. New York.
HOLLISTER, N.
1913. Mammals of the Alpine Club expedition to the Mount Robson region. Canadian Alpine Journal, Special number, 44 pp., 13 pls. February 17.
1923. Report on the National Zoological Park. Smithsonian Inst. Annual Report 1922: 88-103. Washington, D. C.
HOPE, JOHN ARTHUR
1909a. The wolf hunt in northern Ontario. Rod and Gun and Motor Sports in Canada 10 (10): 946-947. March.
1909b. The winter wolf hunt in northern Ontario. Rod and Gun in Canada 11 (1): 3-6, illus. June.
1909c. Wolf hunting in Quebec. Rod and Gun in Canada 11 (6): 633. November.
HORMELL, ROBERT S.
1940. Notes on the history of rheumatism and gout. The New England Journal of Medicine 223 (19): 754-760. November 7.
Discusses use by ancient Greeks of hot wolf oil to cure arthritis.

HORNADAY, WILLIAM TEMPLE
1889. The extermination of the American bison, with a sketch of its discovery and life history. U. S. Natl. Mus., Ann. Rept. 1887: 367-548, pls. 1-22.
1913. Our vanishing wild life. 411 pp. New York.
HOWELL, ARTHUR H.
1921. A biological survey of Alabama. U. S. Dept. Agr., Bur. Biol. Survey. North Amer. Fauna 45: 1-76.
1936. A revision of the American Arctic hares. Jour. Mamm. 17 (4): 315-337.
HUGHES, J. C.
1883. Mammals. American Naturalist 17 (11): 1192. November.
HUME, EDGAR ERSKINE
1942. Ornithologists of the United States Army Medical Corps. 36 biographies, with foreword by Alexander Wetmore: i-xxv; 1-583; 235.
HUMPHREYS, DAVID (COLONEL)
1818. An essay on the life of the Hon. Major General Israel Putnam . . . . with an appendix containing an historical and topographical sketch of Bunker Hill battle by S. Swett. 276 pp. Boston.
HUTYRA, F., MAREK, J., and MANNINGER, R.
1938. Special Pathology and Therapeutics of the Diseases of Domestic Animals. 4th English ed. Chicago.
ILJIN, N. A.
1941. Wolf-dog genetics. Jour. Genetics 42 (3): 360-414, illus. July.
INGERSOL, ERNEST
1906. The life of animals. 555 pp. New York.
INGHAM, THOMAS J.
1899. History of Sullivan County, Pennsylvania. 3 pts. in 1 vol. Chicago.
INMAN, HENRY
1899a. Buffalo Jones' forty years of adventure. 469 pp. Topeka, Kansas.
1899b. The old Santa Fe trail. 493 pp. Topeka, Kansas.
1917. Tales of the trail—short stories of western life. 280 pp., 5th ed. Topeka, Kansas.

IOWA:
THE HISTORY OF APPANOOSE COUNTY
1878. 624 pp. Chicago.
THE HISTORY OF FAYETTE COUNTY
1878. 758 pp. Chicago.
THE HISTORY OF FREMONT COUNTY
1881. 778 pp. Des Moines.
THE HISTORY OF KEOKUK COUNTY
1880. 822 pp. Des Moines.
THE HISTORY OF MARSHALL COUNTY
1878. 696 pp. Chicago.
HISTORY OF MONTGOMERY COUNTY
1881. p. 451.
THE HISTORY OF PAGE COUNTY
1880. P. 374. Des Moines.
THE HISTORY OF WARREN COUNTY
1879. 743 pp. Des Monies.
THE HISTORY OF WOODBURY AND PLYMOUTH COUNTIES
1890-1891. 1022 pp. Chicago.

IOWA, STATE OF
1857a. Journal of Iowa House of Representatives of the Sixth general assembly of the State of Iowa 1856. 664 pp.
1857b. Journal of Iowa Senate of the Sixth general assembly of the State of Iowa 1856: 631 pp.
1860. Journal of the House of Representatives 1859. Pp. 188, 270, 271, 377, 378, 591, 623.

IRVING, WASHINGTON
1855. Astoria; or, anecdotes of an enterprise beyond the Rocky Mountains. 519 pp. New York.
1895. The adventures of Captain Bonneville, U. S. A., in the Rocky Mountains. 2 vols. New York.

JACKSON, C. F.
1922. Notes on New Hampshire mammals. Jour. Mamm. 3 (1): 13-15.

JACKSON, HARTLEY H. T.
1908. A preliminary list of Wisconsin mammals. Bull. Wis. Nat. Hist. Soc. 6 (1-2): 13-34, illus. April.

JACKSON, SHELDON

1900. Ninth annual report on introduction of domestic reindeer into Alaska. Govt. Print. Office, Wash., D. C.: 1-261; illus.

JACKSON, W. H.

1942. Three unlucky wolves. Alaska Sportsman 8 (7): 8-9, 29-30, illus. July. Ketchikan, Alaska.

JAMES, EDWIN, and LONG, STEPHEN H.

1823. Account of an expedition from Pittsburgh to the Rocky Mountains, performed in the years 1819 and 1820. 2 vols. Philadelphia.

JAMES, JAMES ALTON

1942. The first scientific exploration of Russian America and the purchase of Alaska. Northwestern University; pp. i-xii; 1-276; map, 6 illus.

JARDINE, JAMES T.

1908. Preliminary report on grazing experiments in a coyote-proof pasture, with an introduction by Frederick V. Coville. U. S. Dept. Agr., Washington, D. C. Forest Service Circ. 156: 1-32, illus.

JENNISON, GEORGE

1937. Animals for show and pleasure in ancient Rome. 209 pp., illus. Manchester, England.

JENSEN, A. S.

1928-29. Greenland. Pub. by Comm. for Direction of Geol. and Geog. Invest. in Greenland, Copenhagen. 3 vols., illus.

JEWETT, STANLEY G.

1914. Oregon timber wolf. Oregon Sportsman 29 (5): 7-10, illus. May.

1923. *Canis gigas* in the Blue Mountains of Oregon. Jour. Mamm. 4 (1): 54.

JOHNSON, CHARLES EUGENE

1921. A note on the habits of the timber wolf. Jour. Mamm. 2 (1): 11-15.

1922. Notes on the mammals of northern Lake County, Minnesota. Jour. Mamm. 3 (1): 33-39.

JOHNSON, FREDERICK CHARLES
1887-1908. The Historical Record of Wyoming Valley. 14 vols. Wilkes-Barre, Pennsylvania.
JOHNSON, SIR HARRY HAMILTON
1903. British mammals. 405 pp. London.
JONES, DANIEL W.
1890. Forty years among the Indians. 400 pp. Salt Lake City, Utah.
JONES, PAUL A.
1937. Coronado and Quivira. 242 pp., illus. Lyons, Kansas.
JOSSELYN, JOHN
1672. New England Rarities. London. Reprinted Boston, 1865. Pp. 47, 50, 51.
JUDSON, KATHARINE B.
1911. Myths and legends of Alaska. P. 127. Chicago.
KALM, PETER
1937. The America of 1750, Peter Kalm's Travels in North America. The English version of 1770. Revised from original Swedish, edited by Adolph B. Benson, with a translation of new material from Kalm's diary notes. 2 vols. New York.
KANNER, LEO (M.D.)
1928. Folklore of the teeth. 316 pp. New York.
KANSAS STATE HISTORICAL SOCIETY
1896. Governor Medary's administration. Trans. Kans. State Hist. Soc. 5: 561-633. Topeka.
1928. The life of George W. Brown. Kans. Hist. Soc. Coll. 1926-28 17: 98-134.
KEATING, WILLIAM H.
1825. Narrative of an expedition to the source of St. Peter's River, Lake Winnipeg, Lake of the Woods, Etc., performed in the year 1823. 2 vols. London.
KEIM, DE B. R.
1924. On the border with Sheridan's troopers. The Pioneer West—Narratives of the Westward March of Empire. 386 pp. Selected and edited by Joseph Lewis French, with a foreword by Hamlin Garland.
KELLER, OTTO
1887. Thiere des classichen Alterthums. P. 158. Innsbruck.

KELLOGG, REMINGTON
1937. Annotated list of West Virginia mammals. Proc. U. S. Natl. Mus. 84 (3022): 443-479.
1939. Annotated list of Tennessee mammals. Proc. U. S. Natl. Mus. 86 (3051): 245-303.

KENDALL, GEORGE WILKINS
1844. Narrative of the Texan Santa Fe expedition comprising a description of a tour through Texas. 2 vols. New York.

KENDRICK, JOHN B., SENATOR
1931. Control of Predatory Animals. Hearings before the Committee on Agriculture and Forestry, U. S. Senate, 71st Cong., 2nd and 3rd sess., on S. 3483. Pp. 6, 7, 47. May 8, 1930, and January 28 and 29, 1931.

KENNICOTT, ROBERT
1855. Catalogue of animals observed in Cook County, Illinois. Trans. Illinois State Agricultural Society 1: 577-612. Springfield.

KIMBALL, GERTRUDE SELWYN
1900. Pictures of Rhode Island in the Past, 1642-1833. Compiled by Gertrude Selwyn Kimball. 175 pp. Providence.
"A Short Account of the Present State of New England."

KINGSTON, C. S.
1923. Introduction of cattle into the Pacific Northwest. The Washington Historical Quarterly 14 (3): 165-185. July.

KNOX, M. V. B.
1875. Kansas Mammalia. Trans. Kans. Acad. Sci. 4: 18-22.

KUMLIEN, LUDWIG
1879. Contributions to the natural history of Arctic America made in connection with the Howgate Polar Expedition 1877-78. U. S. Natl. Mus. Bull. 15: 1-179.

KUNKEL, G. M.
1930. Report of case of tularemia contracted from a coyote (*Canis lestes*) in New Mexico. Public Health Reports 45 (9): 439-440. February 28. Reprint No. 1356 from Public Health Reports, pp. 1-2.

KURZ, RUDOLPH FRIEDERICK
1937. Journal of Rudolph Kurz. Smithsonian Inst. Bull., Amer. Ethnology No. 115, pp. 1,382, illus.
LA FLECHE, E. R.
1909. The wolves in Algonquin Park. Rod and Gun in Canada 11 (1): 12-15. June.
LAIDLAW, C. M.
1922. The destruction of wolves. Monteith Demonstration Farm Circular, pp. 1-3, 6-7. Ontario Dept. Agr. May.
LAING, HAMILTON M.
1939. Leave it to lobo. Field and Stream 44 (3): 36-38, 63. July.
1944. Wolf at the crossing. Field and Stream 48 (11): 28-29, 73-74; illus. March.
LANE, BOB
1941. Wolves are queer devils. The Alaska Sportsman 7 (1): 10-11, 32-34, illus. January.
LANMAN, CHARLES
1848. A tour to the River Saguenay in lower Canada. 231 pp. Philadelphia.
1854. Adventures in the wilds of North America. 300 pp. Edited by Charles Richard Weld. London.
1885. Farthest north, or, the life and explorations of Lieut. James Booth Lockwood of the Greely Arctic expedition. 333 pp., illus. New York.
LANTZ, D. E.
1908. Bounty laws in force in the United States July 1, 1907. Yearbook, U. S. Dept. Agr., 1907: 560-565.
LARPENTEUR, CHARLES
1898. Forty years a fur trader on the Upper Missouri River, 1833-1872. 2 vols. Edited by Elliott Coues. New York.
LASCELLES, TONY
1939a. You were asking: Food habits of timber wolf? Forest and Outdoors 35: 49-50. February.
1939b. Do wolves hunt in packs? Can a deer escape wolves? Forest and Outdoors 35 (3): 83, 84. Montreal.
1939c. The nature album. Why don't Huskies bark like domestic dogs? Forest and Outdoors 35 (12): 354-356. December. Montreal.

LAUT, AGNES C.
1921. The fur trade of America. 341 pp., illus.
LAWSON, JOHN
1714. The history of North Carolina. 258 pp. London. Edited by Francis Latham Harriss and reissued 1937. Richmond.
LEAVITT, SCOTT
1929. Discourse on the grey wolf, in course of discussion on Agriculture Appropriation bill. Cong. Record, pp. 679-683. December 14. 71st Cong., 2nd sess., from December 2 to December 21, U. S. House of Representatives.
LECHFORD, THOMAS
1642. Plain dealing, or newes from New England. 280 pp. London.
LEE, D., and FROST, J. H.
1844. Ten years in Oregon. 344 pp. New York.
LEESON, MICHAEL A.
1890. History of the counties of McKean, Elk, Cameron, and Potter (Pennsylvania). 1261 pp. J. H. Beers Co., Chicago.
LEINWEBER, MARTIN
1944. Stumbling stampeders. Alaska Sportsman 10 (3) March: 10-11, 27-32; illus.
LEONARD, ZENES
1904. Leonard's Narrative Adventures of Zenes Leonard, Fur Trader and Trapper, 1831-1836. Reprinted from the rare original of 1839, edited by W. F. Wagner, M.D., with maps and illustrations. The Burrows Bros. Co., Cleveland. 282 pp., 6 illus.
LEOPOLD, ALDO
1936. Game management. Chas. Scribner's Sons, New York and London: i-xxi; 1-481; illus.; 35, 36, 86, 247, 251.
LETT, WILLIAM PITTMAN
1890. The Big Game of North America. The wolf. Pp. 453-473, illus. Ed. by G. C. Stiles. Chicago and New York.

LEWIS, MERIWETHER, and CLARK, WILLIAM
1904-05. Original journals of the Lewis and Clark expedition, 1804-1806. 8 vols. Edited by Reuben Gold Thwaites. New York. Edition on Van Gelder handmade paper; 200 copies only printed.

LIGON, J. STOKLEY
1917. Sexes and breeding notes. Excerpt from report to Biological Survey from Albuquerque, New Mexico, August 22. In files of Fish and Wildlife Service, Washington, D. C.
1926. When wolves forsake their ways. Nature Magazine 7: 156-159. March.
1927. Wild life of New Mexico. New Mexico State Game Commission, 212 pp., illus. Santa Fe.

LINDSAY, W. LAUDER
1880. Mind in the lower animals, in health and disease. 2 vols. New York.

LINN, JOHN BLAIR
1877. Annals of Buffalo Valley, Pennsylvania. 620 pp. Harrisburg.
1883. History of Centre and Clinton Counties, Pennsylvania. 672 pp. Philadelphia.

LINNÉ (LINNAEUS), CARL
1766. Systema naturae, vol. 1, 532 pp., 12th ed.
(*Canis*) *mexicanus*, p. 60, based on the "Xoloitzcuintli" of Hernandez (1651, p. 478), and believed to be a wolf until shown by G. M. Allen (1920, p. 478) to be a Mexican "hairless" dog.

LINSEY, JAMES H. (REV.)
1842. A catalogue of the mammals of Connecticut. Amer. Jour. Sci. 43: 345-354. New Haven.

LITTLE, JAMES A.
1890. From Kirtland to Salt Lake City. 260 pp. Salt Lake City, Utah.

LLOYD, T. W.
1929. History of Lycoming County, Pennsylvania. Vol. 1, p. 565. Hist. Pub. Co., Topeka and Indianapolis.

LOMAX, ALFRED L.
1928. History of pioneer sheep husbandry in Oregon. Oregon Hist. Quarterly 29 (2): 99-143. June.
LONG, STEPHEN H., and JAMES, EDWIN
1823. Account of an expedition from Pittsburgh to the Rocky Mountains performed in the years 1819 and 1820. 2 vols. Philadelphia.
LOOMIS, F. B., and YOUNG, D. B.
1912. On the shell heaps of Maine. Amer. Jour. Sci. 34 (4th ser., art. 3): 17-42, illus. July.
LOPEZ, CARLOS M., and LOPEZ, CARLOS
1911. Caza Mexicana. Pp. XIX plus 629, illus.
General account of the wolf in Mexico.
LORD, JOHN KEAST
1866. The naturalist in Vancouver Island and British Columbia. 2 vols., illus. Vol. 1, 358 pp., vol. 2, 375 pp. London.
LORING, J. ALDEN
1905. The Wichita buffalo range. New York Zool. Soc. 10th Ann. Rept., pp. 181-200, illus. New York.
LOWERY, GEORGE H., JR.
1936. A preliminary report on distribution of the mammals of Louisiana. Proc. Louisiana Acad. Sci. 3 (1): 1-39, illus. March.
1943. Check-list of the mammals of Louisiana and adjacent waters. Occas. Papers, Mus. Zool., Louisiana State Univ., 13: 234. Baton Rouge, November 22.
LUDLOW, WILLIAM
1876. Report of a reconnaissance from Carroll, Montana Territory, on the Upper Missouri, to Yellowstone National Park, and return, made in summer of 1875. Pp. 1-155. Govt. Printing Office, Washington, D. C.
LUMMIS, CHARLES F.
1920. The Spanish pioneers. 8th ed. 292 pp., illus. Chicago.
LUTTIG, JOHN C.
1920. Journal of a fur trading expedition on the Upper Missouri, 1812-1813. 192 pp. Edited by Stella M. Drum. Missouri Hist. Society. St. Louis.

LYON, MARCUS W., JR.
1936. Mammals of Indiana. Amer. Midland Nat. 17 (1): 1-384, January.
MACFARLANE, RODERICK ROSS
1905. Notes on mammals collected and observed in the northern Mackenzie River district, Northwest Territories of Canada . . . . Proc. U. S. Natl. Mus. 28 (1405): 673-764.
MAILLIARD, JOSEPH
1927. The birds and mammals of Modoc County, California. Proc. Calif. Acad. Sci., 4th ser., 16 (10): 261-359. April 27. San Francisco.
MANN, ALBERT G.
1899. An ancient bear trap. Proc. Worcester Soc. Antiquity Collections, 1897-99, 16: 405. Worcester, Mass.
MANN, WALTER G., and LOCKE, S. B.
1931. The Kaibab deer—a brief history and recent developments. Mimeographed report with colored map. 67 pp. Prepared by Forest Service, U. S. Dept. Agr. Summary of wolves removed from Kaibab National Forest 1911-1930.
MANNING, T. H.
1943. Notes on the mammals of South and Central Baffin Island. Jour. Mamm. 24 (1): 47-59. February.
MARCY, RANDOLPH B.
1853. Exploration of the Red River of Louisiana in the year 1852. 33rd Cong., 2nd sess., Senate Ex. Doc. 54: 320 pp. Washington, D. C.
1888. Big game hunting in the wild West. Wolves. Outing Magazine 11 (4): 291-299, illus. January.
MARION COUNTY (OREGON)
1887. Marion County Commissioners' Journal 9: 424.
1892. Marion County Commissioners' Journal 12: 434.
MARTIN, HAYES E., and HOLLAND, BEULAH F.
1939. The zoologic distribution of intraoral cancer. Sci. Monthly 49 (3): 262-266. September.
Discussion of occurrence of cancer in domestic and wild animals, including the wolf.

MARTIN, JOHN HILL
1877. Chester (and its vicinity) Delaware County in Pennsylvania; with Genealogical Sketches of Some Old Families. 530 pp. Philadelphia.

MASON, OTIS T.
1902. Traps of the American Indians—a study in psychology and invention. Smithsonian Inst. Annual Report 1901: 461-473.

MASSACHUSETTS
1853-54. Records of the Governor and Company of the Massachusetts Bay in New England. 5 vols. in 6. Boston. Edited by N. B. Shurtleff.
1860. The Massachusetts Code (Law), Ch. 18: 158. Bounty legislation.
1882. The Massachusetts Code (Law), Ch. 27: 227. Bounty legislation.

MATHER, KIRTLEY F.
1940. The future of man as an inhabitant of the earth. Sci. Monthly 50 (3): 193-203. March.

MATHIASSEN, THERKEL
1931. Contributions to the physiography of Southampton Island. Report of the Fifth Thule Expedition 1921-24 . . . . 1 (2): 1-31. Copenhagen.

MATTHEW, W. D.
1930. The phylogeny of dogs. Jour. Mamm. 11 (2): 117-138. May.

MATTSON, EDWIN H.
1939. Bounty trapping in Michigan. Fur, Fish, and Game (Harding Magazine) 69 (3): 8-10, illus. March.

MAXIMILIAN, PRINCE OF WIED
1906. Travels in the interior of North America 1830. Early Western Travels, vols. 22, 23, 24. Edited by Reuben Gold Thwaites, Cleveland.

MAXWELL, HU
1898. The history of Randolph County, West Virginia. 531 pp., illus. Morgantown.
Bounties on wolves.

MAYNARD, C. J.
1872. Catalogue of the mammals of Florida, with notes on their habits, distribution, etc. Bull. Essex Inst. 4 (9-10): 135-150.

McATEE, W. L.
1907. A list of the mammals, reptiles, and batrachians of Monroe County, Indiana. Proc. Biol. Soc. Wash. 20: 1-16. February 25.
1918. A sketch of the natural history of the District of Columbia. Bull. Biol. Soc. Wash. 1: 1-142.

McCLEERY, E. H.
1929. The lone killer. 35 pp. Pittsburgh, Pa.

McCLURE, JAMES R.
1904. Taking the census and other incidents in 1855. Trans. Kansas State Hist. Soc., 1903-1904, 8: 227-250. Topeka.

McCLURE, S. W.
1914. The wolf at the stockman's door. The Country Gentleman 79 (46): 1845-1846, illus. November 14.

McGEHEE, JAMES STEWART
1910. Fremont's fourth expedition, '48-'49. The narrative of Micajah McGehee. Outdoor Life 25: 471-485. May.

McGEHEE, MICAJAH
1891. Rough times in rough places—a personal narrative .... The Century Magazine 41 (5): 771-780. March.

McGOWAN, DAN
1936. Animals of the Canadian Rockies. Pp. 27-31. New York.

McINTYRE, WILLIAM
1904. Rosengarten and sons. Amer. Jour. Pharmacy 76 (7): 303-304.
On date of early manufacture of strychnine in United States. July.

McKNIGHT, W. J.
1881. Pioneer notes of Jefferson County, Pennsylvania. 670 pp. Philadelphia.

McLEAN, JOHN
1932. Notes of a twenty-five years' service in the Hudson Bay territory. P. 276. Edited by W. S. Wallace. Toronto.

McWHORTER, LUCULLUS VIRGIL
1915. The border settlers of northwestern Virginia from 1768 to 1795, 509 pp., illus. Hamilton, Ohio.

MEAD, JAMES R.
1899. Some natural-history notes of 1859. Trans. Kans. Acad. Sci. for 1897-1898 16: 280-281. Edited by the Librarian. Topeka. June.
1906. The Saline River country in 1859. Trans. Kansas State Hist. Soc. 1905-1906 9: 8-19.

MEADER, STEPHEN W.
1936. Trap lines north—a true story of the Canadian woods. 268 pp., illus. New York.

MEARNS, EDGAR ALEXANDER
1907. Mammals of the Mexican boundary of the United States. U. S. Natl. Mus. Bull. 56: 1-530.

MEINTAEFEL, P. A.
1937. Wolf myth exploded. Christian Science Monitor. P. 5. July 7. Re wolves seldom if ever attacking humans.

MENAULT, ERNEST
1870. The intelligence of animals, with illustrative anecdotes. 368 pp., illus. New York.
From the French of Ernest Menault.

MERRIAM, C. HART
1882. The vertebrates of the Adirondack region, northeastern New York. Trans. Linnaean Society 1: 9-107. New York.
1897a. Revision of the coyotes or prairie wolves, with descriptions of new forms. Proc. Biol. Soc. Wash. 2: 19-33. March 15.
All of the coyotes listed are treated as distinct species.
1897b. Suggestions for a New Method of Discriminating between Species and Subspecies. Science (n.s.) 5 (122): 753-758. May 14.

Discussion involving wolves, in reply to Roosevelt (1897).
1923. Wolf attack on humans denied. Outdoor Life 51 (6): 493. June.

MERRIAM, JOHN CAMPBELL
1912. The fauna of Rancho La Brea. 2 vols., illus. Mem. Univ. Calif. Berkeley.

MICHIGAN, STATE OF
0000. Department of Conservation, 10th Biennial Report; Game Division Separate, p. 50. Lansing.
Michigan Senate Documents for 1839. p. 128. Lansing.
Journal of the Senate for 1840. Vol. 1: 101. Lansing.

MILES, BENJAMIN C.
1895a. A letter. Forest and Stream 45 (9): 182. August 31.
1895b. The gray wolf of Tennessee. Forest and Stream 45 (9): 182.

MILLER, GERRIT S., JR.
1899. Preliminary list of New York mammals. New York State Mus. Bull. 6 (29): 271-290. October. Albany.
1912a. The names of the large wolves of northern and western North America. Smiths. Misc. Coll. 59 (15), (publ. 2093: 1-5. June 8.
1912b. The names of two North American wolves. Proc. Biol. Soc. Wash. 25: 93-96. May 4.
Name *Canis lycaon* is fixed for eastern wolf, and *Canis floridanus* is described.
1920. (Review) Lönnberg, Einar. Remarks on some South American Canidae. Arkiv för Zoologi 12 (13): 1-18, figs. 1-4. September 3, 1919. Stockholm. Jour. Mamm. 1 (3): 149-150.

MILLS, ENOS A.
1932. Watched by wild animals. 243 pp., illus. Boston and New York.

MINER, JACK
1908. How I missed a moose and deer and shot a wolf. Rod and Gun and Motor Sports in Canada 10 (6): 547-552. November.

MIVART, ST. GEORGE
1890. Dogs, jackals, wolves, and foxes. Monograph of the Canidae. 216 pp. London.

MOHLER, JOHN R.
1923. Rabies or hydrophobia. U. S. Dept. Agr., Farmers' Bull. 449: 1-23. Washington, D. C.

MONTAGU, M. F. ASHLEY
1943. (Review) J. A. L. Singh and Robert Zingg, Wolf children and feral man. Harper and Bros., New York, XLI+379 pp. 1942. Amer. Anthropologist (n.s.) 45 (3): 462-472. July-September.

MOORE, ELY
1908. A buffalo hunt with the Miamis in 1854. Kansas Hist. Collections, 1907-1908 10: 402-409.

MOORE, E. G.
1932. Alaska sheep and wolves, a timely talk. Outdoor Life 70 (1): 16-17, 68-70.

MORTON, SAMUEL GEORGE
1852a. Observations on the antiquity of some races of dogs. Proc. Acad. Nat. Sci. Phila. 5: 84-89. 1850.
1852b. Communications on the races of dogs. Proc. Acad. Nat. Sci. Phila. 5: 139-140. 1851.

MORTON, THOMAS
1637. New English Canaan or New Canaan. 188 pp. Amsterdam.

MULTNOMAH COUNTY (OREGON)
1897. Multnomah County Commissioners' Journal 20: 502.

MULVANY, BARNEY
1943. The wolves almost got me. Alaska Sportsman 9 (5): 12-13, 16, 19, illus. May.

MURDOCH, JOHN
1883. Expedition to Point Barrow, Alaska. 48th Cong., 2nd sess., Ex. Doc. 44: 93.

MURIE, ADOLPH
1940. Ecology of the coyote in the Yellowstone. U. S. Natl. Park Service, Fauna Ser. No. 4, Conserv. Bull. 4: 1-206, illus.

MURPHY, JOHN MORTIMER
1880. Sporting adventures in the far west. 469 pp., illus. New York.
MURRAY, LOUISE WELLS
1908. A history of Old Tioga and early Athens, Pennsylvania. 656 pp. Raeder Press, Athens, Pa.
MUSGRAVE, MARK E.
1927. The mountain lion is just a "fraidy cat." Farm and Fireside 51 (6): 9. June. Springfield, Ohio.
MUSKEEGO
1887. Wolves in Wisconsin. Forest and Stream 28: 48, February 10. (20 wolves seen in one pack.)
MYERS, ALBERT COOK
1912. Narratives of Early Pennsylvania, West New Jersey and Delaware, 1630-1707. Letters from Wm. Penn to the comm. of the Free Soc. of Traders, 1683. 476 pp. New York, C. Scribner's Sons.
NASH, C. W.
1908. Vertebrates of Ontario, sec. 4 (Mammals). P. 95. Dept. of Education, Toronto, Canada.
NATIONAL LIVESTOCK HISTORICAL ASSOCIATION
1905. Prose and poetry of the livestock industry of the United States. 3 vols., illus.
NEHRING, A.
1887. Zur Abstammung der Hunde-Rassen. Zool. Jahr System. 3: 51-58. November 15.
NELSON, E. W.
1888. Natural history collections in Alaska between the years 1877-1881. Arctic Series of Publications, U. S. Army Signal Service, No. 3. 337 pp. 1887. Washington.
1916. The larger North American mammals. Nat. Geog. Mag. 30 (5): 385-472, with illustrations from paintings by Louis Agassiz Fuertes. November. Washington, D. C.
1921. Lower California and its natural resources. Mem. Nat. Acad. Sci. 16 (1): 1-194, illus., 35 pls. Washington.
NELSON, E. W., and GOLDMAN, EDWARD A.
1929. A new wolf from Mexico. Jour. Mamm. 10 (2): 165-166. May 9. New: *Canis nubilus baileyi* (= *Canis lupus baileyi*).

NEWBERRY, J. S.
1857. Report upon the zoology of the route. Reports expl. and surv. RR. route from Miss. River to Pacific Ocean, 1854-1855. Vol. 6 (2), pt. 4, 114 pp.

NEWHOUSE, SEWELL
1865. Trapper's guide. 118 pp. Oneida Community. Wallingford, Conn.
1869. Trapper's guide. 3rd ed., 215 pp. New York.

NEW YORK (STATE)
1776-1900. Laws of the State of New York. Bounty legislation.
1896. The colonial laws of New York. 5 vols. Albany. Bounty legislation.

NICHOL, A. A.
1936. Large predator animals. Univ. Ariz. Bull. No. 3: 70. Tucson.

NORTON, ARTHUR H.
1930. The mammals of Portland, Maine, and vicinity. Proc. Portland Soc. Nat. Hist. 4 (pt. 1): 1-151.

NUTTALL, THOMAS
1821. Journal of travels into the Arkansas territory during the year 1819. 296 pp., illus. Philadelphia.

OGILVIE, WILLIAM (SIR)
1913. Early Days on the Yukon. 306 pp., illus. London: John Lane, The Bodley Head. New York: John Lane Co. Toronto: Bell & Cockburn.

OLIVER, EDMUND H. (REV.)
1930. The institutionalizing of the prairies. Trans. Royal Soc. Canada, Sec. 2, Ser. 3, vol. 24, pp. 1-21. May 30.

OLSON, SIGURD F.
1938a. A study in predatory relationship, with particular reference to the wolf. Scientific Monthly 46: 323-336.
1938b. Organization and range of the pack. Ecology 19 (1): 168-170, illus. January.

ORR, JAMES E.
1908. How a pioneer outwitted the wolves. Rod and Gun and Motor Sports in Canada 10 (5): 421. October.

ORTON, ALDA
1942. Wolves of the Naha. The Alaska Sportsman 8 (1): 8-9, 28-30, illus. January.

OSBORN, HENRY FAIRFIELD
1930. The romance of the woolly mammoth. Natural History 30 (3): 227-241, illus. May-June.

OSGOOD, WILFRED H.
1904. A biological reconnaissance of the base of the Alaska peninsula. U. S. Dept. Agr., Bur. Biol. Survey. North Amer. Fauna 24: 1-86.

PACKARD, A. S.
1885. Origin of the American varieties of the dog. Amer. Nat. 19 (9): 896-901. September.

PADEREWSKI, IGNACE JAN, and LAWTON, MARY
1938. The Paderewski memoirs. 404 pp. New York.

PALMER, L. J.
1941. Animal and plant resources of Alaska. U. S. Dept. Interior, Fish and Wildlife Service. Wildlife Leaflet 176: 1-12. Mimeographed.
1942. A survey of available duck foods in some areas in S. E. Alaska. Progress Report, pp. 17-18. In files of Fish and Wildlife Service, Washington, D. C.

PALMER, T. S.
1897. Extermination of noxious animals by bounties. U. S. Dept. Agr. Yearbook 1896: 55-68.
1899. Report of Acting Chief, Division of Biological Survey. *In* Rept. Sec'y. Agr. 1899, pp. 59-70.
1912. Chronology and index of the more important events in American game protection, 1776-1911. U. S. Dept. Agr., Biol. Survey Bull. 41: 1-62.

PANCOAST, CHARLES EDWARD
1930. A Quaker forty-niner—the adventures of Charles Edward Pancoast on the American frontier. 402 pp. Edited by Anna Paschall Hannum, with a foreword by John Bach McMaster. Philadelphia.

PARKER, R. R.
1926. The susceptibility of the coyote (*Canis lestes*) to tularemia. Repts. U. S. Public Health Service 41 (28): 1407-1410.

PARKER, SAMUEL (REV.)
1842. Journal of an exploring tour beyond the Rocky Mountains in the years 1835-37. 3d ed., 408 pp., with a map of Oregon Territory. Ithaca, New York.

PARKINSON, JOHN
1640. Theatrum Botanicum. 1755 pp. 1 vol. in 2. London.

PATTIE, JAMES O.
1905. The personal narrative of James O. Pattie, of Kentucky, during an expedition from St. Louis through the vast regions between that place and the Pacific Ocean, and thence back through the city of Mexico to Vera Cruz, during journeyings of six years. . . . [A reprint of the original edition of 1831] in R. G. Thwaite's Early Western Travels, 1748-1846. . . . vol. 18, 379 pp., illus. Cleveland.

PATTON, B. S.
1914. Trapping timber wolves. Oregon Sportsman 2 (11): 4-9. Portland, Oregon.

PATTON, C. P.
1939. A preliminary list of the mammals of Virginia. Pp. 46, 47. Unpubl. MS. to be submitted as thesis for M.S. degree in wildlife management or conservation, V. P. I., Blacksburg, Va.

PAULUS AEGINETA
1844-47. The seven books of Paulus Aegineta. Translated from the Greek by Francis Adams. 3 vols. London.

PAYAN, JULES R.
1927. Will wolves take to water? Two more cases for the affirmative. Rod and Gun 29 (2): 159. July.

PEARCE, STEWART
1860. Annals of Luzerne County, Pennsylvania. 554 pp. J. B. Lippincott & Co., Philadelphia.

PENNANT, THOMAS
1793. History of quadrupeds. 2 vols., 3d ed. London.

PENNSYLVANIA, COMMONWEALTH OF
1782. Laws enacted at the second sitting of the sixth general assembly of the Commonwealth of Pennsylvania. Ch. 17: 59.

1819. Acts of General Assembly of the Commonwealth of Pennsylvania. Ch. 79: 114. Harrisburg.

PENNSYLVANIA, STATE OF
1896. The statutes at large of Pennsylvania from 1682 to 1801. Vol. 2, p. 238.

PENNSYLVANIA STATE DEPARTMENT OF AGRICULTURE
1896. Notes on some fur-bearing animals. Report State Dept. Agr. 1896: 327-344. Harrisburg.

PENNYPACKER, SAMUEL W.
1872. Annals of Phoenixville and its vicinity: From the settlement to the year 1771. 295 pp. Philadelphia.
1882. The Pennsylvania Magazine of History and Biography. Hist. Soc. Pa. 6: 312-328. Philadelphia.

PENOBSCOT
1883. Some wolf stories. Forest and Stream 21 (1): 10-11. August 2.

PERKINS, MRS. G. A. (JULIA ANNA SHEPARD)
1870. Early times on the Susquehanna. 287 pp. Malette & Reed, Binghampton.

PETERS, DEWITT CLINTON
1858. Life and adventures of Kit Carson. 534 pp. New York.

PETERSON, WILLIAM J.
1940. Wolves in Iowa. The Iowa Journal of History and Politics 38 (1): 50-93. January.

PICKENS, A. L.
1928. Mammals of upper South Carolina. Jour. Mamm. 9 (2): 155-157. May.

PIERCE, JAMES
1823a. A memoir on the Catskill Mountains. Amer. Jour. Sci. and Arts (Ser. 1) 6: 86-97.
1823b. Notice of the alluvial district of New Jersey. Amer. Jour. Sci. and Arts 6: 237-242.

PIERCE, MILTON P.
1885. Hybrid wolves. Forest and Stream 24: 426-427. June 25.

PIKE, ZEBULON
1932. Zebulon Pike's Arkansaw Journal. 200 pp. Edited by Hart and Hulbert. Denver.

PLUTARCH
1876. Lives. A. D. 100. 688 pp. Translated by Arthur Hugh Clough.
POCOCK, R. I.
1935. The races of *Canis lupus.* Proc. Zool. Soc. London, pt. 3, pp. 647-686, illus. September.
General review, with original descriptions of *Canis lupus arctos* and *Canis lupus orion.*
1937. Natural History. Mammalia. 1897 ed. 771 pp. Edited by Charles Tate Regan. London.
POCOCK, ROGER S.
1923. The wolf trail. 323 pp. New York.
POLICE, ROYAL NORTHWEST MOUNTED
1919. Report of the Bathurst Inlet Patrol, 1917-1918. Pp. 13, 40. Ottawa.
PORSILD, ERLING
1936. The reindeer industry and the Canadian Eskimo. Geogr. Jour. 88 (1): 1-19, illus. July.
PORTER, J. HAMPDEN
1903. Wild beasts. 380 pp., illus. Charles Scribner and Sons, New York.
PREBLE, EDWARD A.
1902. A biological investigation of the Hudson Bay region. U. S. Dept. Agr., Bur. Biol. Survey. North Amer. Fauna No. 22, 140 pp. Washington, D. C.
1908. A biological investigation of the Athabaska-Mackenzie Region. U. S. Dept. Agr., Bur. Biol. Survey. North Amer. Fauna No. 27, 222 pp. Washington, D. C
1911. Report on condition of elk in Jackson Hole, Wyoming, in 1911. U. S. Dept. Agr., Biol. Survey Bull. No. 40, 23 pp., illus. December 21. Washington, D. C.
PRICE, WILLIAM W.
1893. Notes on a collection of mammals from Sierra Nevada Mountains. Zoe 4 (4): 315-332. December 21.
QUINN, DAVIS
1930. The antelope's S.O.S. 16 pp., 1 map. Emergency Conserv. Comm., New York City, New York.
RAINE, WILLIAM MacLEOD, and BARNES, WILL C.
1930. Cattle. 340 pp. New York.

RANDALL, HENRY S.
1858. The life of Thomas Jefferson. 3 vols. Derby and Jackson, New York.

RATHBUN, MARY J.
1918. The Grapsoid crabs of North America. U. S. Natl. Mus. Bull. 97: 1-461. Washington, D. C.
Fiddler crabs being eaten by wolves (*Canis n. rufus*).

RAY, MRS. GEORGE R.
1940. The mad wolf at Fort Churchill. The Beaver, Outfit 271 (2): 30. September, Winnipeg.

RAY, P. H., and MURDOCH, JOHN
1885. Report of The International Polar Expedition to Point Barrow, Alaska. 1 vol. 695 pp. Washington, D. C.

REEKS, HENRY
1870. Notes on the zoology of Newfoundland. The Zoologist (Ser. 2) 5: 2033-2049. March.

RHOADS, SAMUEL N.
1894. A reprint of The North American Zoology by George Ord, pp. 290-361; Appendix 1-52. Taken from Mr. Ord's private, annotated copy. Published by the author. Haddonfield, N. J.
1895. Notes on the mammals of Monroe and Pike Counties, Pennsylvania. Proc. Acad. Nat. Sci. Phila. 1894: 393.
1896. Contributions to the zoology of Tennessee. No. 3, Mammals. Proc. Acad. Nat. Sci. Phila. 1896: 200.
1897a. A contribution to the mammalogy of central Pennsylvania. Proc. Acad. Nat. Sci. Phila., pp. 220-226. April.
1897b. A contribution to the mammalogy of northern New Jersey. Proc. Acad. Nat. Sci. Phila., pp. 23-33.
1899. Snails on the bill of fare. Forest and Stream 53: 206.
1903. Mammals of Pennsylvania and New Jersey. 266 pp. Philadelphia.

RICHARDSON, JOHN
1829. Fauna Boreali Americana. Part 1, pp. XLVI plus 300 pp., illus.
1836. Zoological remarks, appendix, of narrative of the Arctic Land expedition . . . . pp. 492, 493. London.

1839. The Zoology of Capt. Beechey's voyage of the Blossom 1825-28. 186 pp., illus. London.
New: *Canis lupus* var. *fusca.*

RIDER, SIDNEY S.
1904. The lands of Rhode Island as they were known to Caunounicus and Miantunnomu when Roger Williams came in 1636. 297 pp., illus. Providence, R. I.

RIGGS, THOMAS, JR.
1920. Annual report of the Governor of Alaska on Alaska game law, 1919. U. S. Dept. Agr., Dept. Circ. 88: 1-18.

RISTER, CARL COKE
1928. The southwestern frontier, 1865-1881. 336 pp. Cleveland.

ROBERTS, N. G.
1939. The tricks of trapping wolves. Forest and Outdoors 35 (11): 340-341, 1 photo. Montreal.

ROE, F. G.
1939. From dogs to horses among the western Indian tribes. Trans. Royal Society of Canada, Sec. II, Ser. 3, vol. 33, pp. 209-275.

ROGERS, HARRISON G.
1918. The Ashley-Smith explorations and the discovery of a central route to the Pacific, 1822-1829, with the original journals, edited by Harrison Clifford Dale. 352 pp. Cleveland.

ROLLINAT, RAYMOND
1929. Le loup commun. Revue d'Histoire Naturelle, vol. 10, pt. 1, nos. 4, 7, 9, pp. 105-129, 209-238, 289-308.

ROMER, ALFRED SHERWOOD
1933. Man and the vertebrates. 405 pp. Chicago. 3rd Ed. 1941.

ROOSEVELT, THEODORE
1885. Hunting trips of a ranchman. 318 pp. The Medora edition. New York.
1893. The wilderness hunter. Pp. 386, 396, 403, 409.
1895. Hunting in Many Lands. Hunting in the cattle country. 447 pp. A book of the Boone and Crockett Club. New York.

1897. A Layman's Views on Specific Nomenclature. Science (n.s.) 5 (122): 685-688. April 30.
1900. Hunting trips of a ranchman. 296 pp. New York and London.
(This is probably a reprint of the 1885 edition and not so limited as to copies as the Medora edition, which was only 500 copies.)
1903. The winning of the West. 6 vols. Edition de luxe. Philadelphia.
1904. Hunting trips of a ranchman. 348 pp. The Statesman edition. New York.
1905. A wolf hunt in Oklahoma. Scribner's Mag. 38 (5): 513-532.

ROOSEVELT, THEODORE, VAN DYKE, T. S., ELLIOT, D. G., and STONE, A. J.
1902. The deer family. Macmillan Company, New York. Pp. i-ix; 1-334, illus.; 44, 305-307, 319.

ROSS, ALEXANDER
1849. Adventures of the first settlers on the Oregon, or Columbia, River . . . . 352 pp. London.
1855. The fur hunters of the Far West. 2 vols. London.
1904. Alexander Ross's adventures of the first settlers on the Oregon or Columbia River, 1810-1813. Early Western Travels 7: 332 pp. Edited by Reuben Gold Thwaites. Cleveland.

ROSS, BERNARD ROGAN
1861. A popular treatise on the fur-bearing animals of the Mackenzie River district. Canadian Nat. and Geol. and Proc. Nat. Hist. Soc. Montreal 6: 5-36. Montreal.

ROWE, ROBERT A.
1941. The receding range of the timber wolf in western Oregon. The Murrelet 22 (3): 53-54, illus. December.
1943. A recent record of the timber wolf in western Oregon. The Murrelet 24 (1): 11, January-April.

ROWELL, A. C.
1918. Wolf lore. Outdoor Life 42: 13-15, 92-93.

RUPP, I. DANIEL
1843-45. History of Lancaster and York Counties, Pennsylvania. P. 468. Lancaster.
RUSSELL, OSBORNE
1921. Journal of a trapper, or, nine years in the Rocky Mountains, 1834-1843. 149 pp. Boise, Idaho.
SABINE, JOSEPH
1823. Mammals and birds. Zoological appendix, Sir John Franklin's Narrative of a Journey to the Shores of the Polar Sea . . . . XVI plus 768 pp. London.
Described *Canis lupus griseus* and *Canis lupus albus*, both of which were preoccupied names.
SAGARD, GABRIEL (FATHER)
1939. The long journey to the country of the Hurons. 411 pp. Edited with introduction and notes by George M. Wrong, and translated into English by H. H. Langton. The Champlain Society, Toronto, Canada. First pub. in French in 1632. 380 pp.
SAGER, ABM.
1839. Report of zoologist of geological survey of Ohio. Ohio State Senate No. 13 (1): 1-15. January 12.
SANDOZ, MARI
1935. Old Jules. 424 pp. New York.
SANFORD, LAURA G.
1862. History of Erie County, Pennsylvania. 347 pp. J. B. Lippincott & Co., Philadelphia.
SAWYER, E. J.
1940. American wolves. Western Sportsman 5 (3): 28. August.
SAY, THOMAS
1823 *In* Long's Expedition to Rocky Mountains 1819-1820. 2 vols. Vol. 1, 503 pp., vol. 2, 442 pp.
New: *Canis nubilus* (= *C. l. nubilus*).
SCHAFF, MORRIS
1905. Etna and Kirkersville [Ohio]. 157 pp., 1 map. Boston and New York.
SCHANTZ, VIOLA S.
1936. An unusual specimen of red wolf. Jour. Mamm. 17 (4): 415. November.

SCHAUFFLER, BENNETT F.
1917. Wolving—with complications. Outing 60 (2): 173-176. May.
SCHMID, BASTIAN
1937. Interviewing animals. 223 pp., illus. New York. Trans. by Bernard Miall.
SCHOMBURGK, ROBERT
1829. Traveling and collecting in eastern United States - New Jersey, Virginia, etc., 1804- Okens Isis, Heft: 1-570.
SCHORGER, A. W.
1942. Extinct and Endangered Mammals and Birds of the Upper Great Lakes Region. Trans. Wis. Acad. Sci., Arts and Letters 34: 23-44. Madison.
SCHREBER, JOHANN CHRISTIAN DANIEL von
1774-1846. Die säugthiere in abbildungen nach der Natur mit beschreibungen. 8 vols., separately paged, illus. Erlangen.
Name *Canis lycaon* used on plate 8, 1775, reference to "loup noir" of Buffon, vol. 3, p. 353, 1776, and name again appears in index, p. 585, 1778.
SCHULTZ, JAMES WILLARD
1919. Rising wolf, the white blackfoot, or Hugh Monroe's story of his first year on the plains. 252 pp. New York.
SCLATER, P. L.
1868. On the breeding of mammals in the garden of the Zoological Society of London during the past twenty years. Proc. Zool. Soc. London. Pp. 623-626. December 10.
1874. On the black wolf of Thibet. Proc. Zool. Soc. London. Pp. 654-655, illus. November 17.
SCOTT, H. HAROLD
1928. Carcinoma of the tonsil in a common wolf (*Canis lupus*). Proc. Zool. Soc. London, pt. 1: 43-47, illus.
SCOTT, W. E.
1939. Rare and extinct mammals of Wisconsin. Wisconsin Conservation Bull. 4 (10): 21-28. October.

1940. A seventeen-year summary of data on bountied predacious animals. 33 pp., mimeographed. Wisconsin Department of Conservation. Madison.

SCOTT, WILLIAM BERRYMAN
1913. A history of land mammals in the Western Hemisphere. 693 pp., illus. Also 1937 ed. 786 pp. New York.

SETON, ERNEST THOMPSON
1907. The habits of wolves. American Magazine 64 (6): 636-645, illus. October.
1929. Lives of game animals. 4 vols., each in 2 pts.
1937. Great historical animals. Preface, pp. v, ix. New York.

SETTLE, DIONISE
1810. The second voyage of Master Martin Frobisher, 1577. Hakluyt 3: 62, new ed. London.

SETTLE, RAYMOND W.
1940. The march of the mounted riflemen. 380 pp., illus. Arthur H. Clarke Co., Glendale, Calif.

SEWALL, SAMUEL
1868. The history of Woburn, Middlesex County, Massachusetts, 1640-1860. 657 pp. Wiggin & Lunt, Boston.

SHANTZ, HOMER LeROY, and PIEMEISEL, ROBERT LOUIS
1917. Fungus fairy rings in eastern Colorado and their effect on vegetation. Jour. Agr. Research 9 (5): 191-246, illus., U. S. Dept. Agr., Washington, D. C. October 29.

SHEFFY, L. F.
1929. The lobo as a factor in the cattle industry. The Cattleman 15 (10): 94-99.

SHELDON, CAROLYN
1936. The mammals of Lake Kedgemakooge and vicinity, Nova Scotia. Jour. Mamm. 17 (3): 207-215. August.

SHELDON, CHARLES
1930. The wilderness of Denali. 412 pp. New York and London.

SHELFORD, V. E.
1942. Biological control of rodents and predators. Scientific Monthly, 55: 331-341. October. Illus.

SHEPARD, ERNEST E.
1940. Wolves kill foxes. Hunting and Fishing in Canada 6 (11): 37. Montreal.

SHEPHERD, SAMUEL
1792-1803. Statutes at large of Virginia. 3 vols. Richmond.

SHIRAS, GEORGE, III
1921. The wild life of Lake Superior, past and present. National Geographic Magazine 40 (2): 113-204, illus. August.

SHOCKWILL, GEORGE ARCHIE
1898. Wolf children. Lippincott Monthly Magazine, 61: 115-125; Philadelphia, January-June.

SHOEMAKER, HENRY WHARTON
1913. Stories of Pennsylvania animals. Reprinted from Altoona Tribune. Pp. 5-6. Altoona, Pa.
1914. Black Forest souvenirs. 404 pp. Reading, Pa.
1915. Wolf days in Pennsylvania. Altoona.
1917-19. Extinct Pennsylvania animals. 2 vols. Altoona.

SHUFELDT, R. W.
1897. Chapters on the natural history of the United States. 472 pp. New York and Philadelphia.

SILVER, JAMES
1933. Hunting the den of the timber wolf. The Northern Sportsman 3 (12): 3-4, 14. April. Munising, Mich.

SIMMS, B. T., McCAPES, A. M., and MUTH, O. H.
1932. Salmon poisoning—transmission and immunization experiments. Jour. Amer. Veterinary Medical Assoc. 81 (n.s.) 34 (1): 26-36. July.

SIMPSON, GEORGE GAYLORD
1943. Mammals and the nature of continents. Amer. Jour. Sci. 241 (1): 1-31. January.

SINGER, DANIEL J.
1914. Big game fields of America, North and South. 368 pp., illus. New York.

SINGH, J. A. L., and ZINGG, ROBERT M.
1942. Wolf children and feral man. Pp. XLI plus 379, illus. Harper & Bros., New York.

SKINNER, MILTON P.
1924. The American antelope. Jour. Mamm. 3 (2): 82-105. April 15. (Reprinted as separate from Jour. Mamm. by Roosevelt Wild Life Exp. Station, Syracuse, New York. 32 pp.)
1927. Predatory and fur bearing animals of Yellowstone Park. Roosevelt Wild Life Bull. 4 (2): 156-281. June.

SLAUGHTER, GERTRUDE (MRS. ELIZABETH TAYLOR)
1939. Calabria, the first Italy. 330 pp., illus. Madison, Wis.

SLEEMAN, SIR W. H. (MAJOR GENERAL)
1888. Wolves nurturing children in their dens. The Zoologist, 3d ser., 12: 87-98. London.

SMART, GRAYDON F.
1931. A wolf pack howls in his back yard. American Magazine 111 (2): 81, 129. February.

SMITH, CHARLES HAMILTON
1846. Dogs. 2 vols. The Naturalist's Library, vols. 18-19. Edinburgh.

SMITH, JAMES
1870. An account of the remarkable occurrences in the life and travels of Col. James Smith during his captivity with the Indians, in the years 1755-59. With an appendix of illustrative notes by William M. Darlington. 190 pp. Cincinnati.

SMITH, JOHN (CAPTAIN)
1884. Captain John Smith's works 1608-1631. Edited by Edward Arber. Birmingham. CXXXVI plus 948 pp., with map.
A compilation of the works of Captain John Smith.

SMITH, R. W.
1883. History of Armstrong County, Pennsylvania. P. 30. Waterman, Watkins & Co., Chicago.

SMITH, SAMUEL
1765. The history of the colony of Nova-Caesaria or New Jersey... 573 pp. Burlington, N. J., and Philadelphia, Pa.

SNYDER, L. L.
1928. The mammals of the Lake Abitibi region. Univ. of Toronto Studies, Biol. Series No. 32, pp. 7-15.

SOPER, J. DEWEY
1928. A faunal investigation of southern Baffin Island. Nat. Mus. Canada Bull. 53 (Biol. Ser. 15): 28-76. Ottawa.
1940. Eskimo dogs of the Canadian Arctic. Canad. Geog. Jour. 20 (2): 101, 103. February. Ottawa.
1941. History, range, and home life of the northern bison. Ecological Monographs 11: 347-412. October.
1942. Mammals of Wood Buffalo Park, northern Alberta, and District of Mackenzie. Jour. Mamm. 23 (2): 119-145, illus. May.

SPEELMAN, S. R., and WILLIAMS, J. O.
1926. Breeds of dogs. U. S. Dept. Agr. Farmers' Bulletin 1491: 1-46, 34 figs. May.

SPEER, OTIS H.
1939. Wise old wolves. The Alaska Sportsman 5 (2): 25-27. February.
1944. A foot in a trap—a head in a snare. Alaska Sportsman, 10 (1): 12-13, 28-29, illus. January.

SPERRY, CHARLES C.
1939. Food habits of peg-leg coyotes. Jour. Mamm. 20 (2): 190-194. May.

STANWELL-FLETCHER, JOHN F.
1942. Three years in the wolves' wilderness. Natural History 49 (3): 137-147, illus. March. New York.

STANWELL-FLETCHER, JOHN F., and THEODORA C.
1940. Naturalists in the wilds of British Columbia. The Sci. Monthly 50 (1): 17-32; 50 (2): 128-131.
1943. Some accounts of the flora and fauna of the Driftwood Valley region of north central British Columbia. British Columbia Prov. Mus., Occas. Papers No. 4, 97 pp., illus.

STEARNS, W. A.
1883. Notes on the natural history of Labrador. Proc. U. S. Natl. Mus. 6: 111-137.

STEBLER, A. M.
1944. The status of the wolf in Michigan. Journ. Mammalogy, 25 (1): 37-43.

STEELE, JOHN
1930. Across the plains in 1850. 227 pp. Edited with introduction and notes by Joseph Schaefer, Supt. of State Hist. Soc. of Wisconsin. Chicago.
STEFANSSON, VILHJALMUR
1928. The standardization of error. 110 pp. London.
STEINEL, ALVIN T.
1927. History of Colorado 2 (Ch. 12, The Range Livestock Industry): 668. Denver.
STEPHENS, FRANK
1906. California mammals. 351 pp. San Diego.
STERLING, E.
1883. The old settlers again. Forest and Stream 21 (18): 348. November 29.
STEVENSON, PAUL HUSTON
1939. Factors in early human emergence. The Scientific Monthly 49 (3): 258. September.
STEWART, AGNES
1928. The journey to Oregon—a pioneer girl's diary. Introduction and editing by Claire Warner Churchill. The Oreg. Hist. Quart. 29 (1): 83, 85, 88. March.
STEWART, JOSHUA THOMPSON
1913. Indiana County, Pennsylvania; her people past and present, embracing a history of the county. 2 vols., paged continuously. J. H. Beers & Co., Chicago.
STILES, C. W., and BAKER, EDITH CLARA
1934. Key-catalogue of parasites reported for carnivora (cats, dogs, bears, etc.) Nat. Inst. of Health, U. S. Treas. Dept., Public Health Serv. Bull. 163: 1099-1124. Washington, D. C.
STILLMAN, DONALD
1939. Rod and gun. New York Herald-Tribune. January 20.
STIMSON, A. M.
1910. Facts and problems of rabies. Hygienic Lab., Treasury Dept., Public Health and Marine Hospital of U. S. Bull. 65. 85 pp., illus.
STOCKWELL, GEORGE ARCHIE
1898. Wolf-children. Lippincott's Monthly Magazine 61: 117-124. January. Philadelphia.

STONE, WITMER, and CRAM, WILLIAM EVERETT
1902. American animals. 318 pp. New York.

STORER, TRACY I.
1931. Early trade values of skins in Montana. Jour. Mamm. 12 (1): 77-78. February.

STRANGE, JAMES BARON (2ND DUKE OF ATHOLE)
1749. Report from the committee appointed to enquire into the state and condition of the countries adjoining to Hudson's Bay . . . . Reports of the House of Commons, 1738-1765, 2: 213-266. April 24. London.

STRONG, WM. DUNCAN
1930. Notes on mammals of the Labrador interior. Jour. Mamm. 11 (1): 1-10. February.

STUART, GRANVILLE
1925. Forty years on the frontier as seen in the journals and reminiscences of Granville Stuart. 2 vols. Edited by Paul C. Phillips. Cleveland.

STURGIS, ROBERT S.
1939. The Wichita Mountains wild life refuge. Chicago Nat. 2 (1): 9-20. Chicago Academy of Sciences. Chicago.

SUCKLEY, GEORGE, and GIBBS, GEORGE
1860. Reports of explorations and surveys to ascertain the most practicable and economical route for a railroad from the Mississippi River to the Pacific Ocean 1853-55. 36th Cong., 1st sess., Senate Ex. Doc. No. 56, vol. 12 (bk. 2, ch. 3, Zoology): 110-113, 139.

SURBER, THADDEUS
1932. The mammals of Minnesota. 84 pp., illus. Bull. Minn. Dept. Conserv., Div. Game and Fish, St. Paul.
1942. Our wild dogs and cats. The wolves, foxes, and lynxes. Conservation Volunteer 4 (24): 44-47. September. St. Paul.

SUTTON, GEORGE MIKSCH, and HAMILTON, WILLIAM J., JR.
1932. The mammals of Southampton Island. Mem. Carnegie Mus. 12 (pt. 2, Zoology, sec. 1): 9-111. August 4.

SWANK, JAMES M.
1908. Progressive Pennsylvania. 360 pp. J. B. Lippincott & Co., Philadelphia.

SWARTH, H. S.
1922. Birds and mammals of the Stikine River region of northern British Columbia and southeastern Alaska (Alaska, Sergref Island). Univ. Calif. Publ. Zool. 24 (2): 125-314.
1936. Mammals of the Atlin region, northwestern British Columbia. Jour. Mamm. 17 (4): 398-405. November.

SWEETSER, M. F.
1876. White Mountains—a handbook for travellers. 436 pp. Boston.

SWIFT, ERNEST
1941. The biography of a self-made naturalist. Part II. Wisconsin Conservation Bull. 6 (1): 41-52, illus. January. Madison, Wisconsin.

T., N. A.
1887. Wolves and squirrels in Texas. Forest and Stream 29: 403. December 15.
1888a. More about Texas wolves. Forest and Stream 29: 504. January 19.
1888b. The howl of the wolf. Forest and Stream 30: 24. February 2.
1888c. The ways of wolves. Forest and Stream 30: 45. February 9.

TALBOT, THEODORE
1931. The journals of Theodore Talbot, 1843 and 1849-52; with the Fremont expedition of 1843 and with the first military company in Oregon territory, 1849-1852. 153 pp. Edited by Charles H. Carey. Portland, Oreg.
1939. Journals. Ed. by Charles H. Carey. P. 30. Metropolitan Press, Portland, Oreg.

TAYLOR, JOSEPH HENRY
1891. Twenty years on the trap line. Pp. 70-73. Bismarck, North Dakota, and Avondale, Pennsylvania.

TAYLOR, WALTER P., and SHAW, WILLIAM T.
1927. Mammals and birds of Mt. Rainier National Park. 249 pp. U. S. Dept. Interior, National Park Service, Washington, D. C.

1929. Provisional list of land mammals of the state of Washington. Occasional Papers Charles R. Conner Museum, No. 2, 32 pp. December.

TENCH, C. V.

1940. Yellow gold and brown grizzly. Forest and Outdoors 36 (4): 133-137. April. Montreal.

TEXAS GAME, FISH AND OYSTER COMMISSION

1930. Fur-bearers and predatory animals. Year Book on Texas Conservation of Wild Life, 1929-30, pp. 21-42.

THACHER, JAMES

1832. History of the town of Plymouth from its first settlement in 1620 to the year 1832. 382 pp. Boston.

THOMAS, GABRIEL

1912. The history of west New Jersey, 1698. Narratives of Early Pennsylvania, West New Jersey, and Delaware. P. 348. New York.

THOMPSON, DAVID

1916. David Thompson's narrative of his explorations in western America, 1784-1812. 582 pp. Edited by J. B. Tyrrell. Toronto.

——————, and HENRY, ALEXANDER

1897. New light on the early history of the greater Northwest, 1799-1814. Manuscript journals of Alexander Henry and David Thompson. 3 vols. Edited by Elliott Coues. New York.

THOMPSON, ERNEST E.

1886. A list of the mammals of Manitoba. Trans. Manitoba Sci. and Hist. Soc. 23: 1-26. May. Toronto.

THOMPSON, ZADOCK

1853. Natural history of Vermont. 4 pts. in 1 vol. Burlington.

THORNTON, THOMAS (COLONEL)

1806. A sporting tour through various parts of France in the year 1802. . . . In a series of letters to the Right Hon. Earl of Darlington. To which is prefixed an account of French wolf-hunting. 2 vols. in one. London.

THRASHER, HALSEY (Pseudonym)

1868. The hunter and trapper. 91 pp. New York.

THWAITES, REUBEN GOLD
1902. Daniel Boone. 257 pp. New York.
1904-07. Early Western travels 1748-1846. 32 vols. The Arthur H. Clark Co., Cleveland, Ohio.

TOME, PHILIP
1928. Pioneer life; or, Thirty years a hunter. 173 pp. Aurand Press, Harrisburg.

TOMKINS, IVAN R.
1931. Some late records of the timber wolf in Pennsylvania. Jour. Mamm. 12 (2): 165. May.

TOPSELL, EDWARD
1607. The historie of fovr-footed beastes. 757 pp. London.

TOWNSEND, JOHN K.
1839 and 1905. Narrative of a journey across the Rocky Mountains to the Columbia River. 352 pp. Philadelphia. Also Thwaites Early Western Travels, vol. 21, 336 pp. 1905. Cleveland.
1850. On the giant wolf of North America. Jour. Acad. Nat. Sci. Phila. (ser. 2) 2, 334 pp. Philadelphia.
New: *Lupus gigas* (= *C. l. fuscus*).

TOWNSHEND, FREDERICK TRENCH
1875. Wild life in Florida, with a visit to Cuba. 319 pp. London.

TRAUP, NORMAN E.
1888. Wolves nurturing children. The Zoologist (3d ser.) 12 (138): 221. London.

TRAUTMAN, MILTON B.
1939. The numerical status of some mammals throughout historic time in the vicinity of Buckeye Lake, Ohio. Ohio Jour. Sci. 39 (3): 133-143. May.

TREMBLEY, HELEN LOUISE, and BISHOP, F. C.
1940. Distribution and hosts of some fleas of economic importance. Jour. Economic Entomology 33 (4): 701-703. September 28.

TRIPPE, T. MARTIN
1871. Some differences between western and eastern birds. Amer. Nat. 5: 632-636.
Incidental reference to retirement with advancing civilization of buffalo, elk, antelope, deer, and wolf.

TRUE, ALFRED CHARLES

1937. A history of agricultural experimentation and research in the United States, 1607-1925 . . . . U. S. Dept. Agr. Misc. Publ. 251: 1-321. Washington, D. C.

TRUMBULL, BENJAMIN

1818. A complete history of Connecticut 1630-1764. 2 vols. New Haven.

TURNBULL, T.

1913. T. Turnbull's travels from the United States across the plains to California. Edited by Frederick L. Paxon. Proc. Wis. State Hist. Soc. Pp. 151-225.

TURNER, L. M.

1886. Contributions to the natural history of Alaska. Arctic Series of Publications, 226 pp. Signal Service, U. S. Army.

UMFREVILLE, EDWARD

1790. The present state of Hudson's Bay. 230 pp. London.

UNION, COUNTY OF (OREGON)

1885. County Commissioners' Journal C: 526.

UNITED STATES COMMISSIONER OF AGRICULTURE

1863. Condition and prospects of sheep husbandry in the United States. Report for the year 1862. Pp. 2-285. Washington, D. C.

UNITED STATES CONGRESS

1929. Control of predatory animals. 70th Cong., 2nd sess., House Doc. No. 496. 17 pp.

1930. Control of predatory animals. Hearing before the Committee on Agriculture, House of Representatives, 71st Cong., 2nd sess., on H. R. 9599, by Mr. Scott Leavitt, of Montana. April 29 and 30 and May 1. 100 pp.

1936. The western range. Senate Doc. No. 109, 74th Cong., 2nd sess. 620 pp.

1939. Hearings before a sub-committee of the Committee on Indian Affairs, U. S. Senate, 74th Cong., 2nd sess., pt. 36. Alaska (including reindeer): 19,977, 19,981, 19,982, 20,329, 20,334.

UNITED STATES DEPARTMENT OF AGRICULTURE
1899. Report of the Acting Chief of the Division of Biological Survey Work. Rept. of the Sec. of Agr. Pp. 59-70.
1908. Report of the Secretary of Agriculture to the President, 1907. Bureau of Biological Survey, U. S. Dept. Agr. Yearbook 1907. Pp. 95-101. Washington, D. C.

UNITED STATES GOVERNMENT
1918. Joint report upon the survey and demarcation of the international boundary between the United States and Canada. P. 282. Washington, D. C.
1940. The status of wildlife in the United States. Report of the special committee on the conservation of wildlife sources. 76th Cong., 3d sess., Senate Report 1203. 457 pp.

UNITED STATES HOUSE OF REPRESENTATIVES
1939. Congressional Record 84 (156): 14,969. 76th Cong., 1st sess. August 2.

UNITED STATES SENATE
1907. Report on work of the Biological Survey. 60th Cong., 1st sess., Document No. 132. 29 pp. December 21.
1930. Control of Predatory Animals (Confidential Report). Hearing before the Committee on Agriculture and Forestry. U. S. Senate, 71st Congress, 2d sess., Senate Report 3483, 28 pp. May 8.
1931. Control of Predatory Animals. Hearings before the Committee on Agriculture and Forestry, U. S. Senate, 71st Congress, 2d and 3d sessions, Senate Report 3483, May 8, 1930, and January 28 and 29, 1931. 192 pp.

VALLEJO, GUADALUPE
1890. Ranch and mission days in Alto, California. Century Illustrated Monthly Magazine (n.s.) 19: 183-192. December.

VAN WAGENEN, J. A.
1907. Chased by wolves. Sports Afield 39 (3): 245-246. September.

VICTOR, FRANCES FULLER (MRS.)
1870. The river of the West. 602 pp. Hartford, Conn., and San Francisco, Calif.

VIRGINIA
1804-1938. Laws. (Bounty legislation.)
1849. The Virginia Code (Law). P. 456. (Bounty legislation.)
1887. The Code of Virginia (Law), Section 834: 256. (Bounty legislation.)
1930. The Virginia Code (Law)? Section 2729, Chapter 109. (Bounty legislation.)
(See also Hening, William Waller, 1823.)

WAGGONER, GEORGE A.
1905. Stories of old Oregon. 292 pp. Salem.

WAILES, BENJAMIN LEONARD COVINGTON
1854. Report on the agriculture and geology of Mississippi. 371 pp. Philadelphia.

WALKER, THOMAS
1898. Journal of Dr. Thomas Walker. Filson Club Publ. No. 13, 84 pp. Louisville, Ky.

WALL, THOMAS LINCOLN
1925. Clearfield County, Pennsylvania, Present and Past. (Library ed.) Published by author. 296 pp. Clearfield, Pa.

WALLS, GORDON LYNN
1942. The Vertebrate Eye and its Adaptive Radiation. Cranbrook Institute of Science, Bull. No. 19, 785 pp., illus. August. Bloomfield Hills, Mich.

WARD, HENRY GEORGE
1828-29. Mexico in 1827. 2 vols. London.

WARDEN, D. B.
1819. Statistical, political, and historical account of the United States of North America. . . . 3 vols. Edinburgh.

WARREN, EDWARD ROYAL
1910. The mammals of Colorado. 300 pp. New York and London.
1927. The beaver, its work and its ways. Monog. Amer. Soc. Mamm. 2: 1-177, illus. Baltimore.

WASHINGTON, GEORGE
1801. Letters from his excellency General Washington to Arthur Young, Esq., London. 172 pp. London.

WATKINS, M. G.
1885. Gleanings from the natural history of the ancients. 258 pp. London.
WATSON, JOHN F.
1833. Historic tales of old times. E. Littell and Thomas Holden, Philadelphia.
1844. Annals of Philadelphia and Pennsylvania. 2 vols. Philadelphia.
WEBB, DAVID K., and STEVENS, JOHN M.
1934. Early bounty hunters of Butler County, Pennsylvania. 27 pp. Publ. privately, Chillicothe, Ohio.
WEBB, JAMES JOSIAH
1931. Adventures in the Santa Fe trade. 301 pp. Ed. by Ralph P. Bieber. Glendale, California.
WEBB, WM. E.
1872. Buffalo land. 503 pp. Chicago.
WEBBER, CHARLES WILKINS
1875. Wild scenes and wild hunters; or the romance of sporting. 610 pp., illus. Philadelphia.
WEBSTER, E. B.
1920. The king of the Olympics. 227 pp., illus. Port Angeles, Washington.
WHEELER, OLIN D.
1904. The trail of Lewis and Clark. 2 vols., illus. G. P. Putnam's Sons, New York and London. Vol. 2: 298, 323, 362, 367.
WHIPPLE, A. W., EUBANK, T., and TURNER, W. W.
1856. Report upon the Indian tribes. U. S. Exec. Doc. 91, 33d Cong., 3d sess., Pac. R. R. Repts., vol. 2, 127 pp.
WHITE, BOUCK
1913. The call of the carpenter. 355 pp. Doubleday, Page & Co., Garden City, New York.
WHITE, DALE
1944. Man-sized wolf. Field & Stream, 48 (9): 75, illus. January.
WHITE, ELIJAH (DR.)
1850. Ten years in Oregon . . . . 430 pp. Compiled by Miss A. J. Allen. Ithaca, New York.

WHITE, JIM
1906. Traps and poison. Hunter, Trader, Trapper, 13 (1): 41-42. October.
WHITE, SAM O., and RHODE, CLARENCE J.
1939. Report on Alaska-Yukon Boundary Patrol, March 9-April 7, 9 pp. (mimeog.). Alaska Game Commission, Juneau, Alaska. In files of Fish and Wildlife Service, Washington, D. C.
WHITE, WILLIAM
1853. Records of the Governor and Company of the Massachusetts Bay in New England. Printed by order of the Legislature, Boston, 1853, vol. 1.
WHITEHEAD, CHARLES E.
1891. The campfires of the Everglades; or wild sports in the South. 298 pp. Edinburgh.
WHITING, A. B.
1912. Account of a blizzard in 1856. Kansas Hist. Coll. 1911-1912, vol. 12, pp. 118-120.
WHITTAKER, J. S.
1864. Wayne. [Annual Report of the Wayne County Agricultural Society.] 9th report State Agr. Soc. 1863. Pp. 483-485.
WHITTAKER, M. W.
1911. Strange adventures with a wolf. Rod and Gun in Canada 12 (11): 1425-1427. April.
WIGRAM, P.
1896. Supposititious wild man. The Field 87 (2246): 36-37. January 11. London.
WILBERT, M. I.
1904. Progress in pharmacy. Amer. Jour. Pharmacy 76 (12): 581-591. December.
WILKES, CHARLES
1845. Narrative of the United States exploring expedition during the years 1838, 1839, 1840, 1841, 1842. 5 vols. and an atlas. Philadelphia.
WILLIAMS, JOHN LEE
1837. The territory of Florida—civil and natural history. 304 pp. New York.

WILLIAMS, ROGER
1827. A key into the language of America. 205 pp. London. Reprinted in Collections Rhode Island Hist. Soc. 1: 17-163. Providence.
WILLIAMS, ROGER D.
1895. Hunting in Many Lands. Wolf coursing. 447 pp., illus. A book of the Boone and Crockett Club. New York.
1909. Hunting the gray wolf. Recreation 29 (1): 3-7, illus. January.
WILLIAMS, SAMUEL
1809. The natural and civil history of Vermont. 2 vols. 2nd Ed. Burlington.
WILLIAMS, SAMUEL COLE
1928. Early travels in the Tennessee country 1540-1800. 540 pp. Johnson City, Tennessee.
WILLIAMSON, WILLIAM D.
1839. The history of the State of Maine. 2 vols.
WILLIS, A. R.
1940. Talking sticks. The Beaver, outfit 271: 50. June. Winnipeg.
WILSON, CLIFFORD
1937. The wolves are always after us. Forest and Outdoors 33 (2): 37-38, 62, illus.
WILSON, GILBERT LIVINGSTONE
1924. The horse and the dog in Hidatsa culture. Amer. Mus. Nat. Hist. Anthrop. Papers 15 (2): 125-311, illus. New York.
WINEMAN, ELVA
1930. White wolf, foe of cattlemen, is dead. Montana Wild Life 2 (12): 6-7. Helena, Montana.
WINSHIP, GEORGE PARKER
1896. The Coronado expedition, 1540-1542. 14th Ann. Rept. Bur. Ethnology to Sec. Smithsonian Inst., 1892-1893, pp. 329-613, illus. In 2 parts. Washington, D. C.
WOOD, ABRAHAM
1928. A letter. Samuel Cole Williams' Early Travels in the Tennessee Country. P. 27. Johnson City, Tennessee.

WOOD, NORMAN A.

1914. An annotated check-list of Michigan mammals. Univ. Mich. Mus. Zool., Occas. Papers 4: 1-13. April 1.

1922. The mammals of Washtenaw County, Michigan. Univ. Mich. Mus. Zool., Occas. Papers 123: 1-23. July 10.

WOOD, WILLIAM

1635. New England's prospect. 83 pp. London.

WOODHOUSE, S. W.

1852. The North American jackal—*Canis frustror*. Jour. Acad. Nat. Sci. Phila. 2 (2d ser.): 87-88.

1853. Report on the natural history of the country passed over by the exploring expedition under the command of Brevet Capt. L. Sitgreaves' U. S. Topographical Engineers . . . . 32d Cong., 2d sess., Senate Exec. Doc. No. 59, 147 pp. Washington, D. C.

1854. Report on the natural history of the country passed over by the exploring expedition under command of Brevet Capt. L. Sitgreaves. 33d Cong., 1st sess., Senate Exec. Doc., 198 pp. Washington, D. C.

WRIGHT, GEORGE M.

1935. Big game of our national parks. Scientific Monthly 41: 141-147, illus. August.

———— DIXON, JOSEPH S., and THOMPSON, BEN H.

1933 Fauna of the national parks of the United States. A preliminary survey of faunal relations in national parks. U. S. Dept. Interior, contribution of wildlife survey fauna series, 1: i-v; 1-157; illus. 44, 47, 49, 88, 94-95, 106, 110, 117, 122, 127-130, 139, 143, 145.

WRIGHT, R. M.

1902. Personal reminiscences of frontier life in southwest Kansas. Trans. Kans. State Hist. Soc. 1901-1902, 7: 47-83. Topeka.

XENOPHON

1925. Scripta Minora. The cavalry commander. 365 B. C. English translation by E. C. Marchant, Sub-Rector of Lincoln College, Oxford. A volume of the Loeb Classical Library. London, William Heinemann. 463 pp. G. P. Putnam's Sons, New York.

YARHAM, E. R.
1941. Canada's fight for the musk oxen. Amer. Forests 47 (9): 424-425, 448, illus. September.
YEAGER, DORR G.
1931. Our wilderness neighbors. 160 pp., illus. Chicago.
YEAGER, LEE E.
1938. Otters of the Delta Hardwood Region of Mississippi. Jour. Mamm. 19 (2): 195-201. May.
YOUNG, STANLEY P.
1925. The old wolf "Three Toes" of Harding County, South Dakota. Daily Science News Bull. August 13.
1930a. Conquering wolfdom and catdom. Southwest Wilds and Waters 2 (1): 6-7, 47, illus. Oklahoma City.
1930b. Hints on wolf and coyote trapping. U. S. Dept. Agr., Bur. Biol. Survey Leaflet 59: 1-8, illus.; also Amer. Field 114 (36): 219-220.
1934. Our federal predator control work. Trans. 20th American Game Conference, pp. 172-176.
1940. It's "red," but truly American. Western Sportsman 5 (6): 10-11, 26, illus. Denver. November.
1941a. The evolution of the steel wolf trap in North America. Western Sportsman 6 (3): 10-11, 30-31, illus. Denver.
1941b. The return of the musk oxen. American Forests 47 (8): 368-372, illus. August.
1941c. Hints on coyote and wolf trapping. U. S. Dept. of the Interior, Fish and Wildlife Service Circular No. 2, 8 pp., illus.
1942a. Fading trails—a story of endangered wildlife. Pp. XV plus 279, illus. Ch. XI, The Wolf. New York.
1942b. The war on the wolf. American Forests 48 (11): 492-495, 526, illus.; 48 (12): 552-555, 572-574, illus.
1943. What was the early Indian dog? Amer. Forests, 49 (12): 571-573, 594, 603; 4 illus. December.
1944. What was the early Indian dog? Amer. Forests, 50 (1): 26-28, 32, 45; 4 illus. January.
ZINGG, ROBERT M.
1941. India's wolf children—two human infants reared by wolves. Scientific American 164 (3): 135-137, illus. March.

PHOTOGRAPHS OF SKULLS OF NORTH AMERICAN WOLVES

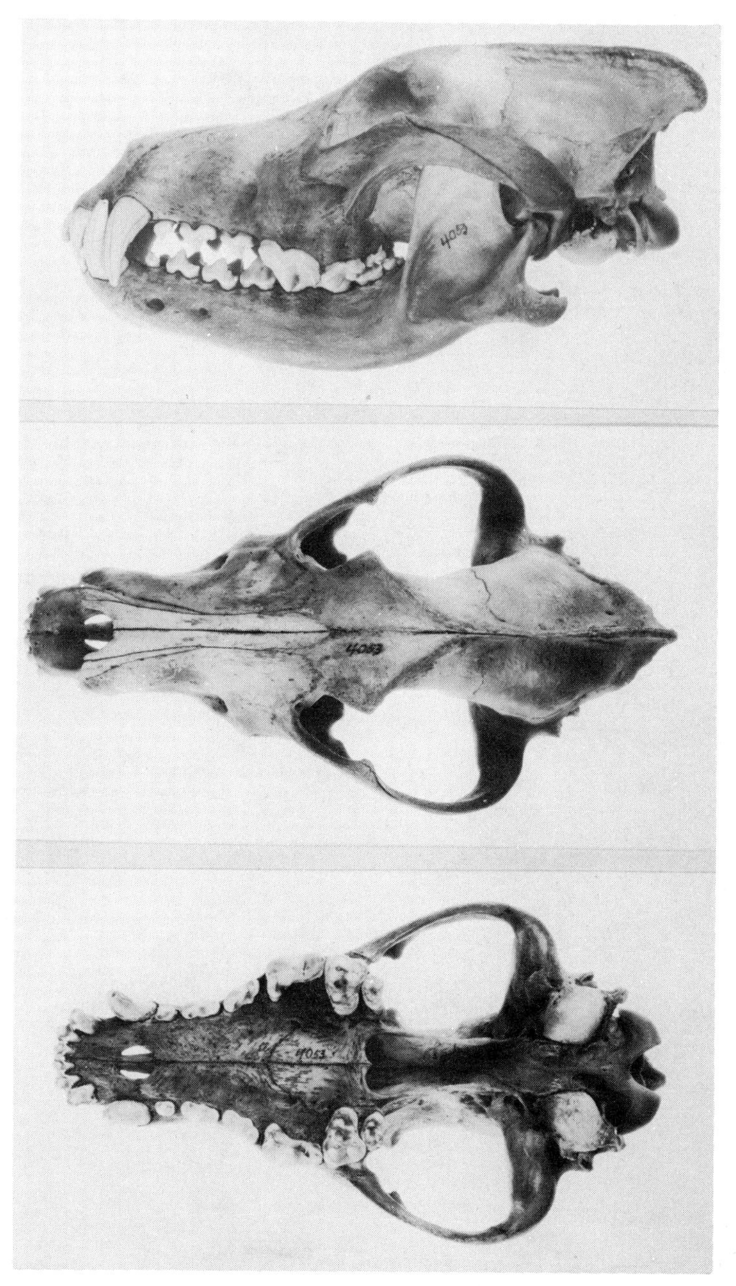

Plate 88. *Canis lupus tundrarum* Miller; male adult; Mead River, near Point Barrow, Alaska. (No. 4053, Colo. Mus. Nat. Hist.) Note relatively large second and third upper premolars. [One-third natural size]

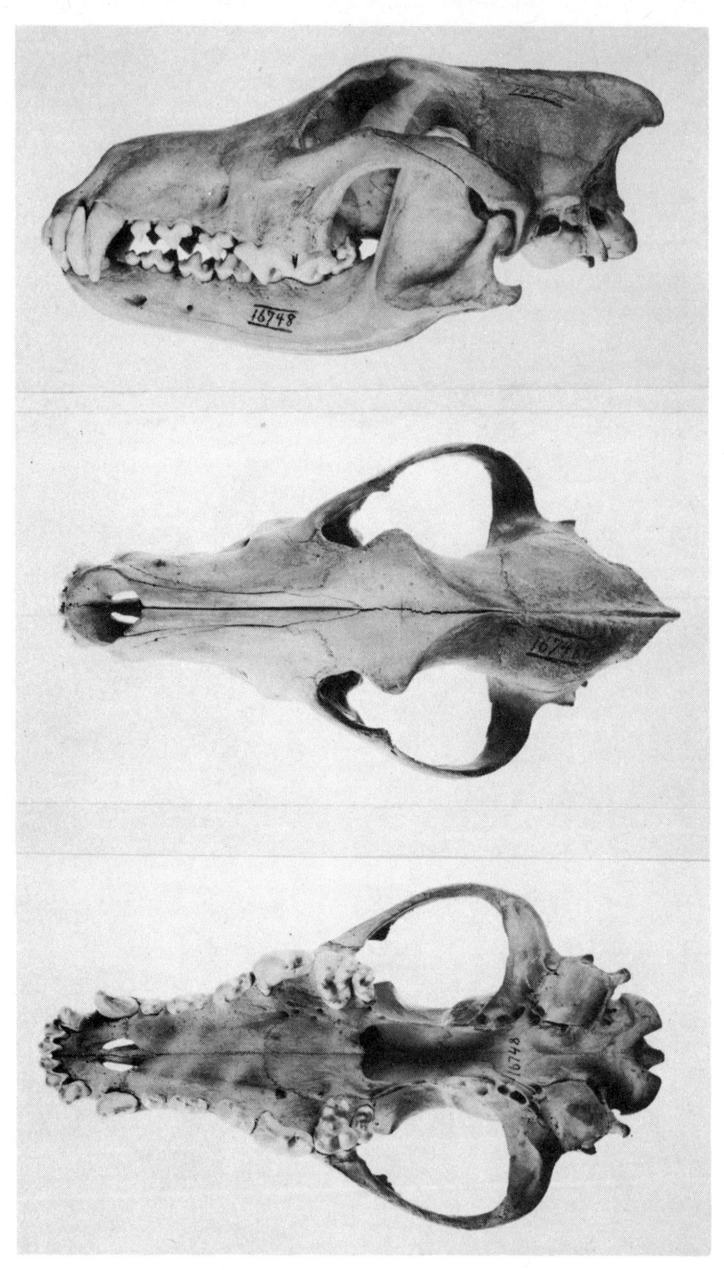

Plate 89. *Canis lupus tundrarum* Miller; type; female adult; Point Barrow, Alaska. (No. 16748, U. S. Nat. Mus.) Note relatively large second and third upper premolars. [One-third natural size]

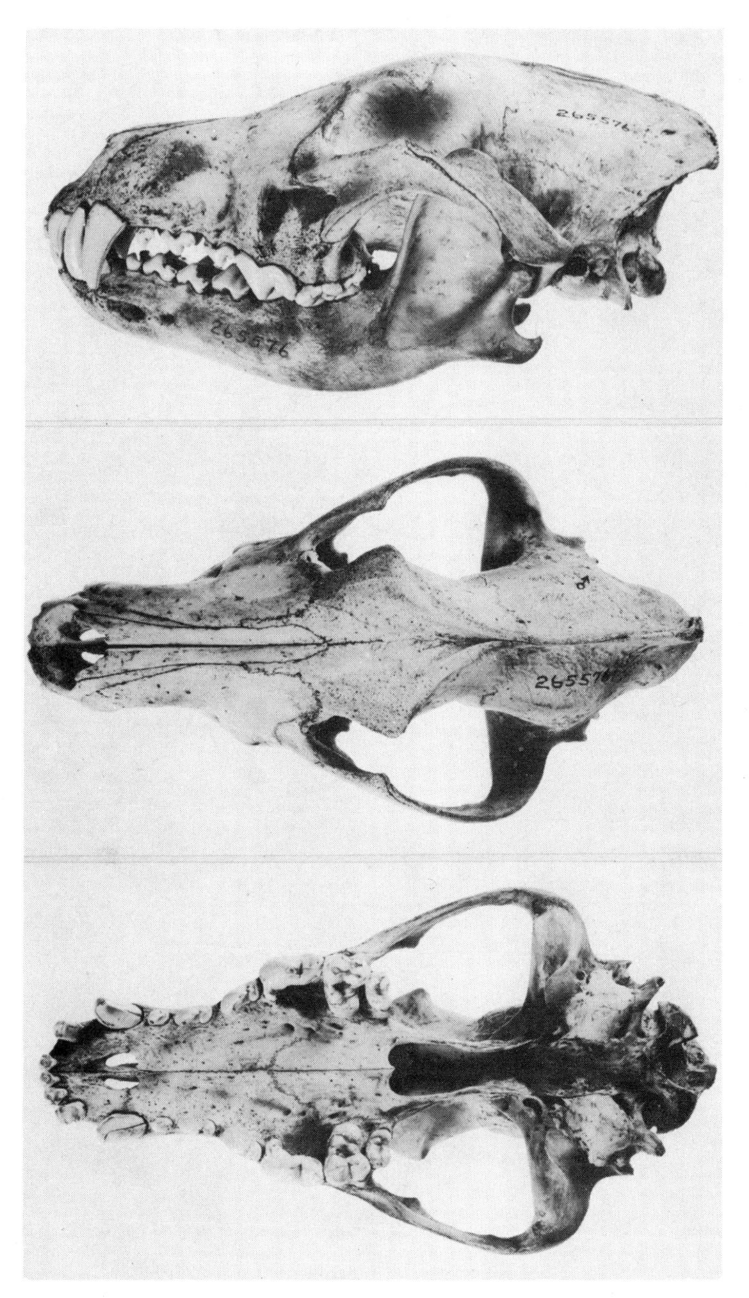

Plate 90. *Canis lupus pambasileus* Elliot; male adult; Big Delta, Tanana River, Alaska. (No. 265576, U. S. Nat. Mus., Biological Surveys collection.) Note large size and tendency toward elongation. [One-third natural size]

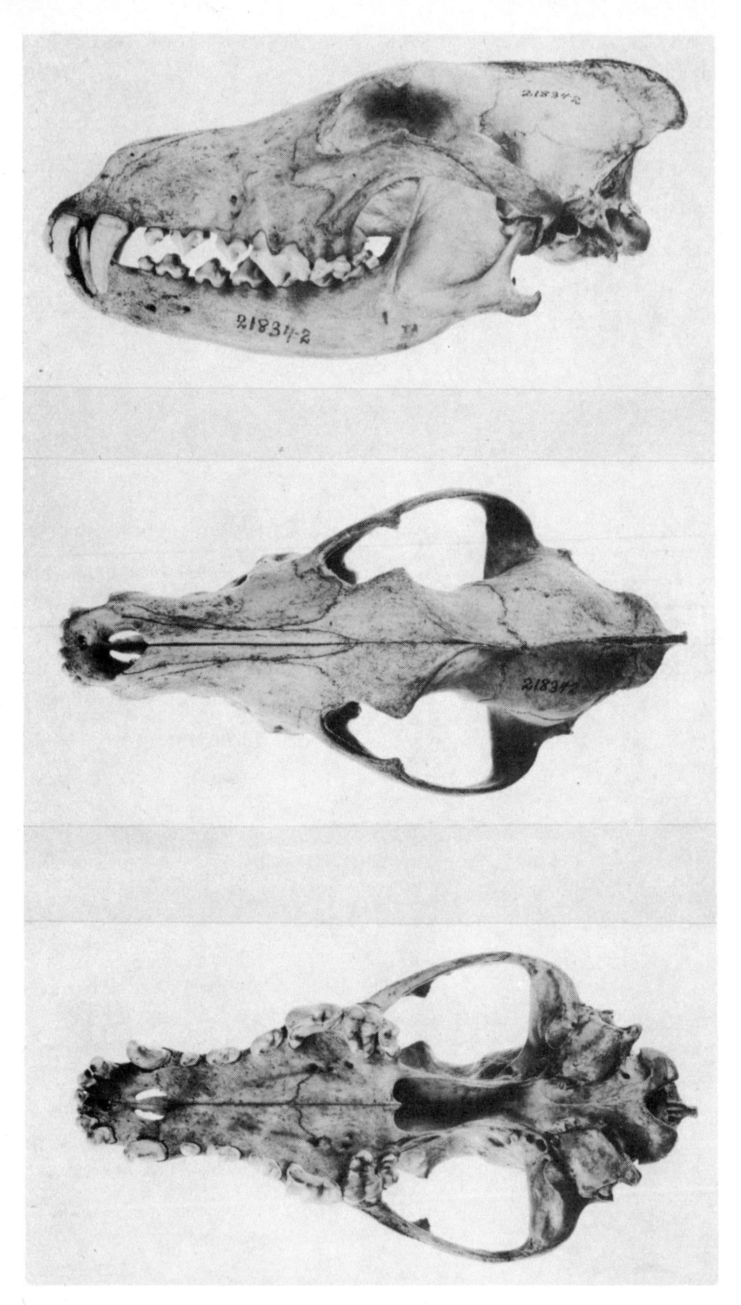

Plate. 91. *Canis lupus pambasileus* Elliot; female adult; Tanana, Alaska. (No. 218342, U. S. Nat. Mus.) Note large size and tendency toward elongation. [One-third natural size]

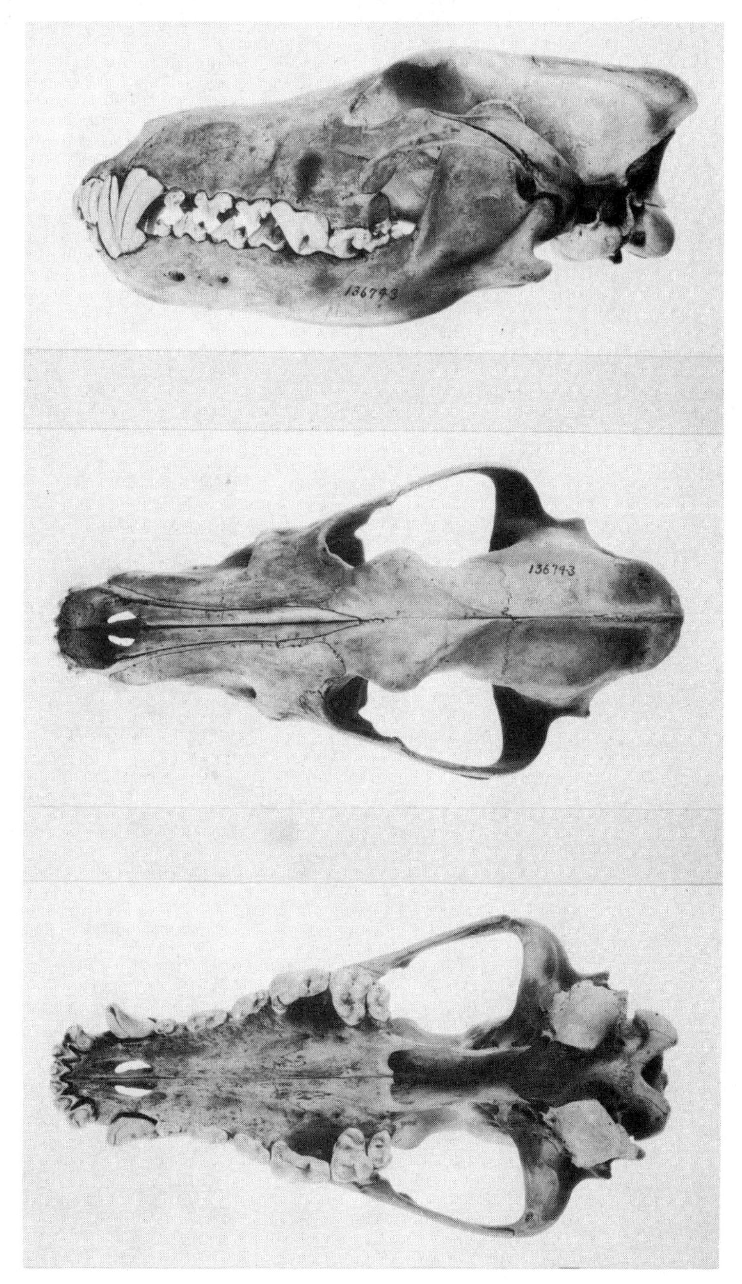

Plate 92. *Canis lupus alces* Goldman; topotype; male subadult; Kachemak Bay, Alaska. (No. 136743, U. S. Nat. Mus., Biological Surveys collection.) Note large size, slightly spreading zygomata, broad supraoccipital shield, and relatively small teeth. [One-third natural size]

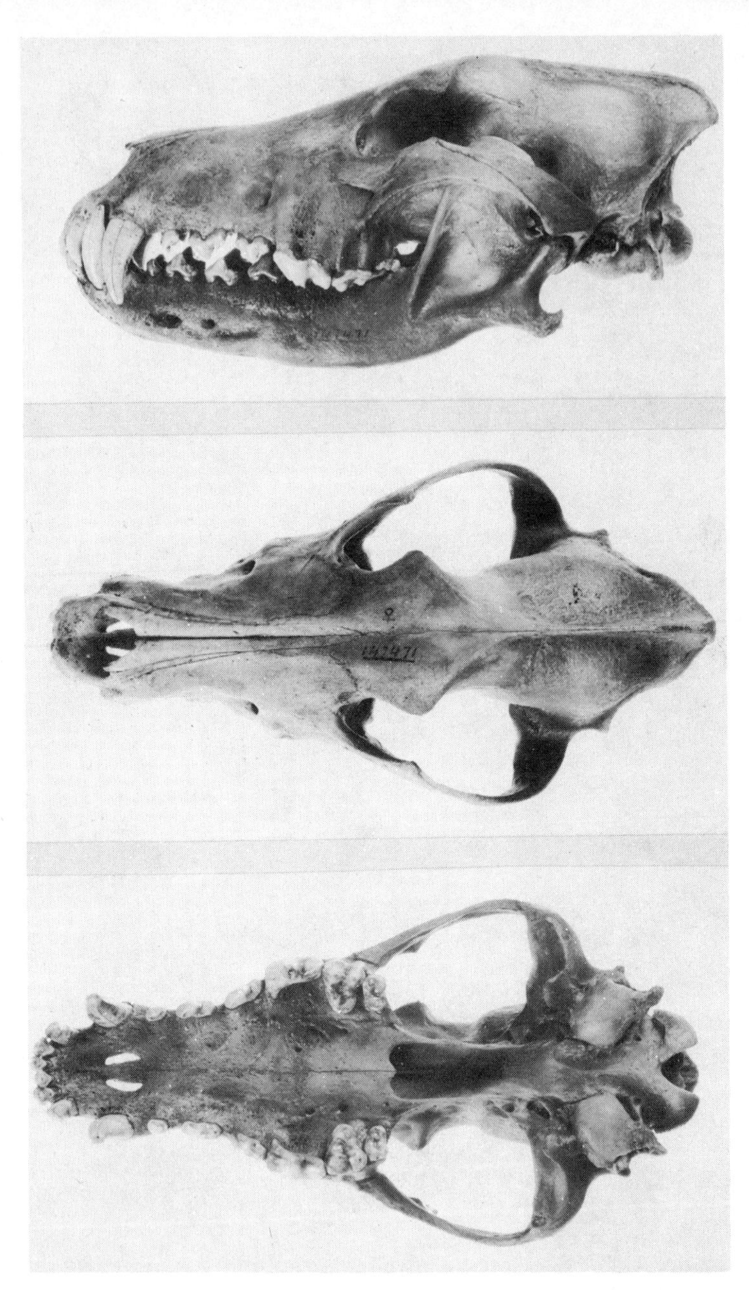

Plate 93. *Canis lupus alces* Goldman; type; female adult; Kachemak Bay, Kenai Peninsula, Alaska. (No. 147471, U. S. Nat. Mus., Biological Surveys collection.) Note large size, slightly spreading zygomata, broad supraoccipital shield, and relatively small teeth. [One-third natural size]

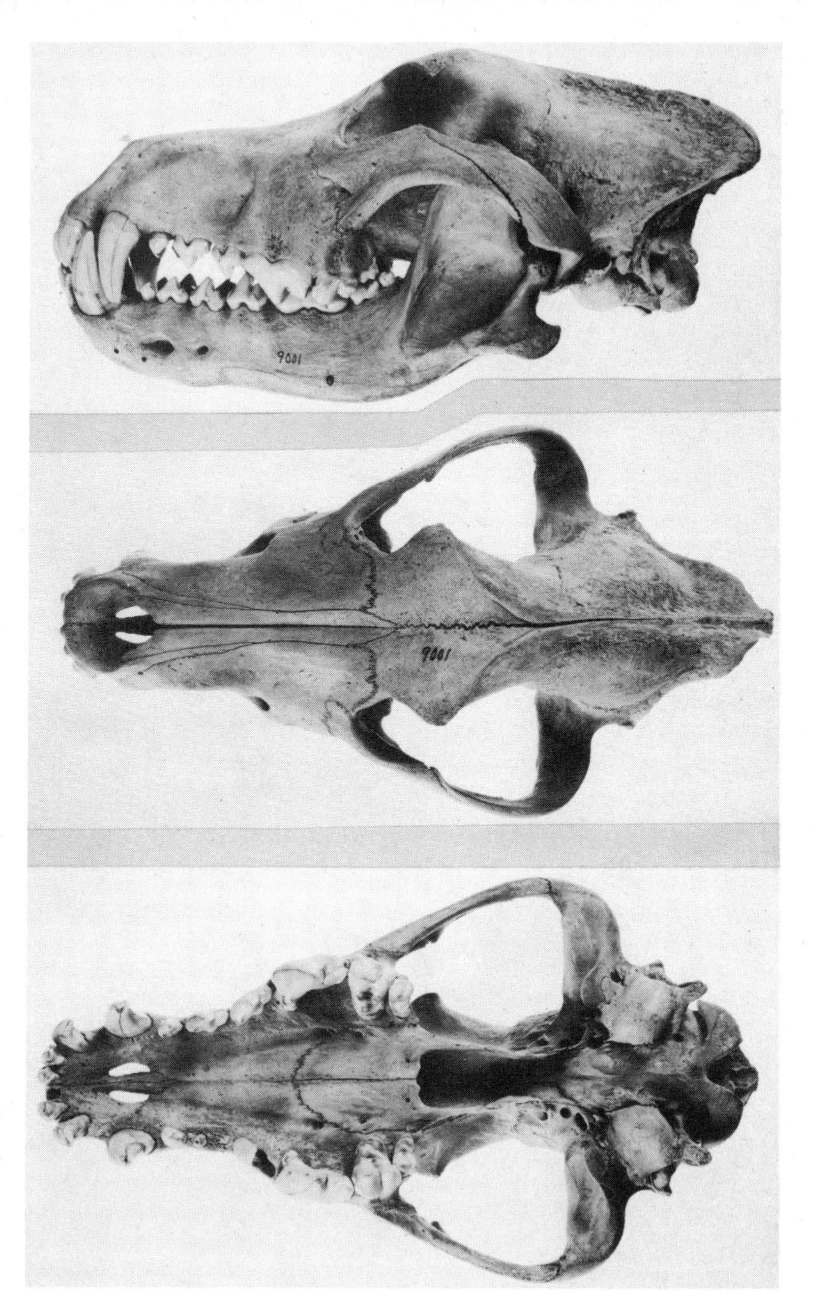

Plate 94. *Canis lupus occidentalis* Richardson; male adult; Simpson, Mackenzie, Canada. (No. 9001, U. S. Nat. Mus.) Note large size and general massiveness. [One-third natural size]

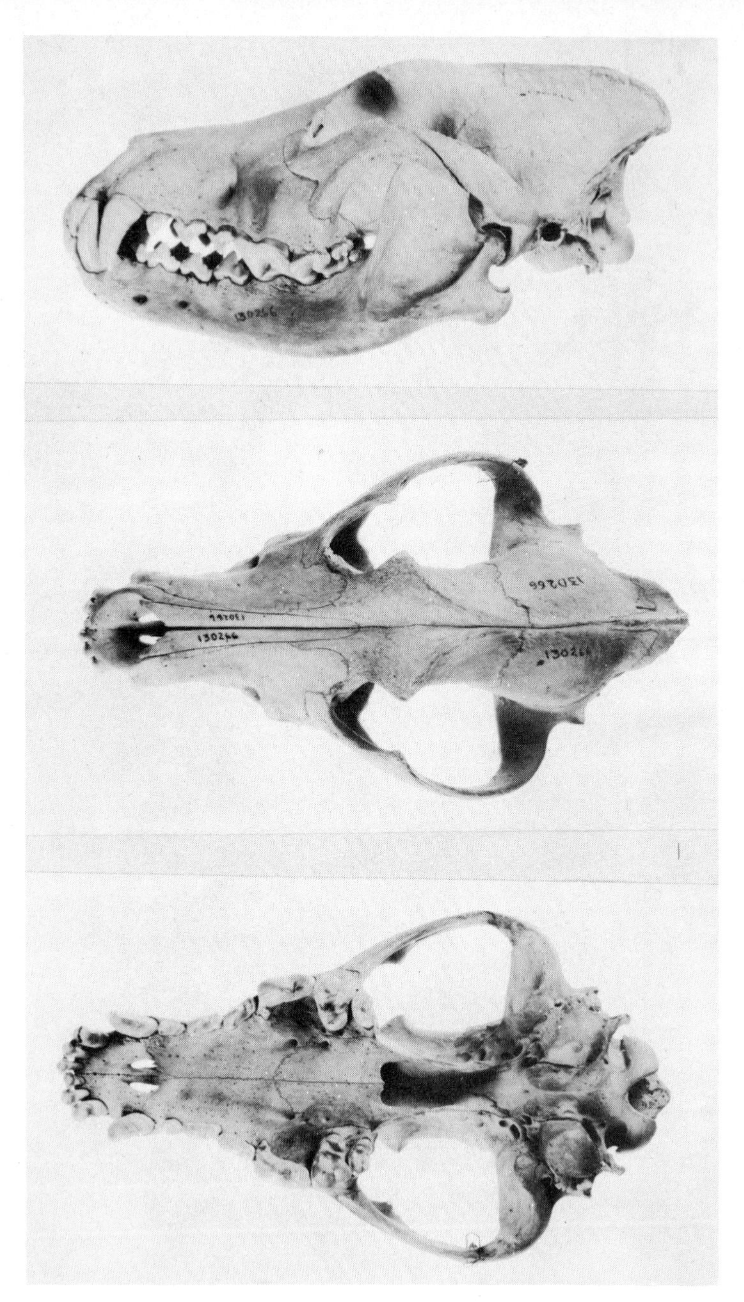

Plate 95. *Canis lupus occidentalis* Richardson; female adult; Wood Buffalo Park, Alberta, Canada. (No. 130266, Amer. Mus. Nat. Hist.) Note large size and general massiveness. [One-third natural size]

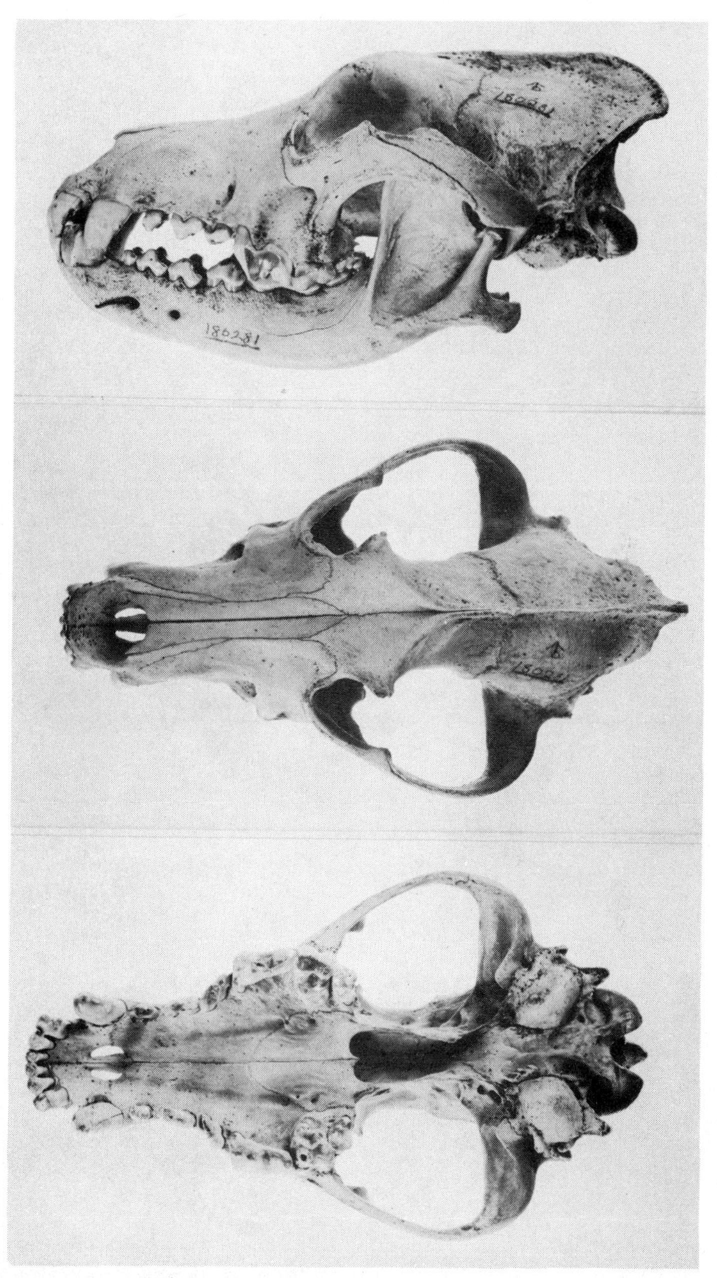

Plate 96. *Canis lupus hudsonicus* Goldman; type; male adult; head of Schultz Lake, Keewatin, Canada. (No. 180281, U. S. Nat. Mus., Biological Surveys collection.) Note medium size, broad postorbital region, and narrow, acutely pointed postorbital processes. [One-third natural size]

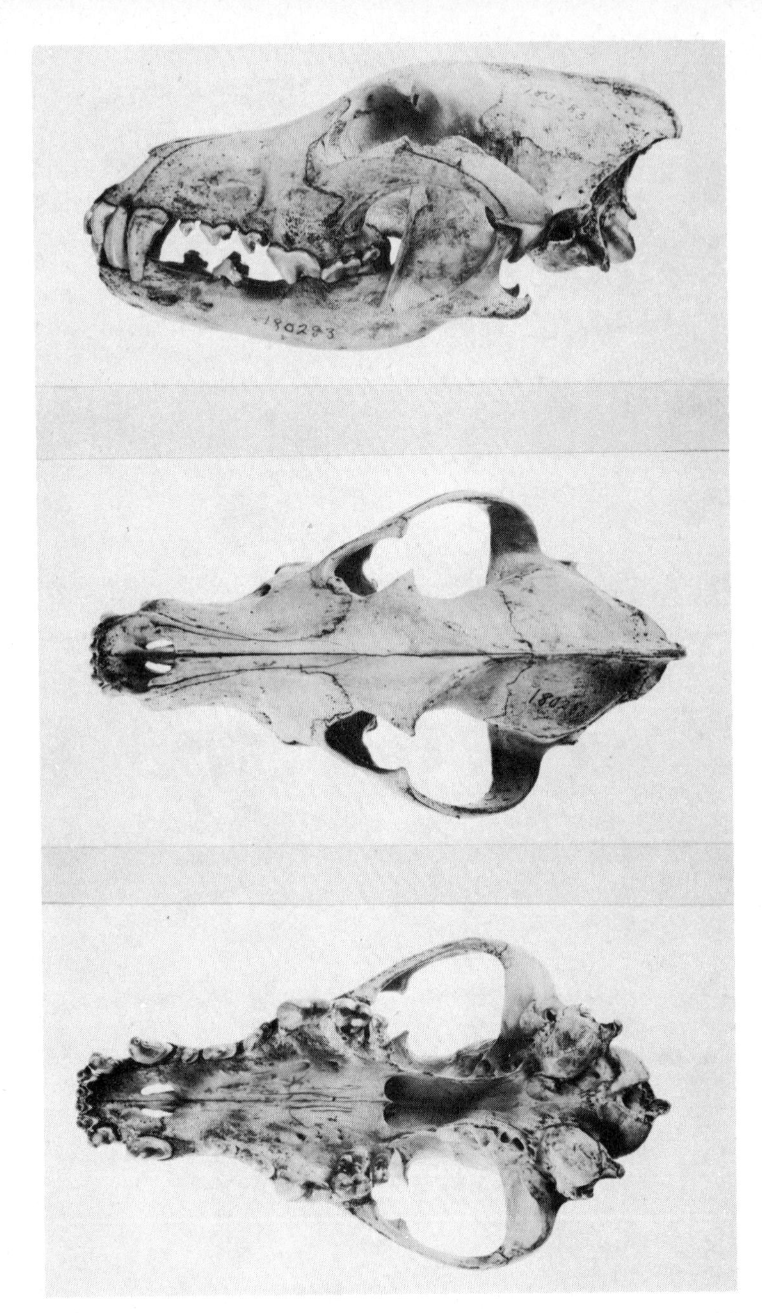

Plate 97. *Canis lupus hudsonicus* Goldman; topotype; female adult; head of Schultz Lake, Keewatin, Canada. (No. 180283, U. S. Nat. Mus., Biological Surveys collection.) Note medium size, broad postorbital region, and narrow, acutely pointed postorbital processes. [One-third natural size]

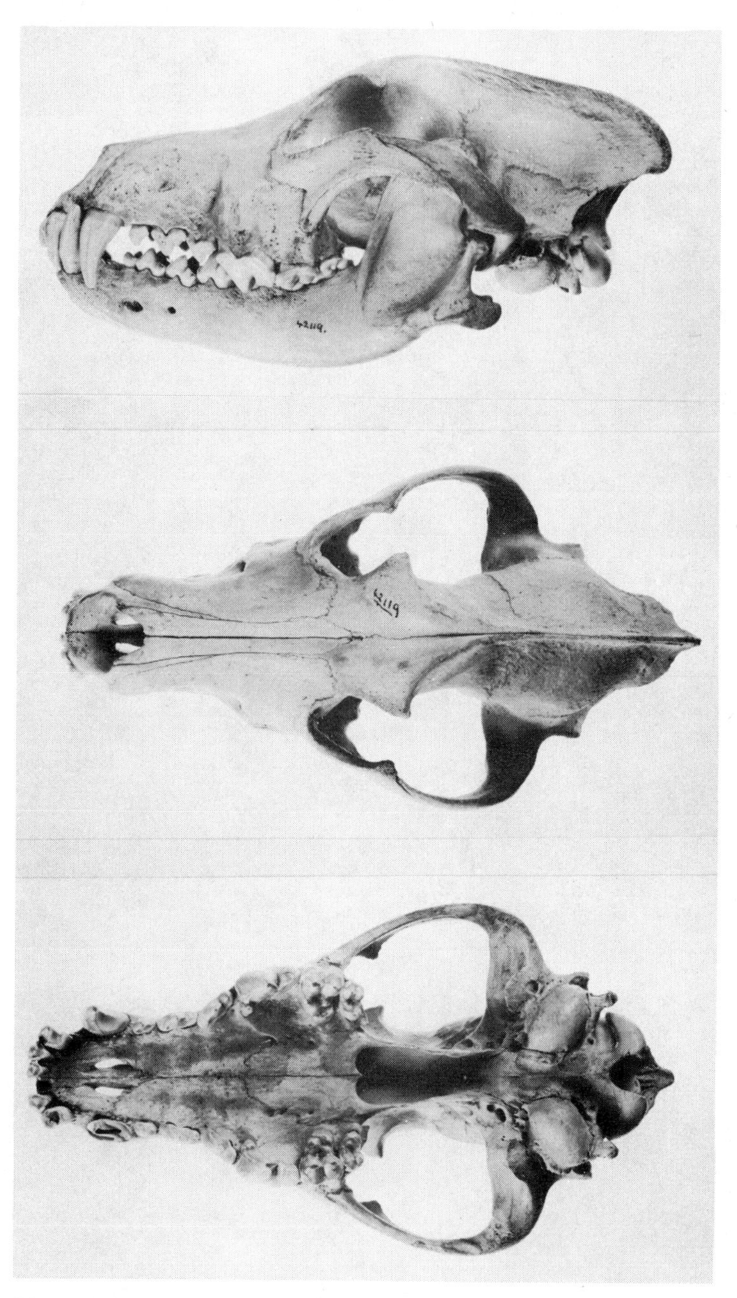

Plate 98. *Canis lupus arctos* Pocock; male adult; Ellesmere Island, Arctic America. (No. 42119, Amer. Mus. Nat. Hist.) Note narrow, highly arched braincase. [One-third natural size]

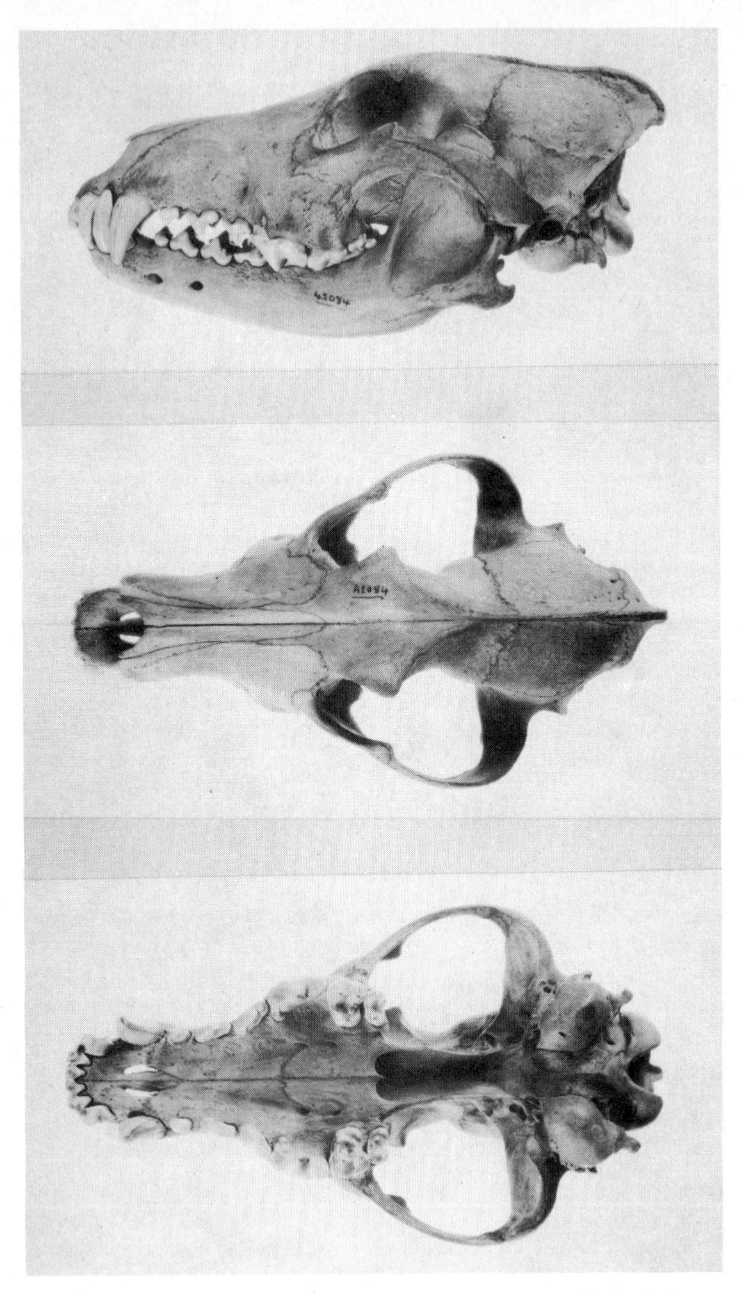

Plate 99. *Canis lupus orion* Pocock; female adult; Greenland, Arctic America. (No. 42084, Amer. Mus. Nat. Hist.) Note smaller size and narrower braincase as compared with mainland wolves. [One-third natural size]

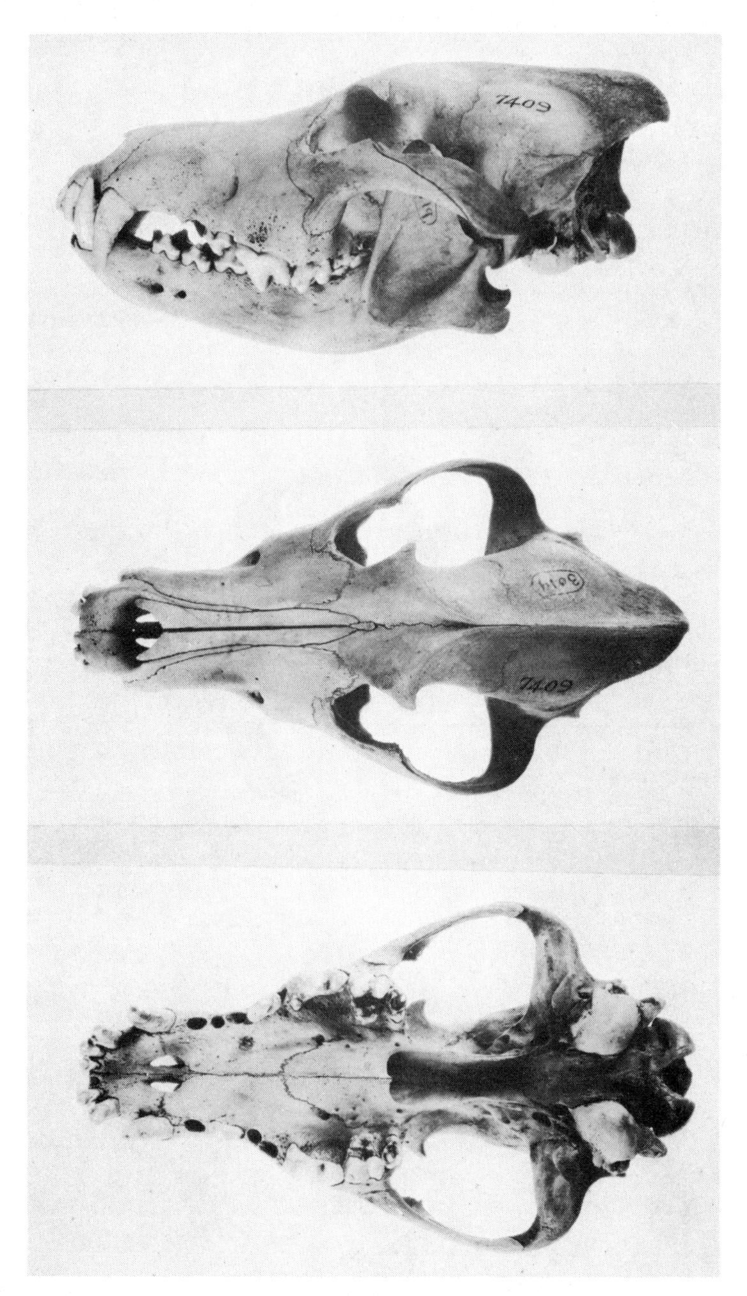

Plate 100. *Canis lupus labradorius* Goldman; male adult; Hopedale, Labrador, Canada. (No. 7409, Mus. Comp. Zool.) Note broad postorbital region. [One-third natural size]

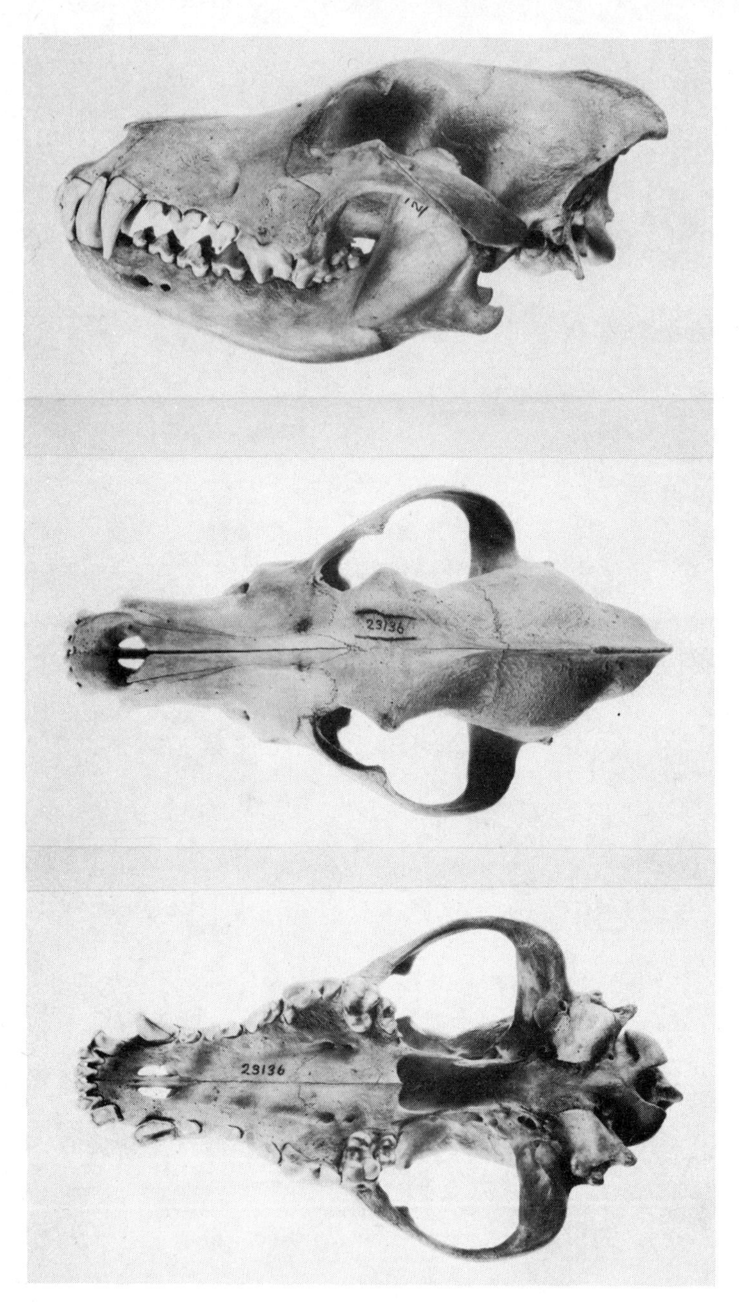

Plate 101. *Canis lupus labradorius* Goldman; type; female adult; Chimo, Quebec, Canada. (No. 23136, U. S. Nat. Mus., Biological Surveys collection.) Note broad postorbital region. [One-third natural size]

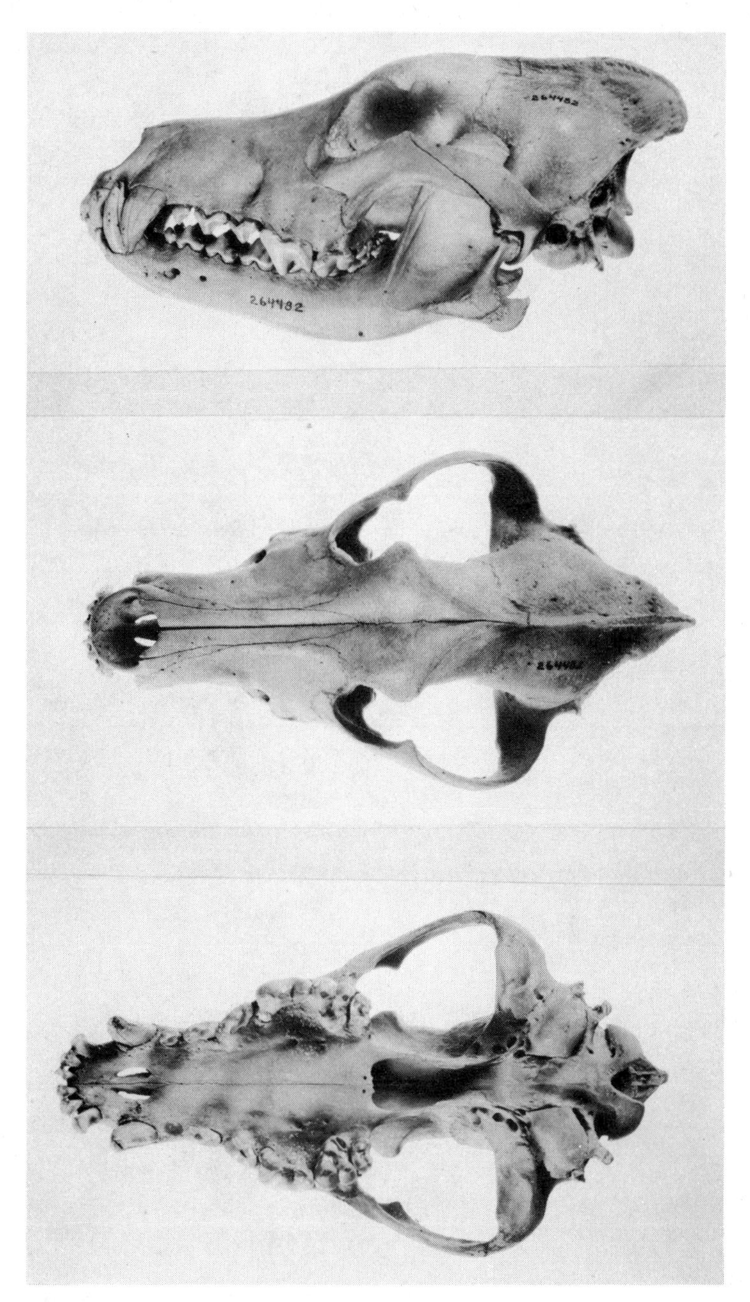

Plate 102. *Canis lupus beothucus* Allen and Barbour; probably male, adult; Newfoundland. (No. 264482, U. S. Nat. Mus., Biological Surveys collection.) Note narrow supraoccipital region and obtuse postorbital processes. [One-third natural size]

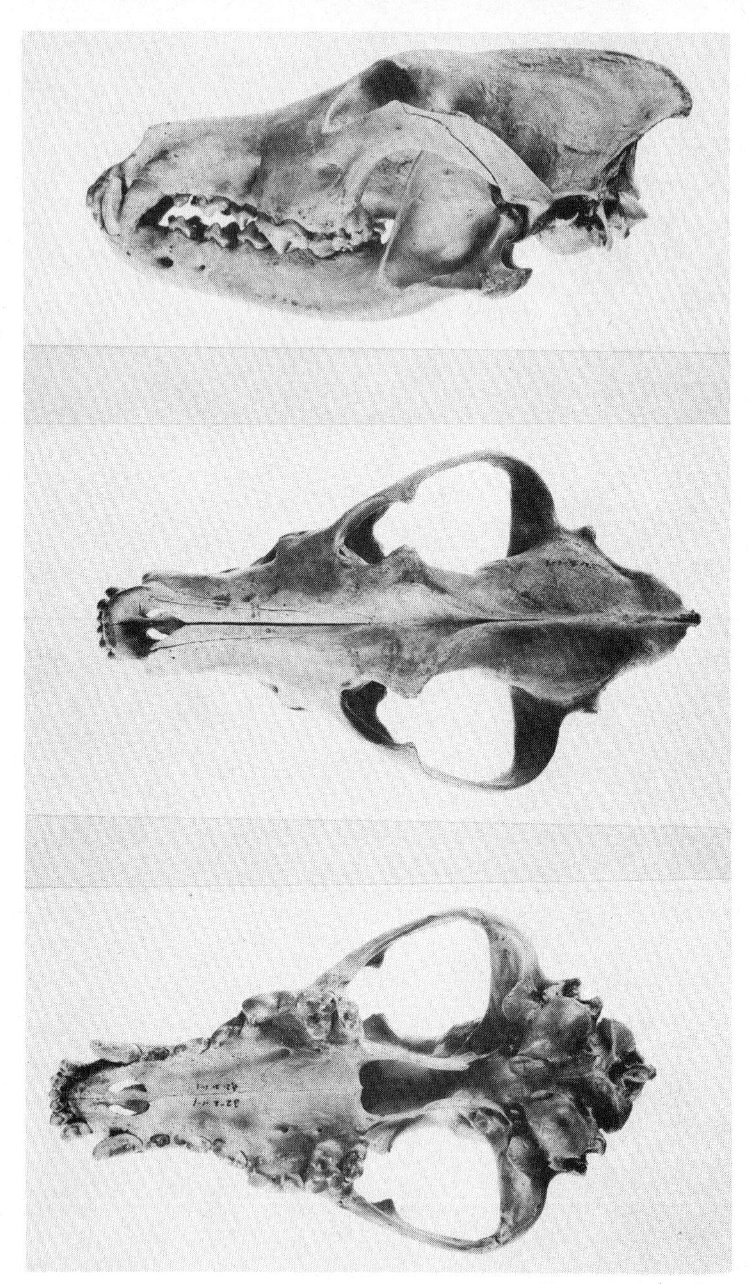

Plate 103. *Canis lupus lycaon* Schreber; male adult; Montebello, Quebec, Canada. (No. 32.2.1.1, Roy. Ont. Mus. Zool.) Note slenderness, especially of rostrum. [One-third natural size]

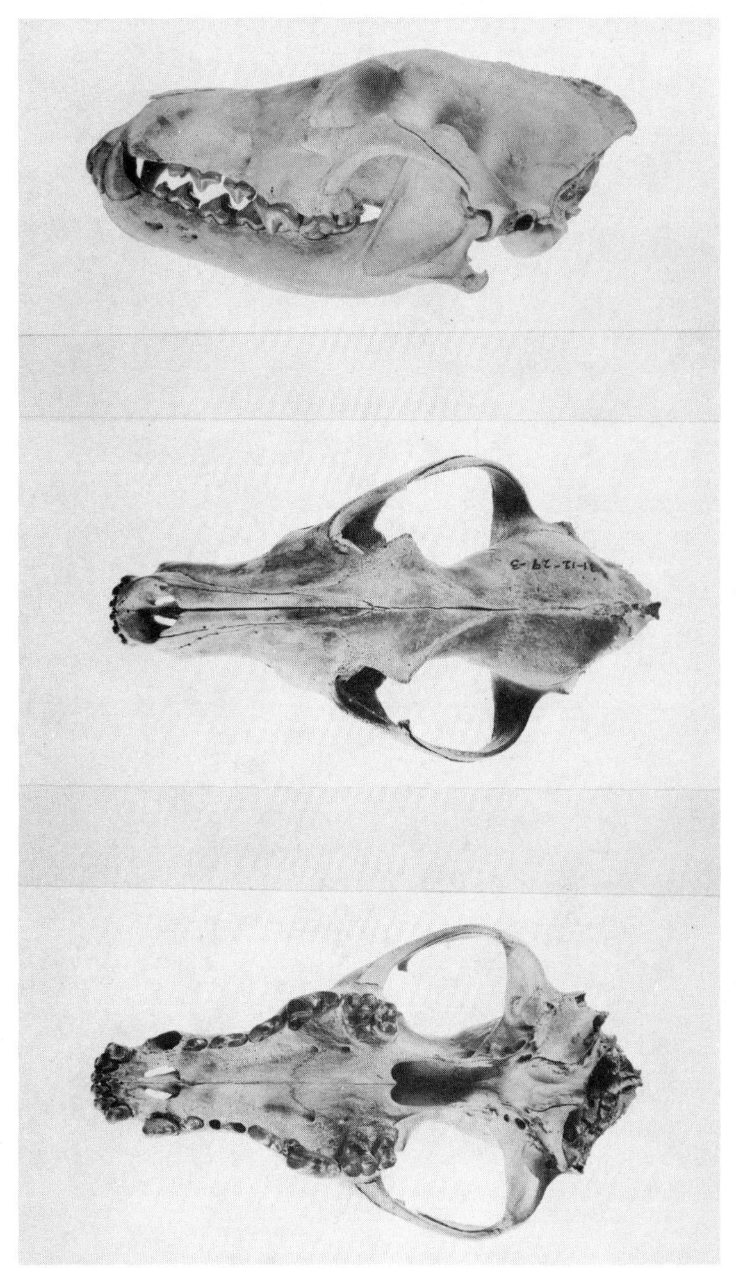

Plate 104. *Canis lupus lycaon* Schreber; female adult; Montebello, Quebec, Canada. No. 31.12.29.3, Roy. Ont. Mus. Zool.) Note slenderness, especially of rostrum. [One-third natural size]

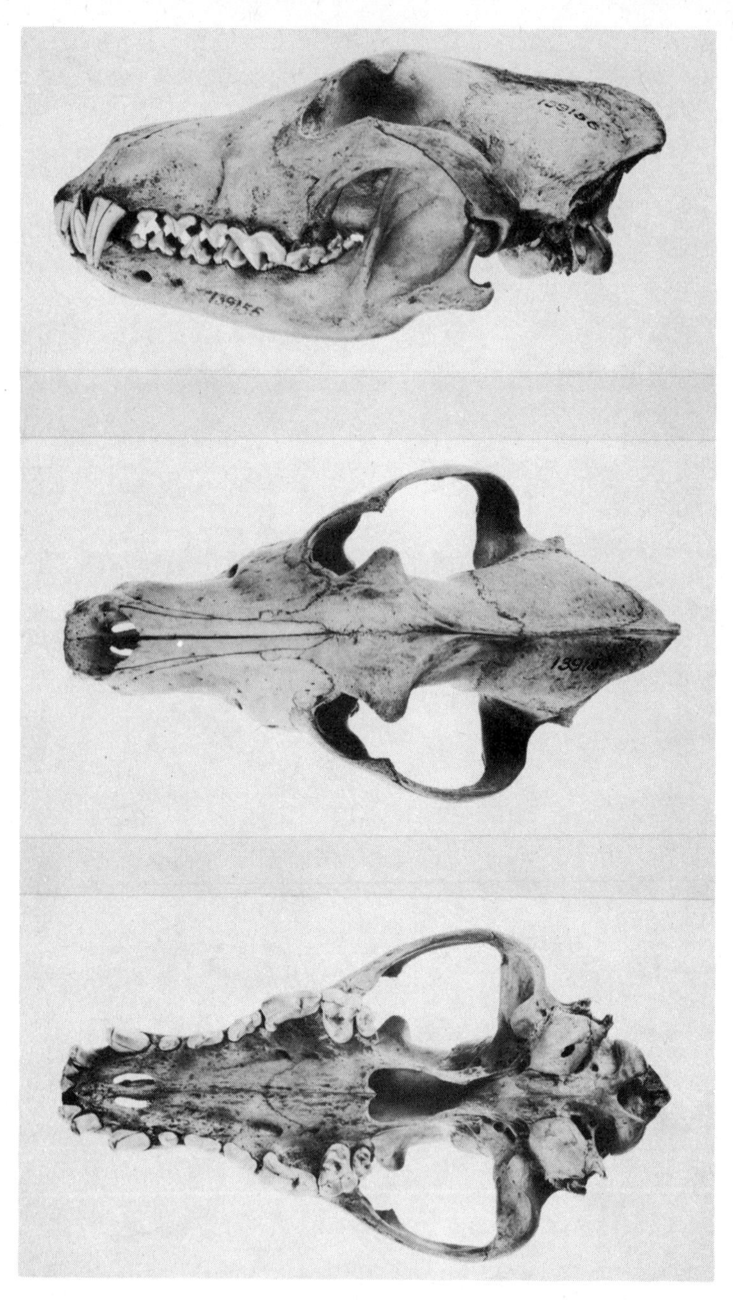

Plate 105. *Canis lupus nubilus* Say; male adult; Gove County, Kansas. (No. 139156, U. S. Nat. Mus., Biological Surveys collection.) Note narrow supraoccipital shield and posterior projection of inion well behind plane of occipital condyles. [One-third natural size]

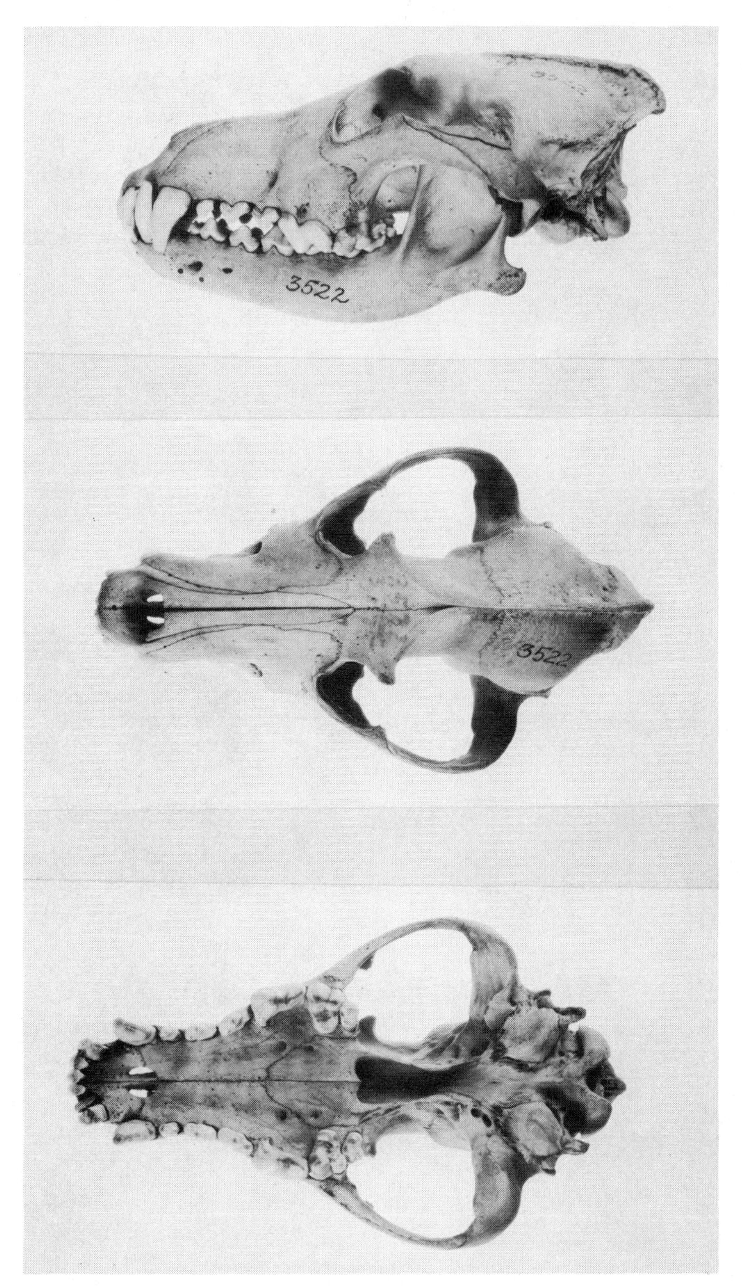

Plate 106. *Canis lupus nubilus* Say; female adult; Platte River Nebraska. (No. 3522/3575, U. S. Nat. Mus.) Note narrow supraoccipital shield and posterior projection of inion well behind plane of occipital condyles. [One-third natural size]

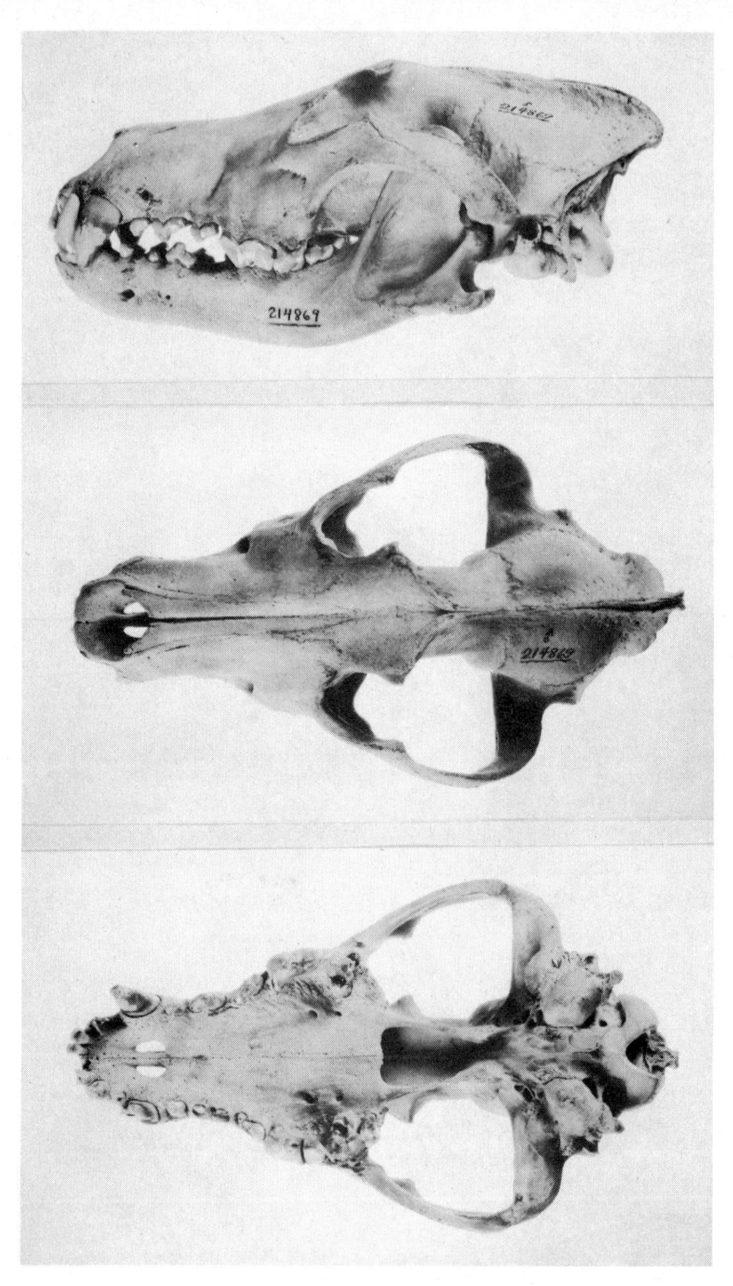

Plate 107. *Canis lupus irremotus* Goldman; type; male adult; Red Lodge, Carbon County, Montana. (No. 214869, U. S. Nat. Mus., Biological Surveys collection.) Note narrow postorbital constriction. [One-third natural size]

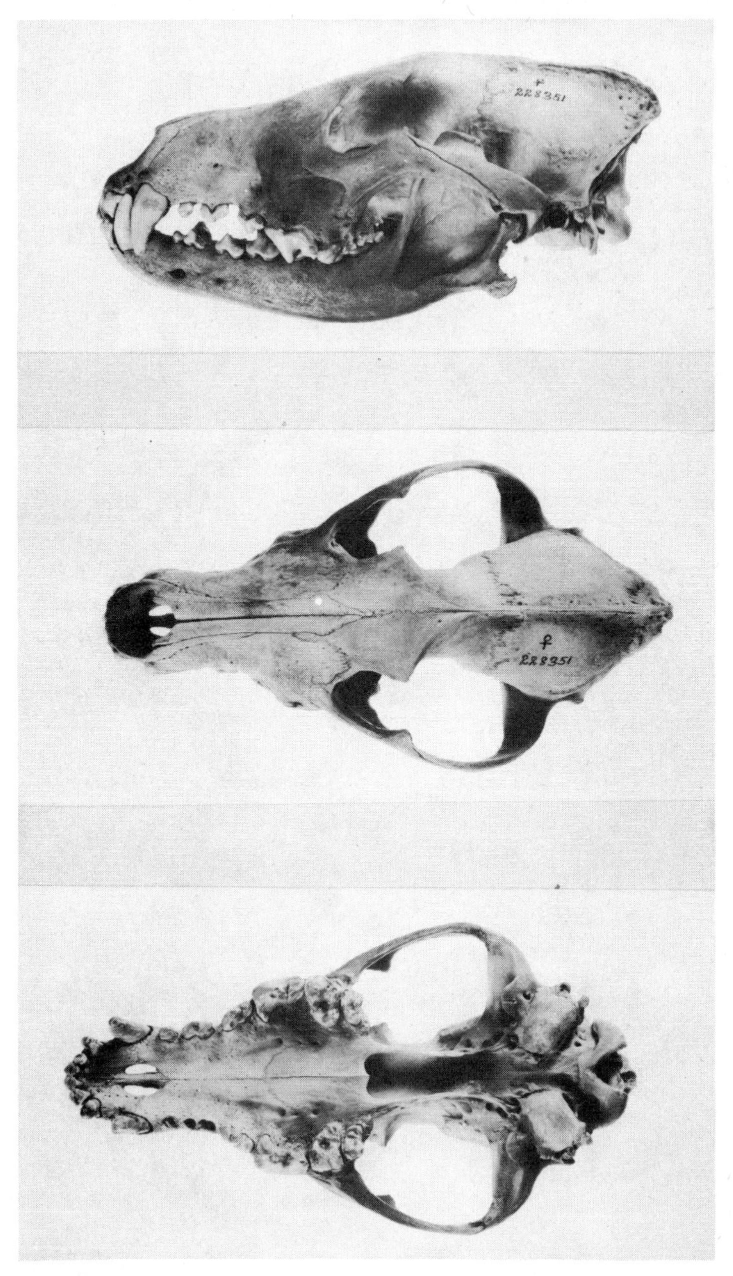

Plate 108. *Canis lupus irremotus* Goldman; female adult; Continental Divide, Montana side, 20 miles east of Leadore, Idaho. (No. 228351, U. S. Nat. Mus., Biological Surveys collection.) Note narrow postorbital constriction. [One-third natural size]

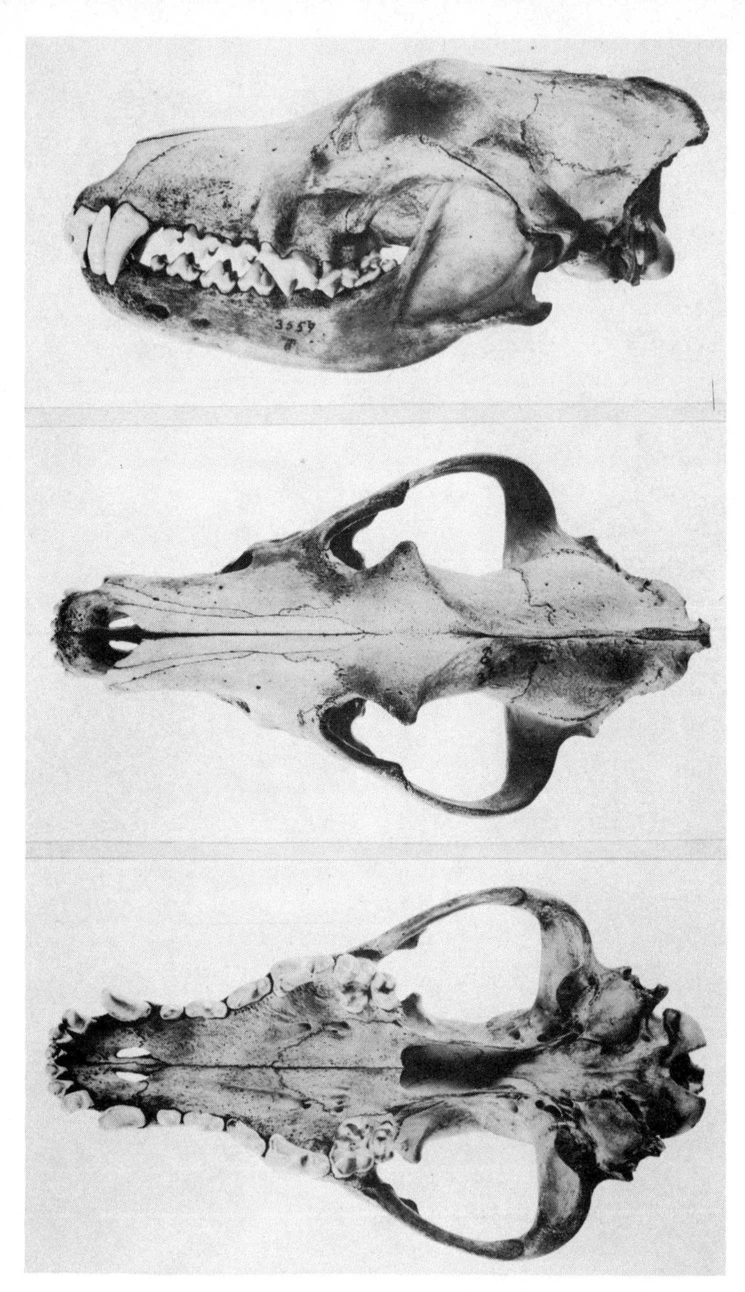

Plate 109. *Canis lupus columbianus* Goldman; type; male adult; Wistaria, north side of Ootsa Lake, Coast District, British Columbia. (No. 3559, Brit. Col. Prov. Mus.) Note large size, broad supraoccipital shield, and narrow carnassials. [One-third natural size]

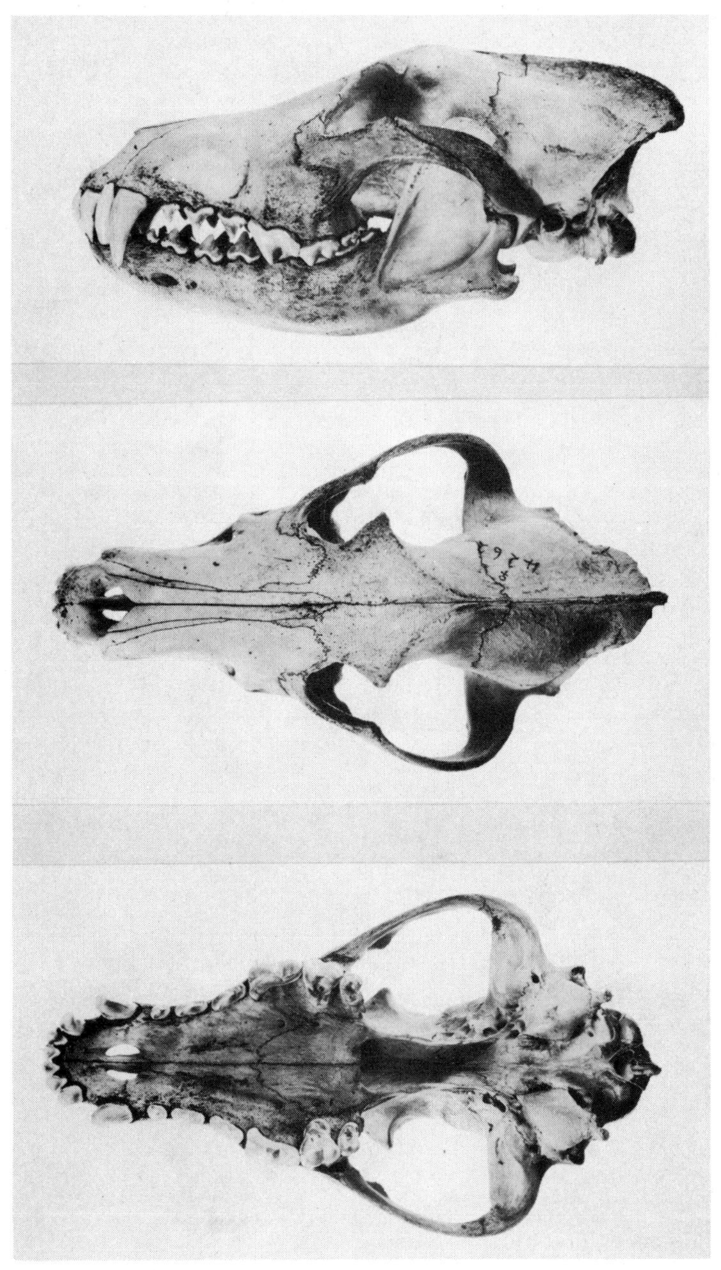

Plate 110. *Canis lupus columbianus* Goldman; topotype; female adult; Wistaria, north side of Ootsa Lake, Coast District, British Columbia. (No. 4262, Brit. Col. Prov. Mus.) Note large size, broad supraoccipital shield, and narrow carnassials. [One-third natural size]

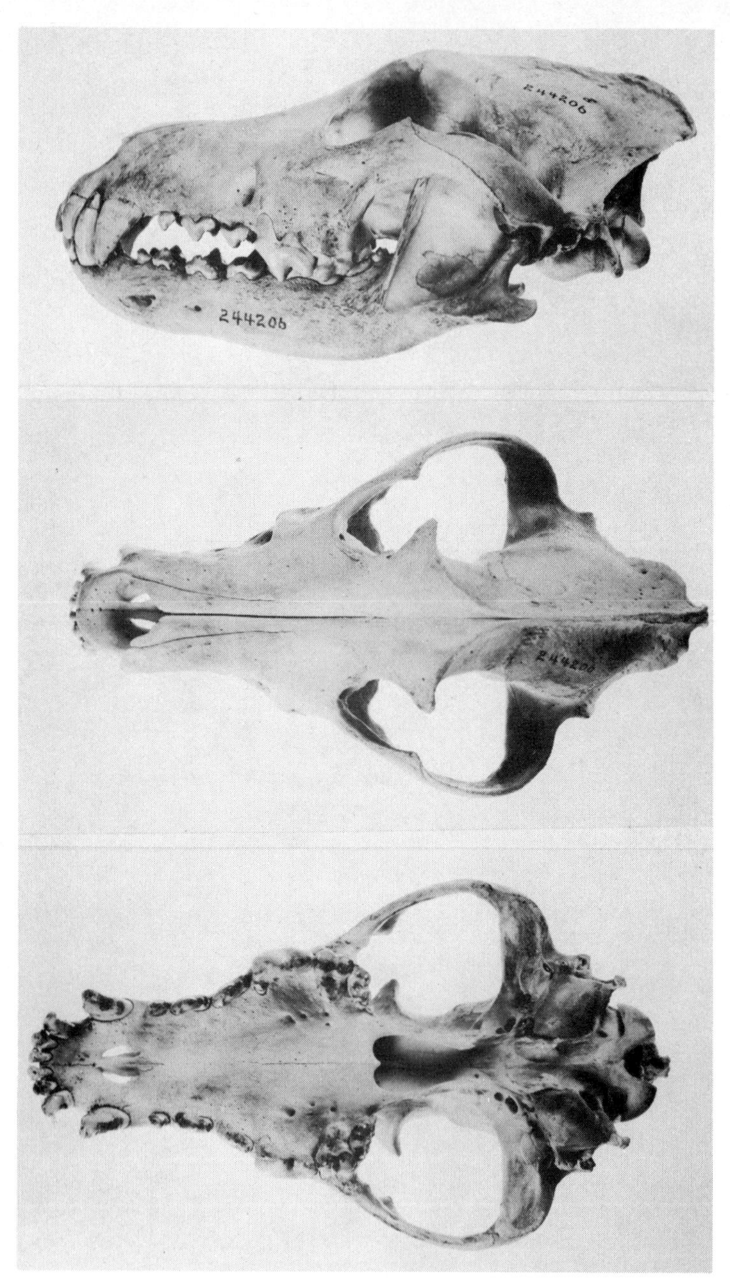

Plate 111. *Canis lupus ligoni* Goldman; male adult; Wrangell, Alaska. (No. 244206, U. S. Nat. Mus., Biological Surveys collection.) Note smaller size, compared with neighboring mainland races. [One-third natural size]

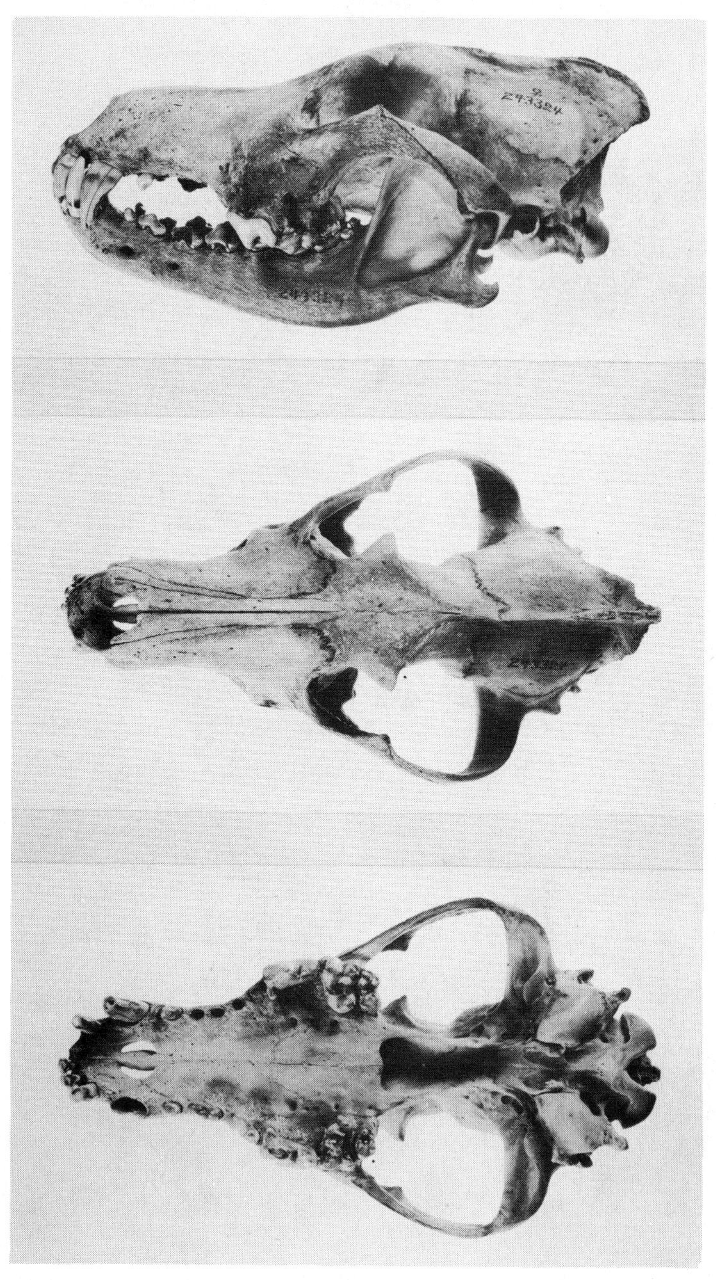

Plate 112. *Canis lupus ligoni* Goldman; female adult; Kupreanof Island, Alaska. No. 243324, U. S. Nat. Mus., Biological Surveys collection.) Note smaller size, compared with neighboring mainland races. [One-third natural size]

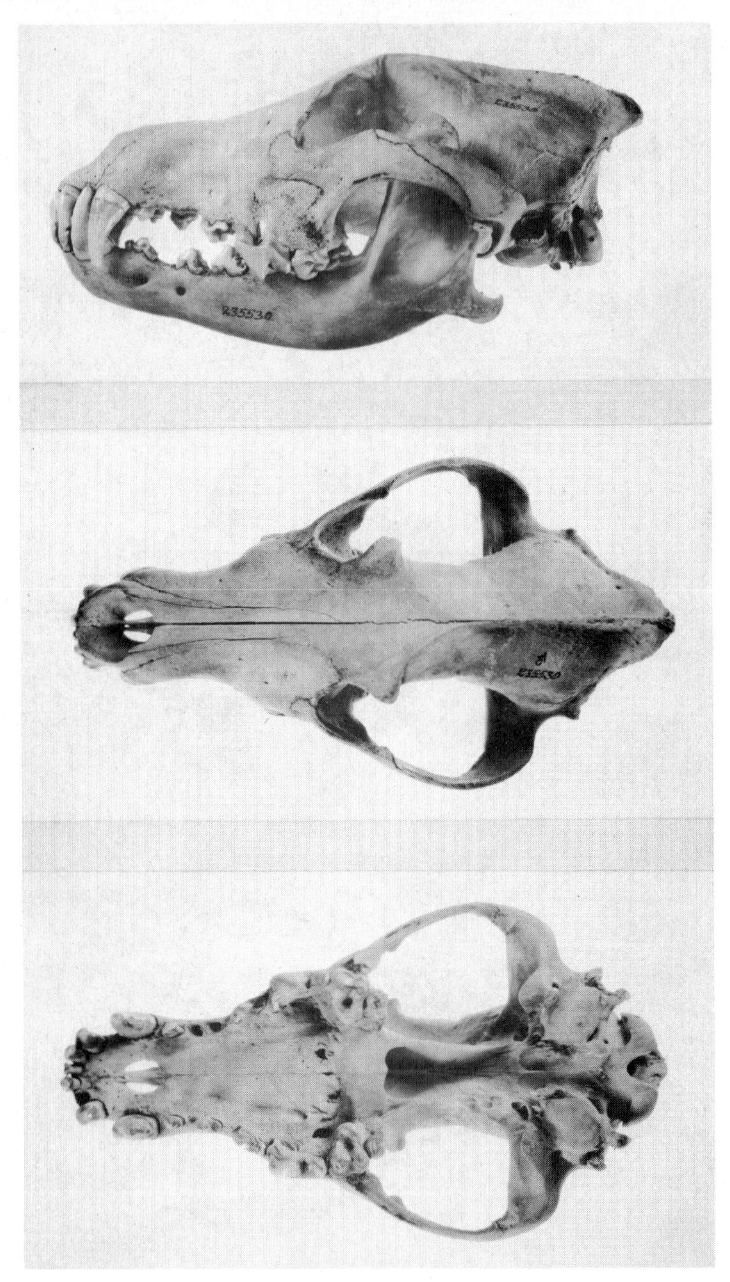

Plate 113. *Canis lupus fuscus* Richardson; male adult; Cascadia, Oregon. (No. 235530, U. S. Nat. Mus., Biological Surveys collection.) Note nasals ending posteriorly in same transverse plane as maxillae, instead of extending beyond this plane as in other races. [One-third natural size]

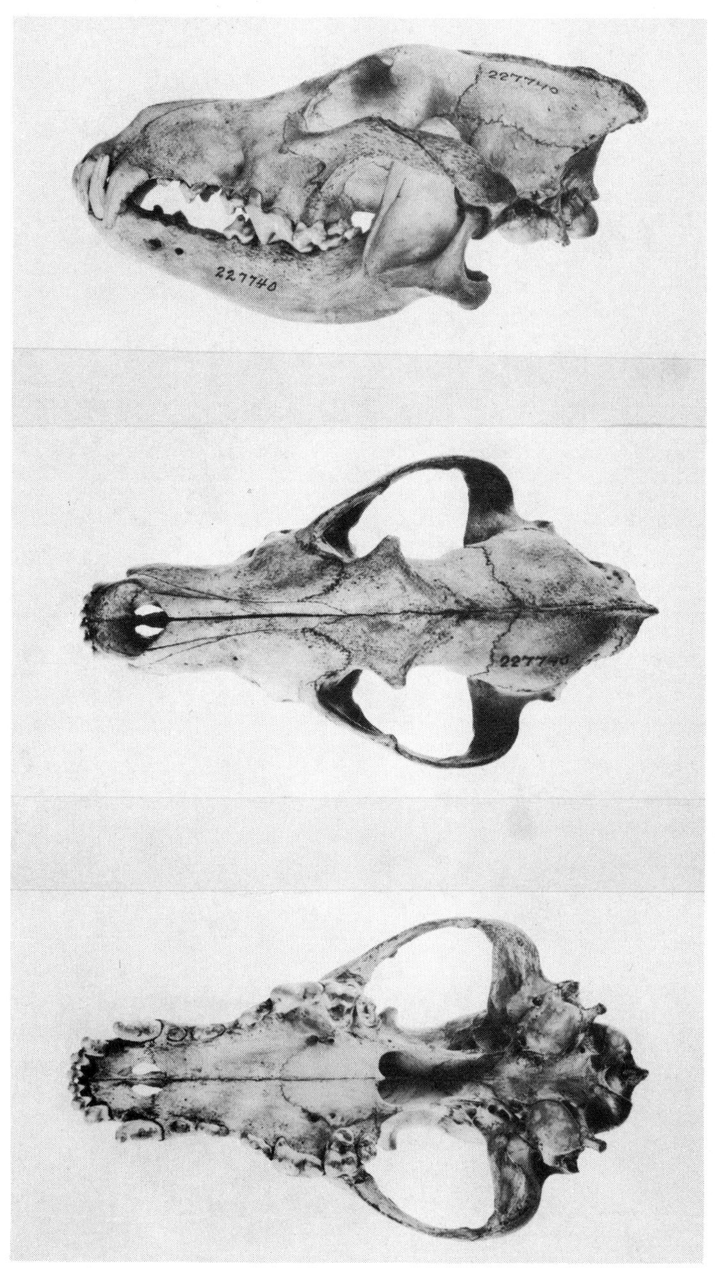

Plate 114. *Canis lupus fuscus* Richardson; female adult; Estacada, Oregon. (No. 227740, U. S. Nat. Mus., Biological Surveys collection.) Note nasals ending posteriorly in same transverse plane as maxillae, instead of extending beyond this plane as in other races. [One-third natural size]

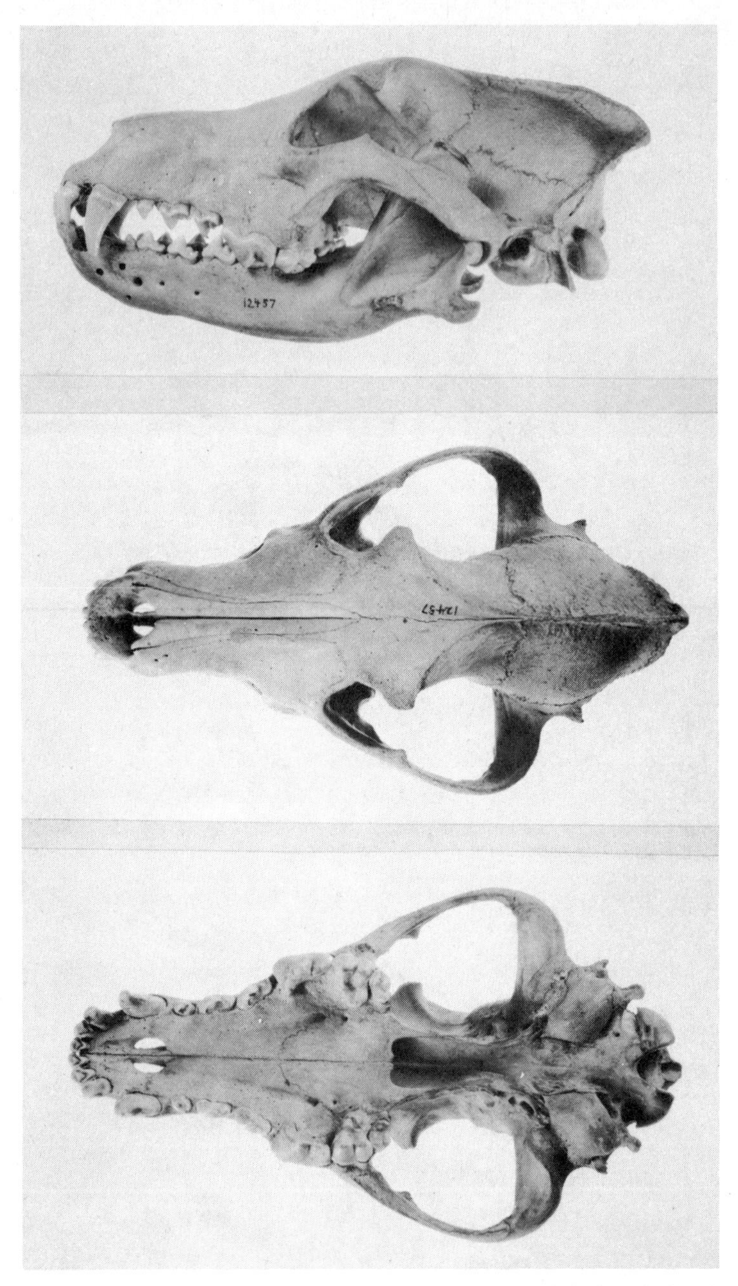

Plate 115. *Canis lupus crassodon* Hall; topotype; male adult; Tahsis Canal, Nootka Sound, Vancouver Island, British Columbia, Canada. (No. 12457, Mus. Vert. Zool.) Note heavy dentition, and form of upper carnassial with outer side longer than inner side. [One-third natural size]

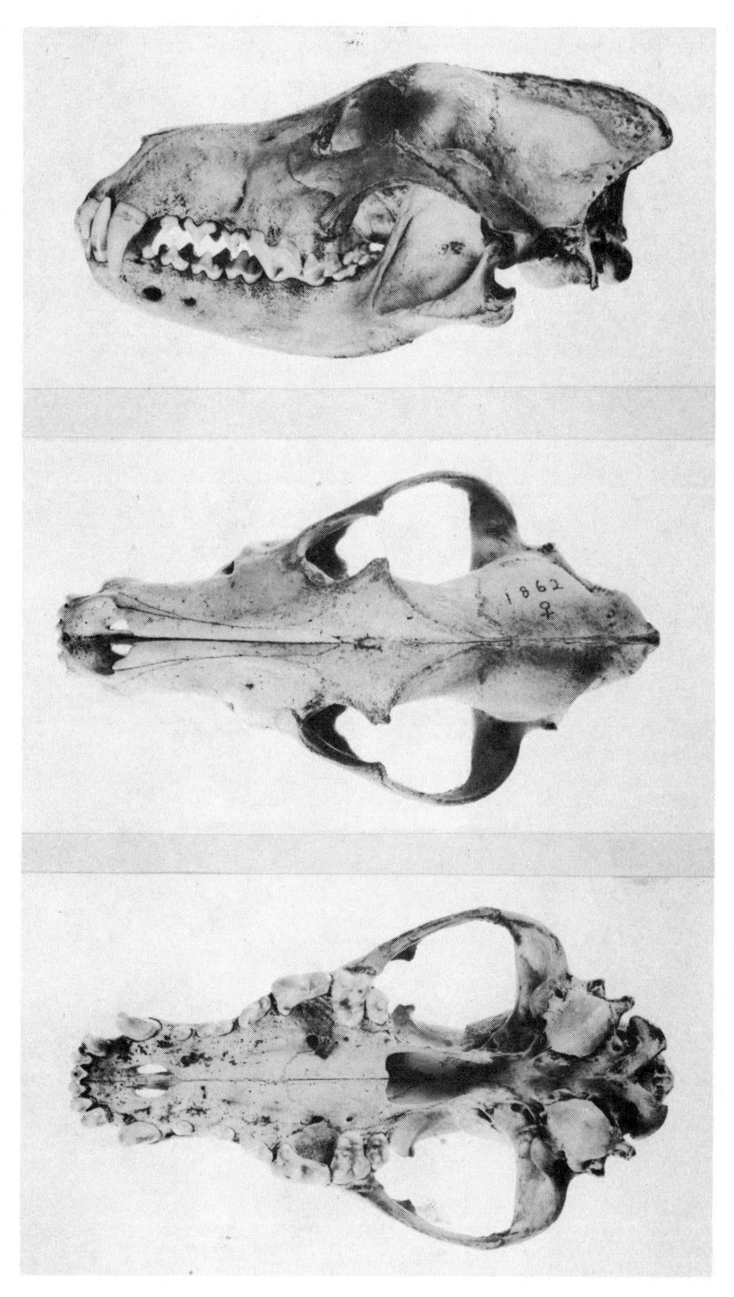

Plate 116. *Canis lupus crassodon* Hall; female adult; Alberni, British Columbia, Canada. (No. 1862, Brit. Col. Prov. Mus.) Note heavy dentition and form of upper carnassial with outer side longer than inner side. [One-third natural size]

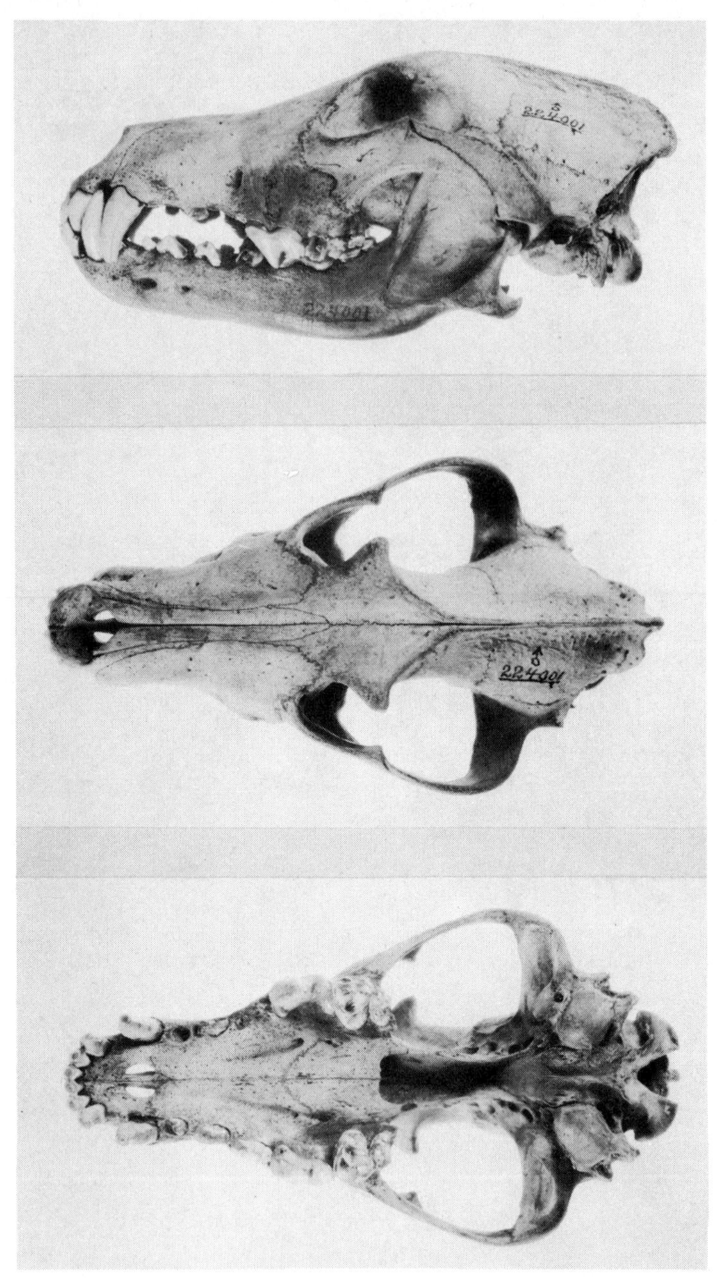

Plate 117. *Canis lupus youngi* Goldman; type; male adult; Harts Draw, 20 miles northwest of Monticello, Utah. (No. 224001, U. S. Nat. Mus., Biological Surveys collection.) Note large size, wide supraoccipital shield, and slight posterior projection of inion. [One-third natural size]

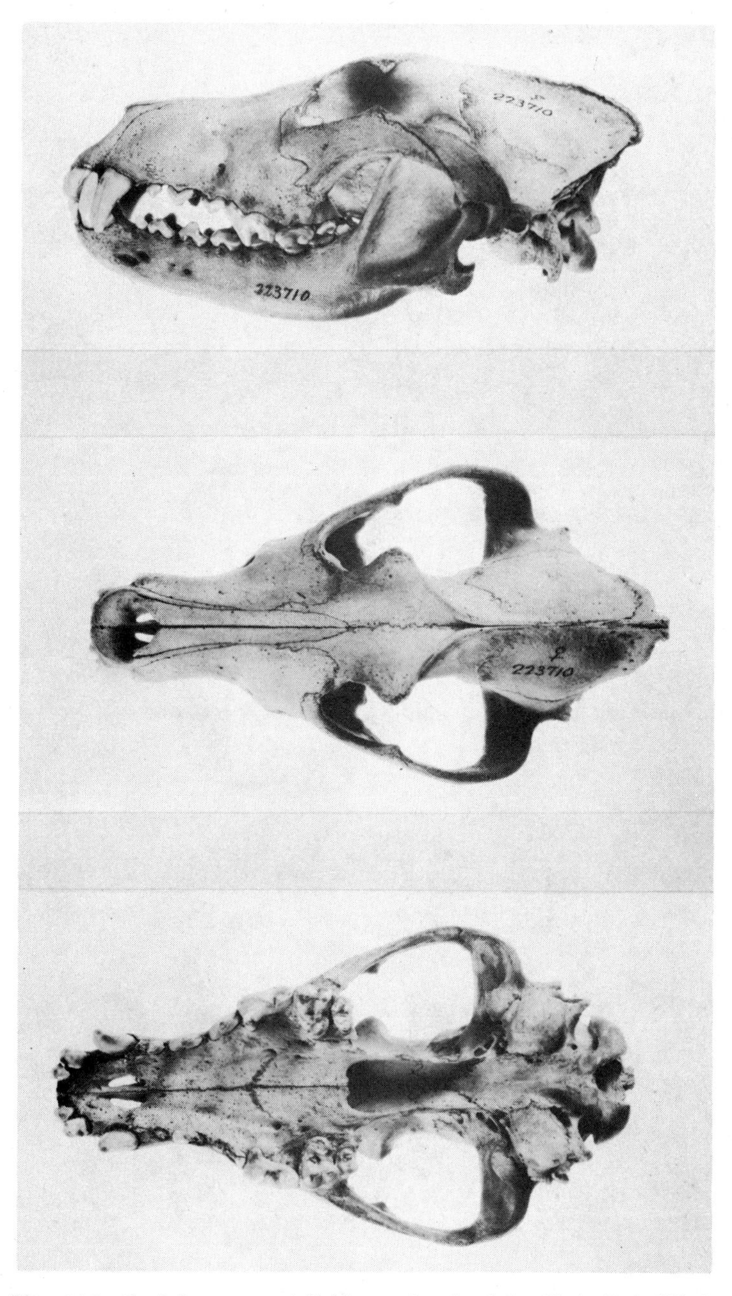

Plate 118. *Canis lupus youngi* Goldman; female adult; Glade Park (Black Ridge), Mesa County, Colorado. (No. 223710, U. S. Nat. Mus., Biological Surveys collection.) Note large size, wide supraoccipital shield, and slight posterior projection of inion. [One-third natural size]

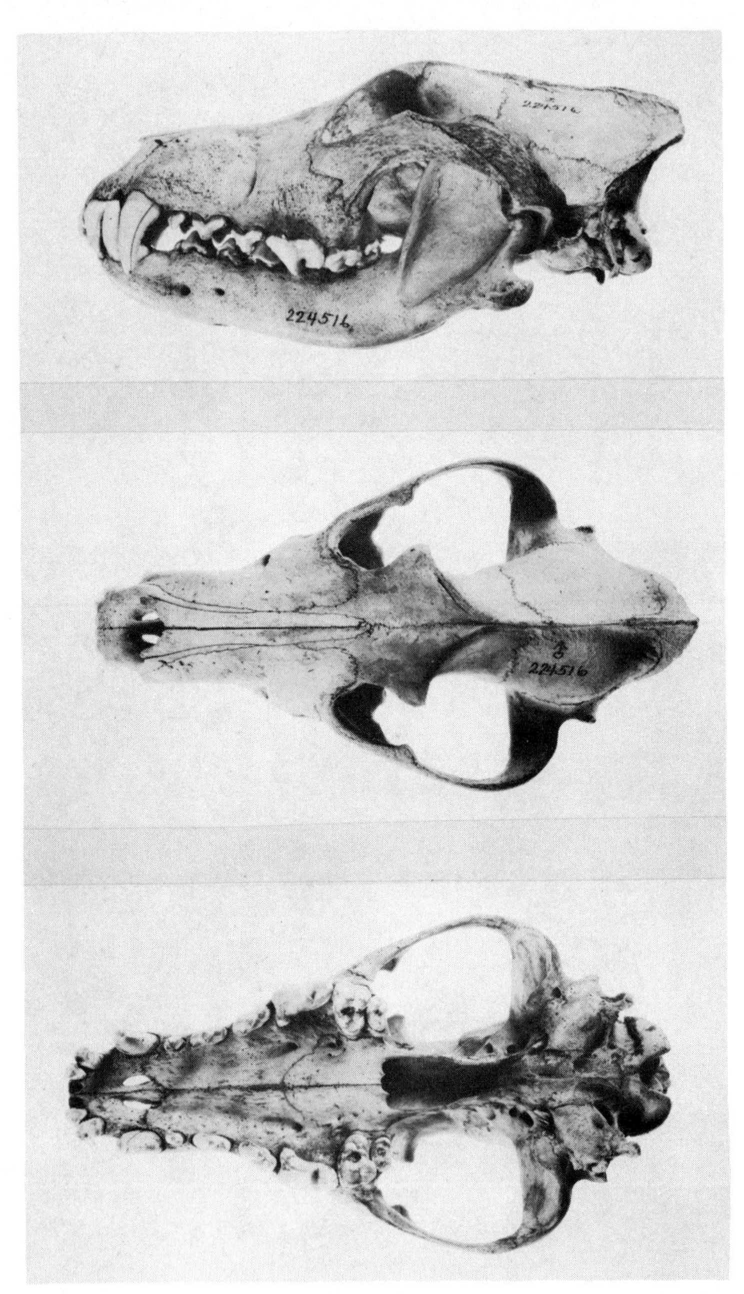

Plate 119. *Canis lupus mogollonensis* Goldman; male adult; Chloride, New Mexico. (No. 224516, U. S. Nat. Mus., Biological Surveys collection.) Note medium size (between *youngi* and *baileyi*). [One-third natural size]

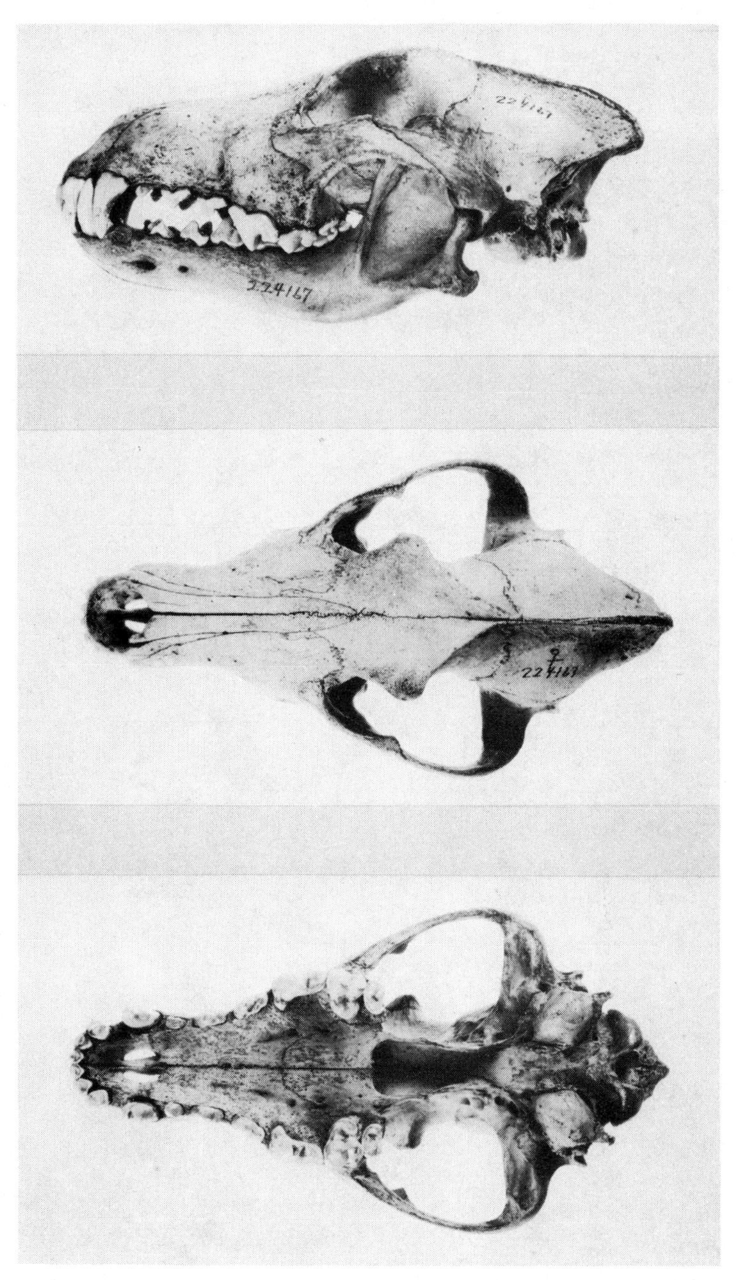

Plate 120. *Canis lupus mogollonensis* Goldman; female adult; Chloride, New Mexico. (No. 224167, U. S. Nat. Mus., Biological Surveys collection.) Note medium size (between *youngi* and *baileyi*). [One-third natural size]

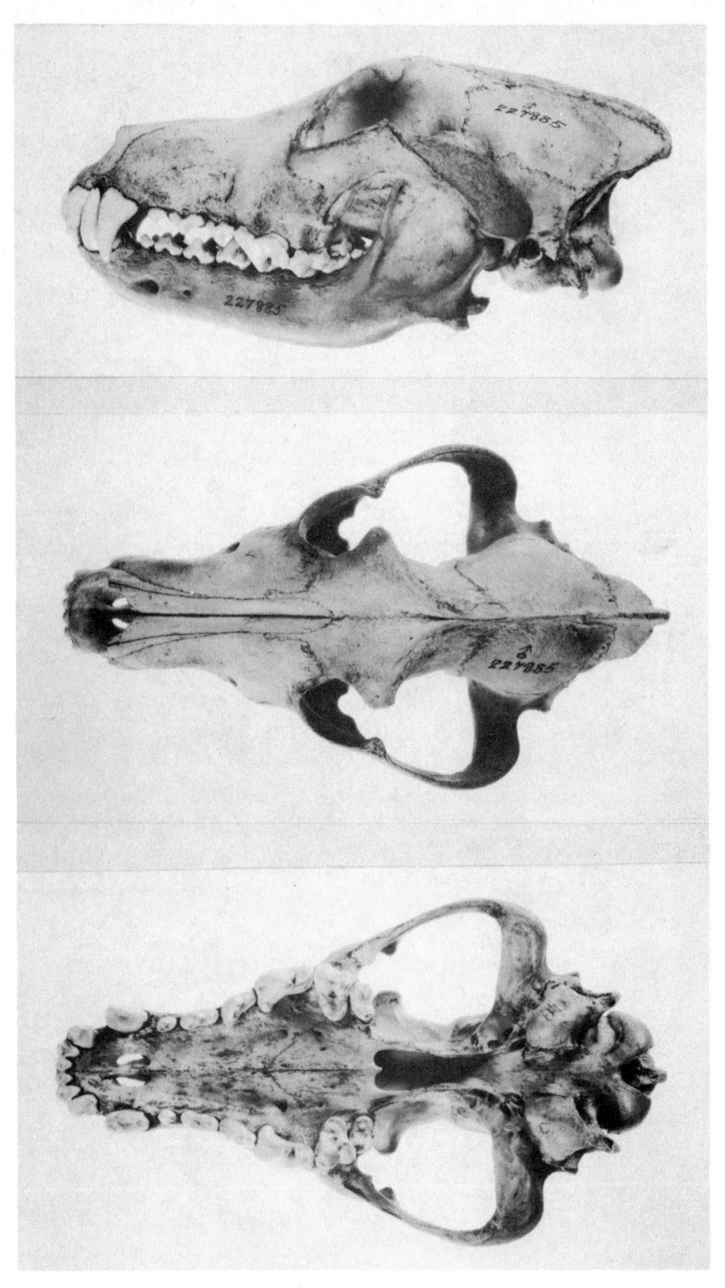

Plate 121. *Canis lupus monstrabilis* Goldman; male adult; Ozona (25 miles west), Texas. (No. 227885, U. S. Nat. Mus., Biological Surveys collection.) Note high arch of braincase. [One-third natural size]

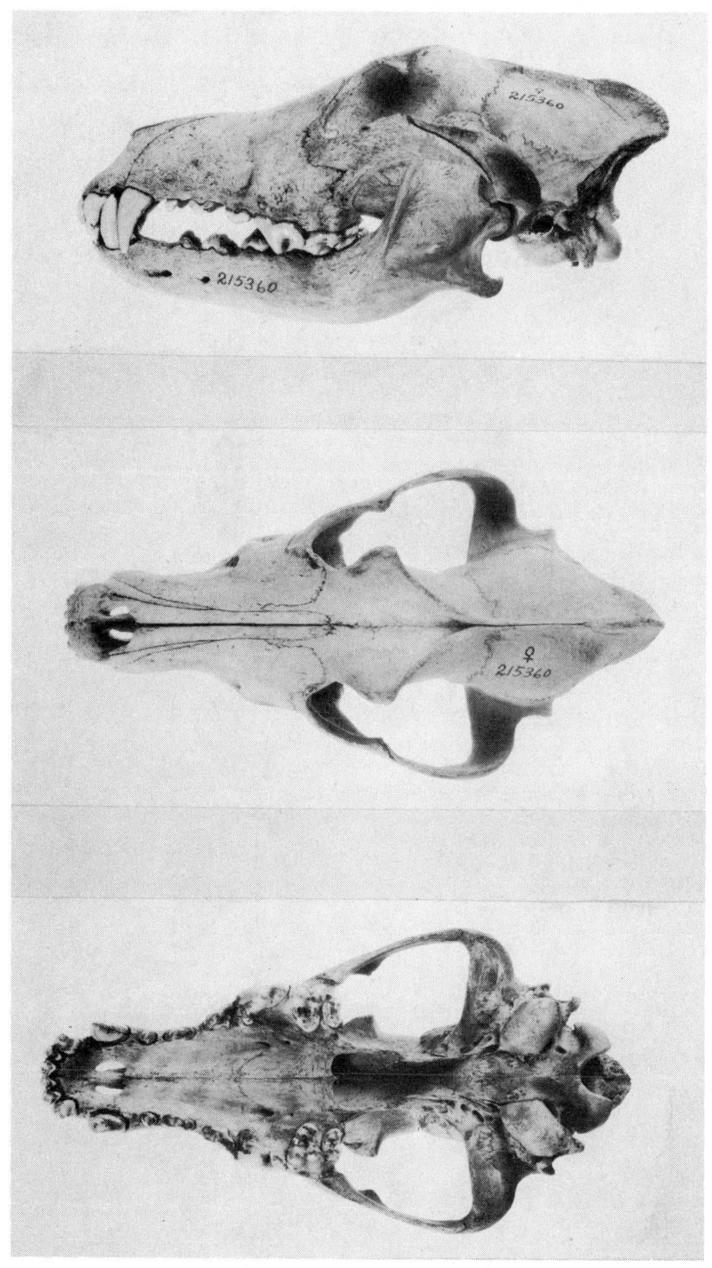

Plate 122. *Canis lupus monstrabilis* Goldman; female adult; Rankin (18 miles southeast), Texas. (No. 215360, U. S. Nat. Mus., Biological Surveys collection.) Note high arch of braincase. [One-third natural size]

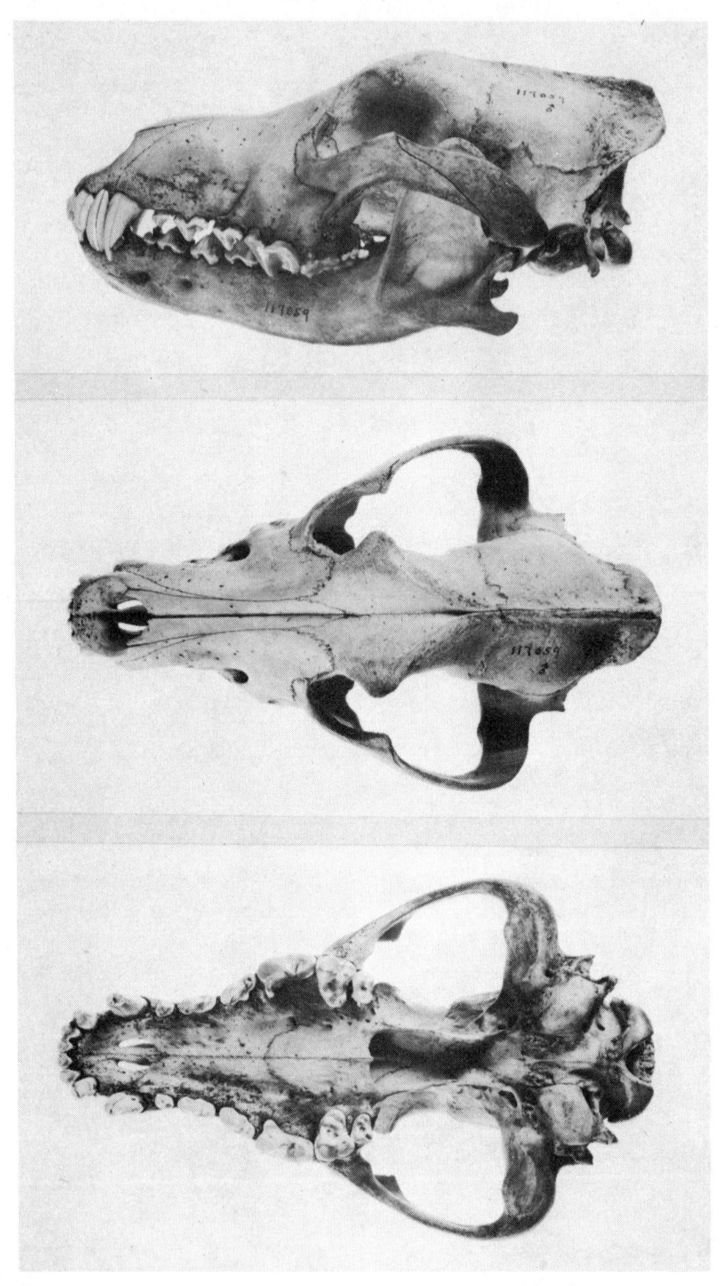

Plate 123. *Canis lupus baileyi* Nelson and Goldman; topotype; male adult; Colonia Garcia, Chihuahua, Mexico. (No. 117059, U. S. Nat. Mus. Biological Surveys collection.) Note small size, slender rostrum, and widely spreading zygomata. [One-third natural size]

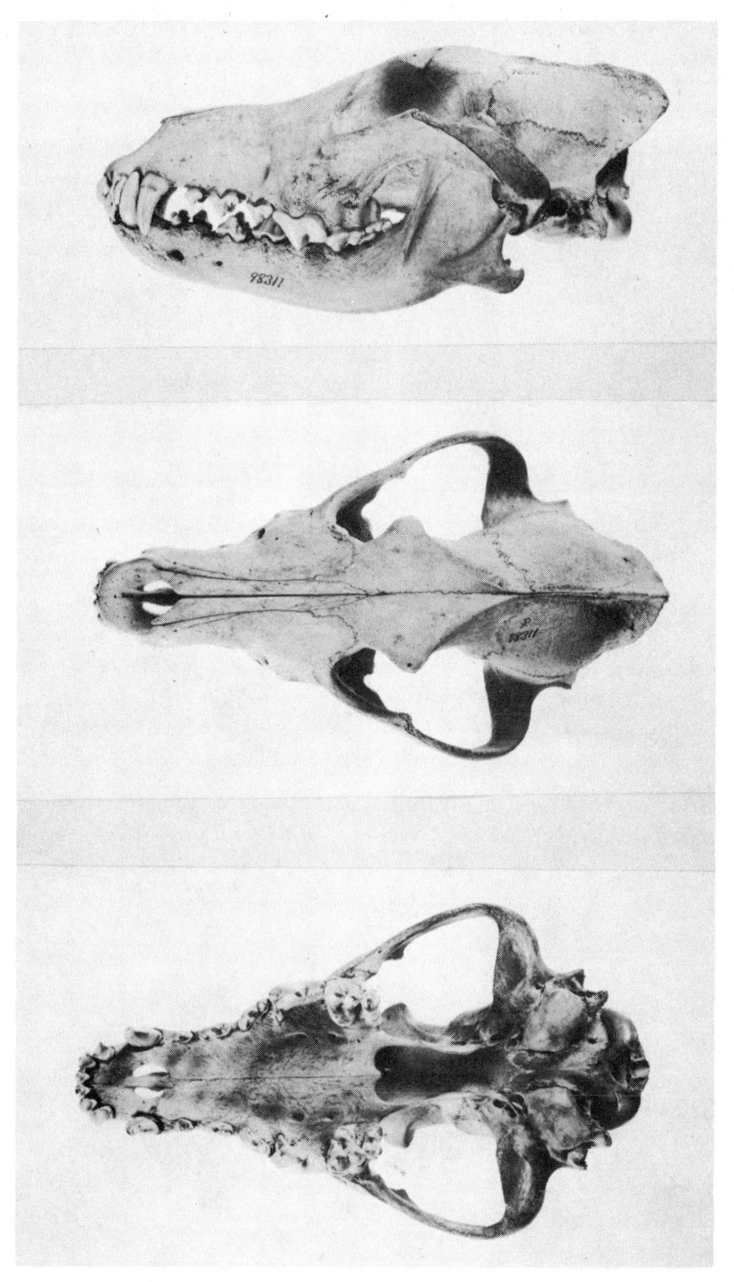

Plate 124. *Canis lupus baileyi* Nelson and Goldman; topotype; female adult; Colonia Garcia, Chihuahua, Mexico. (No. 98311, U. S. Nat. Mus., Biological Surveys collection.) Note small size, slender rostrum, and widely spreading zygomata. [One-third natural size]

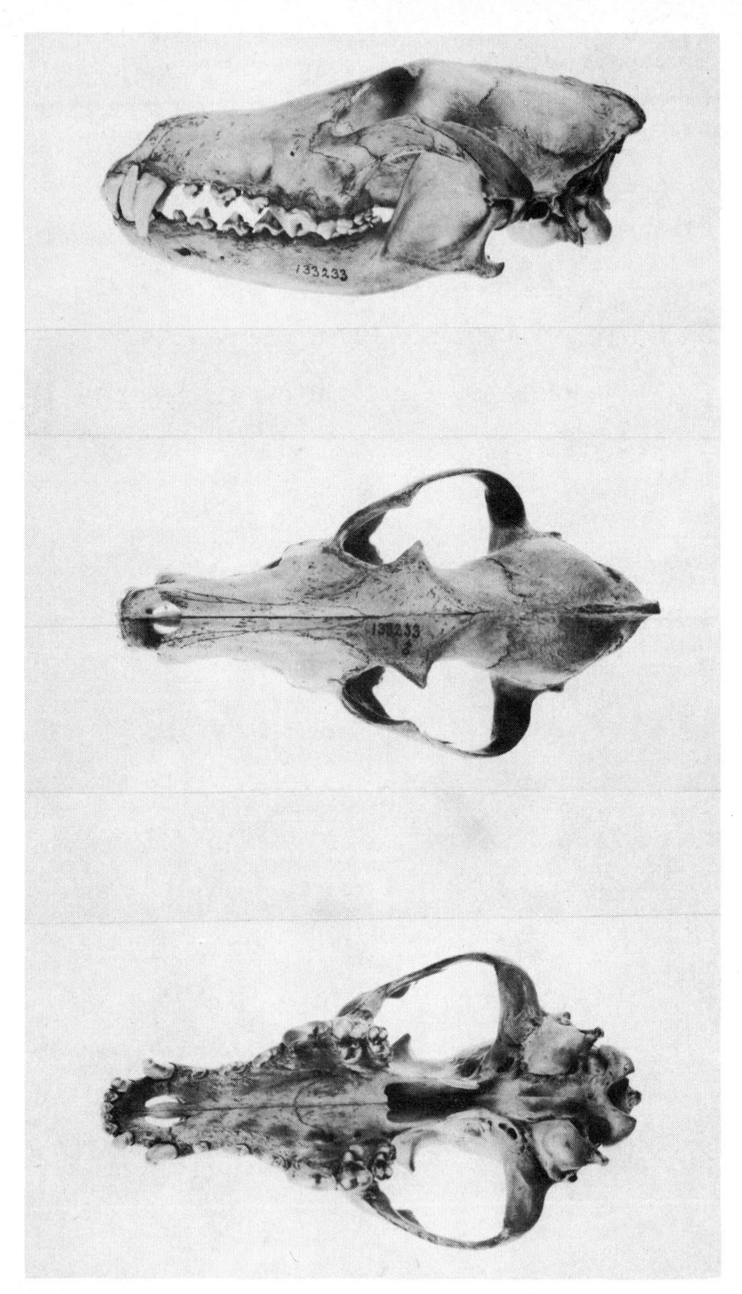

Plate 125. *Canis niger rufus* Audubon and Bachman; male adult; Red Fork, Oklahoma. (No. 133233, U. S. Nat. Mus., Biological Surveys collection.) Note small size and general resemblance to *Canis latrans;* orbits more strongly bowed outward; rostrum deeper. [One-third natural size]

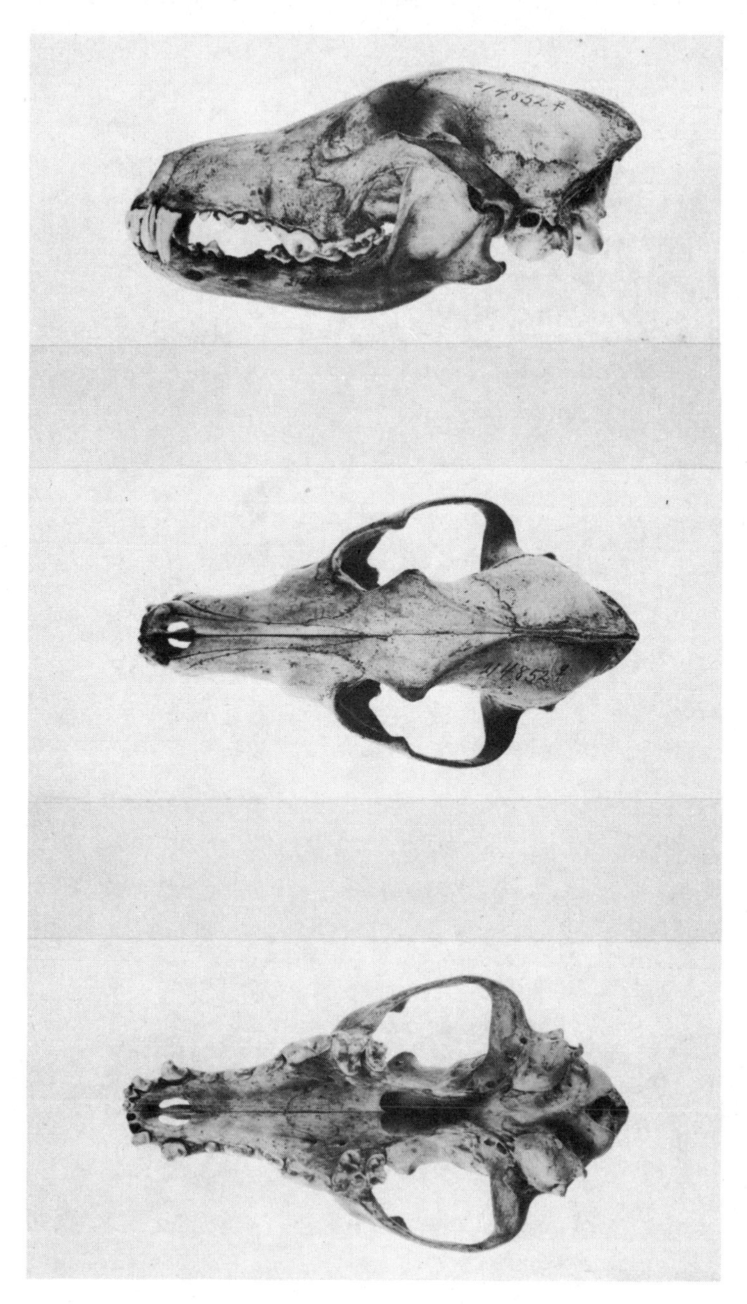

Plate 126. *Canis niger rufus* Audubon and Bachman; female adult; Llano (seven miles northwest), Texas. (No. 214852, U. S. Nat. Mus., Biological Surveys collection.) Note small size and general resemblance to *Canis latrans;* orbits more strongly bowed outward; rostrum deeper. [One-third natural size]

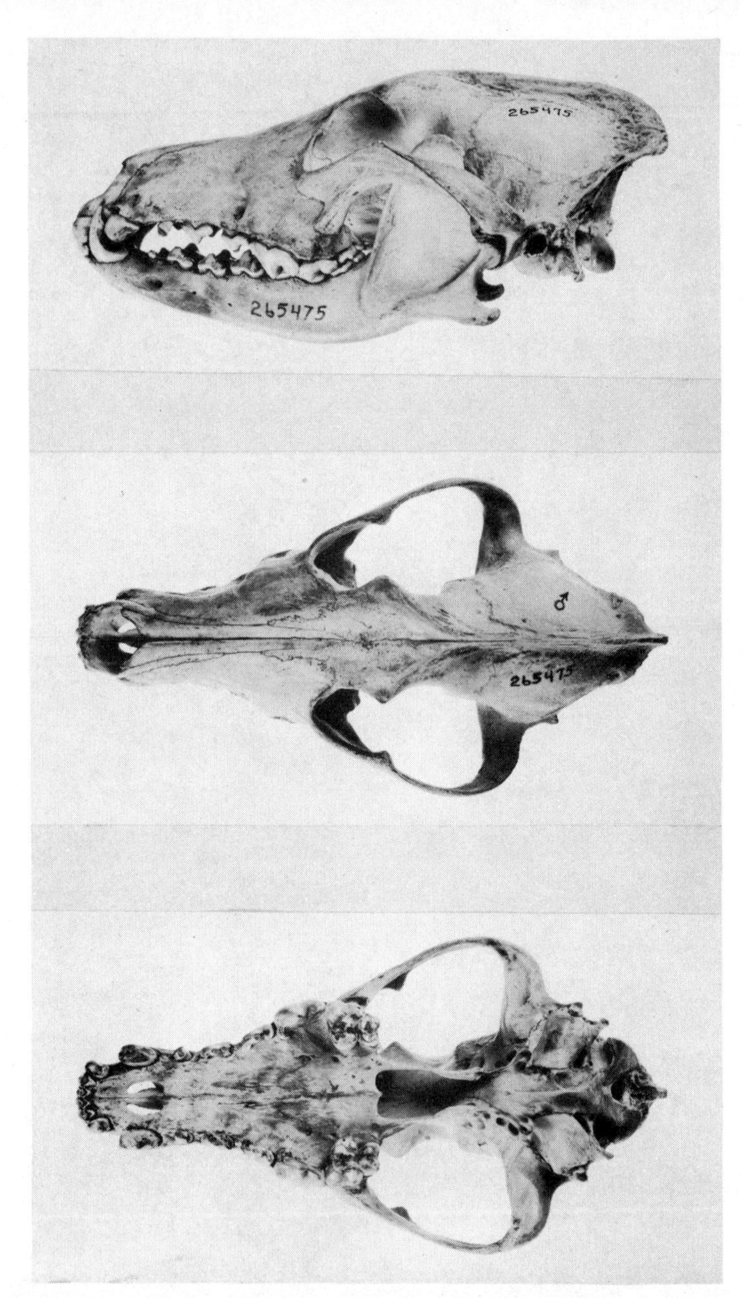

Plate 127. *Canis niger gregoryi* Goldman; male adult; Winn Parish, Louisiana. (No. 265475, U. S. Nat. Mus., Biological Surveys collection.) Note slender proportions and slight elevation of braincase. [One-third natural size]

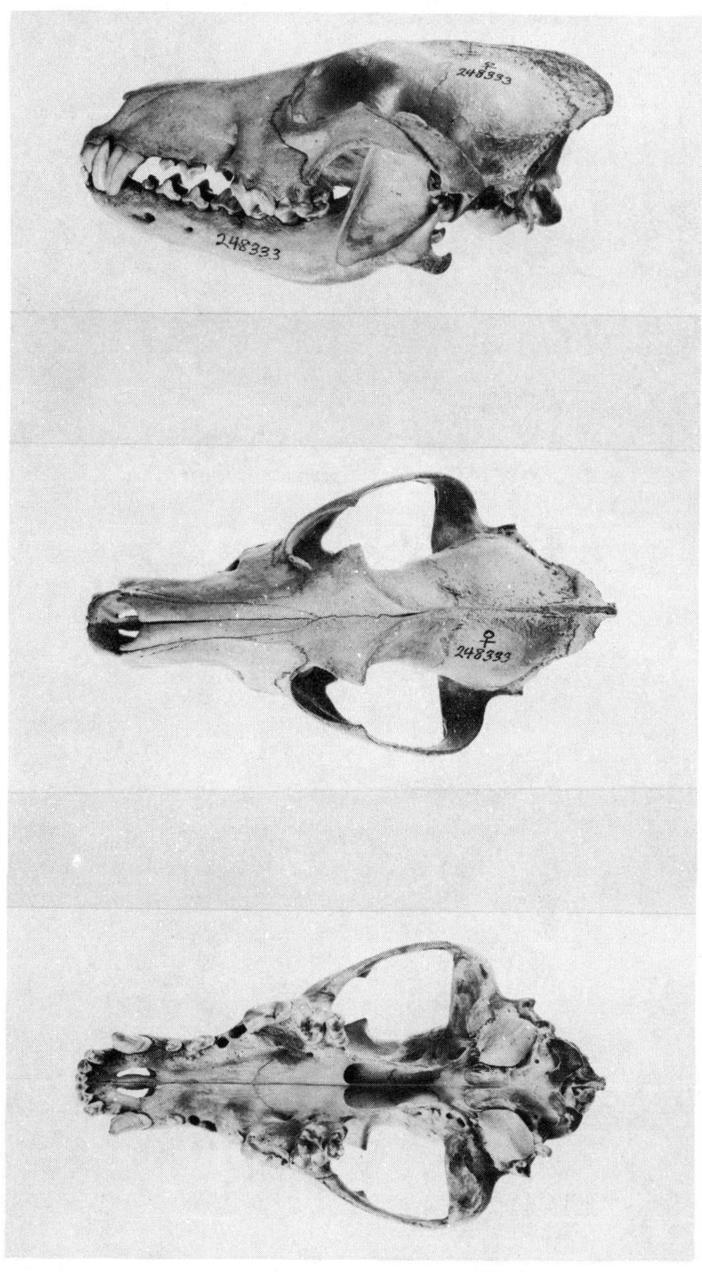

Plate 128. *Canis niger gregoryi* Goldman; female adult; Sabine River, Beauregard Parish, Louisiana. (No. 248333, U. S. Nat. Mus., Biological Surveys collection.) Note slender proportions and slight elevation of braincase. [One-third natural size]

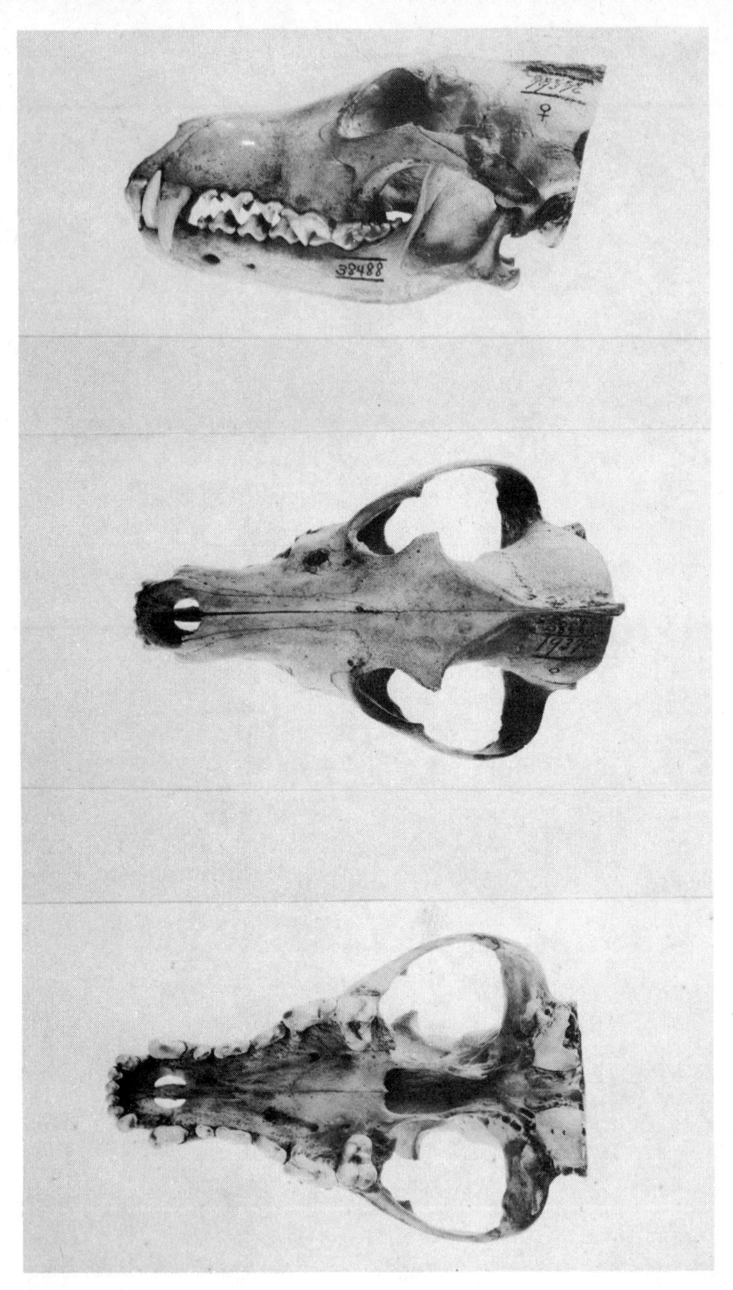

Plate 129. *Canis niger niger* Miller; female adult; Horse Landing, St. Johns River, about 12 miles south of Palatka, Florida. (No. 38488/19376 U. S. Nat. Mus.) Note large teeth. [One-third natural size]

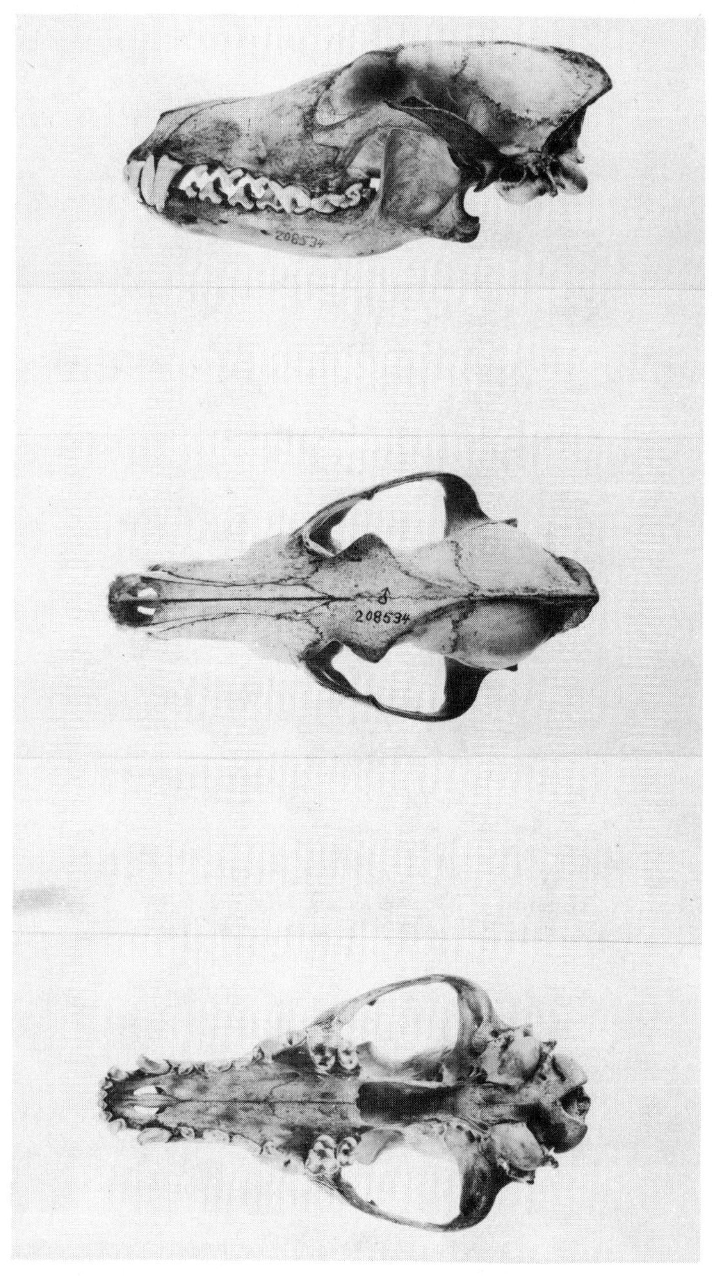

Plate 130. *Canis latrans texensis* Bailey; male adult; San Angelo, Texas. (No. 208534, U. S. Nat. Mus., Biological Surveys collection.) Note similarity to *Canis niger rufus*. [One-third natural size]

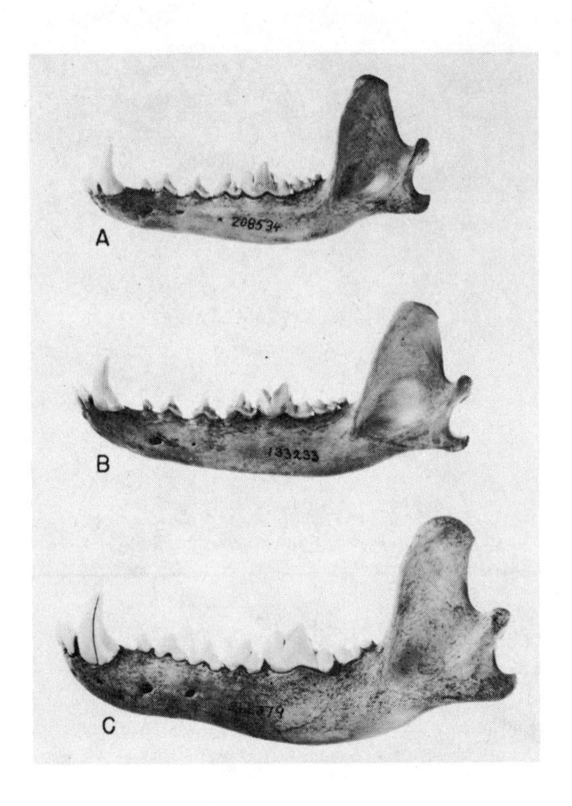

Plate 131. A. *Canis latrans texensis* Bailey; male adult; San Angelo, Texas. (No. 208534, U. S. Nat. Mus., Biological Surveys collection.) Note small size and deeply cleft crowns of cheek teeth. [One-third natural size]

B. *Canis niger rufus* Audubon and Bachman; male adult; Redfork, Oklahoma. (No. 133233, U. S. Nat. Mus., Biological Surveys collection.) Note resemblance to *Canis latrans texensis;* size larger. [One-third natural size]

C. *Canis lupus pambasileus* Elliot; male adult; Toklat River, Mount McKinley National Park, Alaska. (No. 266379, U. S. Nat. Mus., Biological Surveys collection.) Note large size and shallowly cleft crowns of cheek teeth. [One-third natural size]

INDEX

[Principal page references to a species in **boldface** type; synonyms in *italics*]

CATALOG OF DOVER BOOKS

Nature, Biology

NATURE RECREATION: Group Guidance for the Out-of-doors, William Gould Vinal. Intended for both the uninitiated nature instructor and the education student on the college level, this complete "how-to" program surveys the entire area of nature education for the young. Philosophy of nature recreation; requirements, responsibilities, important information for group leaders; nature games; suggested group projects; conducting meetings and getting discussions started; etc. Scores of immediately applicable teaching aids, plus completely updated sources of information, pamphlets, field guides, recordings, etc. Bibliography. 74 photographs. + 310pp. 5⅜ x 8½. T1015 Paperbound **$1.75**

HOW TO KNOW THE WILD FLOWERS, Mrs. William Starr Dana. Classic nature book that has introduced thousands to wonders of American wild flowers. Color-season principle of organization is easy to use, even by those with no botanical training, and the genial, refreshing discussions of history, folklore, uses of over 1,000 native and escape flowers, foliage plants are informative as well as fun to read. Over 170 full-page plates, collected from several editions, may be colored in to make permanent records of finds. Revised to conform with 1950 edition of Gray's Manual of Botany. xlii + 438pp. 5⅜ x 8½. T332 Paperbound **$1.85**

HOW TO KNOW THE FERNS, F. T. Parsons. Ferns, among our most lovely native plants, are all too little known. This classic of nature lore will enable the layman to identify almost any American fern he may come across. After an introduction on the structure and life of ferns, the 57 most important ferns are fully pictured and described (arranged upon a simple identification key). Index of Latin and English names. 61 illustrations and 42 full-page plates. xiv + 215pp. 5⅜ x 8. T740 Paperbound **$1.25**

MANUAL OF THE TREES OF NORTH AMERICA, Charles Sprague Sargent. Still unsurpassed as most comprehensive, reliable study of North American tree characteristics, precise locations and distribution. By dean of American dendrologists. Every tree native to U.S., Canada, Alaska, 185 genera, 717 species, described in detail—leaves, flowers, fruit, winterbuds, bark, wood, growth habits etc. plus discussion of varieties and local variants, immaturity variations. Over 100 keys, including unusual 11-page analytical key to genera, aid in identification. 783 clear illustrations of flowers, fruit, leaves. An unmatched permanent reference work for all nature lovers. Second enlarged (1926) edition. Synopsis of families. Analytical key to genera. Glossary of technical terms. Index. 783 illustrations, 1 map. Two volumes. Total of 982pp. 5⅜ x 8. T277 Vol. I Paperbound **$2.00**
T278 Vol. II Paperbound **$2.00**
The set **$4.00**

TREES OF THE EASTERN AND CENTRAL UNITED STATES AND CANADA, W. M. Harlow. A revised edition of a standard middle-level guide to native trees and important escapes. More than 140 trees are described in detail, and illustrated with more than 600 drawings and photographs. Supplementary keys will enable the careful reader to identify almost any tree he might encounter. xiii + 288pp. 5⅜ x 8. T395 Paperbound **$1.35**

GUIDE TO SOUTHERN TREES, Ellwood S. Harrar and J. George Harrar. All the essential information about trees indigenous to the South, in an extremely handy format. Introductory essay on methods of tree classification and study, nomenclature, chief divisions of Southern trees, etc. Approximately 100 keys and synopses allow for swift, accurate identification of trees. Numerous excellent illustrations, non-technical text make this a useful book for teachers of biology or natural science, nature lovers, amateur naturalists. Revised 1962 edition. Index. Bibliography. Glossary of technical terms. 920 illustrations; 201 full-page plates. ix + 709pp. 4⅝ x 6⅜. T945 Paperbound **$2.25**

FRUIT KEY AND TWIG KEY TO TREES AND SHRUBS, W. M. Harlow. Bound together in one volume for the first time, these handy and accurate keys to fruit and twig identification are the only guides of their sort with photographs (up to 3 times natural size). "Fruit Key": Key to over 120 different deciduous and evergreen fruits. 139 photographs and 11 line drawings. Synoptic summary of fruit types. Bibliography. 2 Indexes (common and scientific names). "Twig Key": Key to over 160 different twigs and buds. 173 photographs. Glossary of technical terms. Bibliography. 2 Indexes (common and scientific names). Two volumes bound as one. Total of xvii + 126pp. 5⅝ x 8⅜. T511 Paperbound **$1.25**

INSECT LIFE AND INSECT NATURAL HISTORY, S. W. Frost. A work emphasizing habits, social life, and ecological relations of insects, rather than more academic aspects of classification and morphology. Prof. Frost's enthusiasm and knowledge are everywhere evident as he discusses insect associations and specialized habits like leaf-rolling, leaf-mining, and case-making, the gall insects, the boring insects, aquatic insects, etc. He examines all sorts of matters not usually covered in general works, such as: insects as human food, insect music and musicians, insect response to electric and radio waves, use of insects in art and literature. The admirably executed purpose of this book, which covers the middle ground between elementary treatment and scholarly monographs, is to excite the reader to observe for himself. Over 700 illustrations. Extensive bibliography. x + 524pp. 5⅜ x 8. T517 Paperbound **$2.45**

CATALOGUE OF DOVER BOOKS

COMMON SPIDERS OF THE UNITED STATES, J. H. Emerton. Here is a nature hobby you can pursue right in your own cellar! Only non-technical, but thorough, reliable guide to spiders for the layman. Over 200 spiders from all parts of the country, arranged by scientific classification, are identified by shape and color, number of eyes, habitat and range, habits, etc. Full text, 501 line drawings and photographs, and valuable introduction explain webs, poisons, threads, capturing and preserving spiders, etc. Index. New synoptic key by S. W. Frost. xxiv + 225pp. 5⅜ x 8. T223 Paperbound **$1.35**

THE LIFE STORY OF THE FISH: HIS MANNERS AND MORALS, Brian Curtis. A comprehensive, non-technical survey of just about everything worth knowing about fish. Written for the aquarist, the angler, and the layman with an inquisitive mind, the text covers such topics as evolution, external covering and protective coloration, physics and physiology of vision, maintenance of equilibrium, function of the lateral line canal for auditory and temperature senses, nervous system, function of the air bladder, reproductive system and methods—courtship, mating, spawning, care of young—and many more. Also sections on game fish, the problems of conservation and a fascinating chapter on fish curiosities. "Clear, simple language . . . excellent judgment in choice of subjects . . . delightful sense of humor," New York Times. Revised (1949) edition. Index. Bibliography of 72 items. 6 full-page photographic plates. xii + 284pp. 5⅜ x 8. T929 Paperbound **$1.50**

BATS, Glover Morrill Allen. The most comprehensive study of bats as a life-form by the world's foremost authority. A thorough summary of just about everything known about this fascinating and mysterious flying mammal, including its unique location sense, hibernation and cycles, its habitats and distribution, its wing structure and flying habits, and its relationship to man in the long history of folklore and superstition. Written on a middle-level, the book can be profitably studied by a trained zoologist and thoroughly enjoyed by the layman. "An absorbing text with excellent illustrations. Bats should have more friends and fewer thoughtless detractors as a result of the publication of this volume," William Beebe, Books. Extensive bibliography. 57 photographs and illustrations. x + 368pp. 5⅜ x 8½. T984 Paperbound **$2.00**

BIRDS AND THEIR ATTRIBUTES, Glover Morrill Allen. A fine general introduction to birds as living organisms, especially valuable because of emphasis on structure, physiology, habits, behavior. Discusses relationship of bird to man, early attempts at scientific ornithology, feathers and coloration, skeletal structure including bills, legs and feet, wings. Also food habits, evolution and present distribution, feeding and nest-building, still unsolved questions of migrations and location sense, many more similar topics. Final chapter on classification, nomenclature. A good popular-level summary for the biologist; a first-rate introduction for the layman. Reprint of 1925 edition. References and index. 51 illustrations. viii + 338pp. 5⅜ x 8½. T957 Paperbound **$1.85**

LIFE HISTORIES OF NORTH AMERICAN BIRDS, Arthur Cleveland Bent. Bent's monumental series of books on North American birds, prepared and published under auspices of Smithsonian Institute, is the definitive coverage of the subject, the most-used single source of information. Now the entire set is to be made available by Dover in inexpensive editions. This encyclopedic collection of detailed, specific observations utilizes reports of hundreds of contemporary observers, writings of such naturalists as Audubon, Burroughs, William Brewster, as well as author's own extensive investigations. Contains literally everything known about life history of each bird considered: nesting, eggs, plumage, distribution and migration, voice, enemies, courtship, etc. These not over-technical works are musts for ornithologists, conservationists, amateur naturalists, anyone seriously interested in American birds.

BIRDS OF PREY. More than 100 subspecies of hawks, falcons, eagles, buzzards, condors and owls, from the common barn owl to the extinct caracara of Guadaloupe Island. 400 photographs. Two volume set. Index for each volume. Bibliographies of 403, 520 items. 197 full-page plates. Total of 907pp. 5⅜ x 8½. Vol. I T931 Paperbound **$2.35**
Vol. II T932 Paperbound **$2.35**

WILD FOWL. Ducks, geese, swans, and tree ducks—73 different subspecies. Two volume set. Index for each volume. Bibliographies of 124, 144 items. 106 full-page plates. Total of 685pp. 5⅜ x 8½. Vol. I T285 Paperbound **$2.35**
Vol. II T286 Paperbound **$2.35**

SHORE BIRDS. 81 varieties (sandpipers, woodcocks, plovers, snipes, phalaropes, curlews, oyster catchers, etc.). More than 200 photographs of eggs, nesting sites, adult and young of important species. Two volume set. Index for each volume. Bibliographies of 261, 188 items. 121 full-page plates. Total of 860pp. 5⅜ x 8½. Vol. I T933 Paperbound **$2.35**
Vol. II T934 Paperbound **$2.35**

THE LIFE OF PASTEUR, R. Vallery-Radot. 13th edition of this definitive biography, cited in Encyclopaedia Britannica. Authoritative, scholarly, well-documented with contemporary quotes, observations; gives complete picture of Pasteur's personal life; especially thorough presentation of scientific activities with silkworms, fermentation, hydrophobia, inoculation, etc. Introduction by Sir William Osler. Index. 505pp. 5⅜ x 8. T632 Paperbound **$2.00**

AMERICAN WILDLIFE AND PLANTS: A GUIDE TO WILDLIFE FOOD HABITS, Alexander C. Martin, Herbert S. Zim, and Arnold L. Nelson. A tremendous amount of material from 25 years of concentrated researches by U.S. Fish and Wildlife Service is collected, correlated, condensed into this 500-page volume. Learn of food, feeding habits of more than 1,000 species of U.S. mammals, birds, fish, their distribution and migratory habits, the most important plant-animal relationships. Last third of book devoted to all genera of plants that furnish food to American wildlife. ". . . should prove a classic in its field and a must for every naturalist," Harold E. Anthony, NATURAL HISTORY. Republication of first (1951) edition. Index. Hundreds of illustrations, tables, range maps, etc. ix + 500pp. 5⅜ x 8. T793 Paperbound **$2.25**

RACING PIGEONS, C. Osman. A complete, practical, up-to-date, and authoritative book on racing pigeons by a British expert. Covers the anatomy of the pigeon, the homing instinct, the pigeon's life cycle, food and feeding, lofts and aviaries, breeding winners, preparing for races, winning systems, common diseases, and much more. Indispensable for beginner and expert alike. 24 photographs by the author. 10 line drawings. Index. 192pp. 5⅛ x 7⅛.
T513 Clothbound **$3.00**

ANTONY VAN LEEUWENHOEK AND HIS "LITTLE ANIMALS," selected, translated, and edited from his printed works, unpublished manuscripts, contemporary records by Clifford Dobell. 100-page biographical study of the first microbiologist, bacteriologist, micrologist. 4 chapters of the papers that founded protozoology, bacteriology, with many of Leeuwenhoek's illustrative drawings, observations and letters to Royal Society, discussion of Leeuwenhoek's name, language, dwelling, draughtsmen, method, microscope bring to life an excited, naive, completely self-taught genius. 25 years of research went into its compilation by a Fellow of the Royal Society. More than an important book for students and workers in the sciences, it may also be read with pleasure by anyone interested in meeting one of the most interesting and remarkable men in history of science. 32 illustrations. Bibliography of over 400 items. Index. vii + 435pp. 5⅜ x 8. S594 Paperbound **$2.25**

MICROGRAPHIA, Robert Hooke. Hooke, 17th-century British universal genius, was a major pioneer in celestial mechanics, optics, gravity, and many other fields, but his greatest contribution was this book, now reprinted in its entirety from the original 1655 edition, which gave microscopy its first great impetus. With all the freshness of discovery, he describes his microscope, and his observations of cork, the edge of a razor, insects' eyes, fabrics, and dozens of other objects. 38 plates, full-size or larger, contain all the original illustrations. A fundamental classic in the fields of combustion and heat theory, light and color theory, botany and zoology, hygrometry, and many others. Contains such farsighted predictions as the famous anticipation of artificial silk. Final section is concerned with Hooke's observations of the moon and stars. 348pp. 5⅜ x 8½. T8 Paperbound **$2.00**

THE AUTOBIOGRAPHY OF CHARLES DARWIN AND SELECTED LETTERS, edited by Francis Darwin. The personal record of the professional and private life of the author of "Origin of Species," whose ideas have shaped our thinking as have few others. His early life; the historic voyage aboard the "Beagle"; the furor surrounding evolution and his replies; revealing anecdotes; reminiscences by his son; letters to Henslow, Lyell, Hooker, Huxley, Wallace, Kingsley, and others; his thought on religion and vivisection. Appendix. Index. 365pp. 5⅜ x 8.
T479 Paperbound **$1.65**

THE MALAY ARCHIPELAGO, Alfred Russel Wallace. A great classic of natural history and travel. The observations of one of the founders of modern biology whose work also provides foundation for scientific study of botany and zoology in many parts of the world. Based on 8 years' personal exploration. Descriptions of the island groupings and peoples, accounts of abundant, strange animals, startling birds and insects—many previously unknown—on either side of the Wallace line, dividing animal life into Indian on the West and Australian on the East and named for the author. Unrivalled travel experience, packed full of intellectual excitement, infectious enthusiasm, this will arouse the empathy of any lay reader interested in strange places and new theories. 62 drawings and maps. Three appendices on crania, 59 languages, and vocabularies. Index. xvii + 515pp. 5⅜ x 8½.
T187 Paperbound **$2.00**

STUDIES ON THE STRUCTURE AND DEVELOPMENT OF VERTEBRATES, Edwin S. Goodrich. This definitive study by the greatest modern comparative anatomist covers the skeleton, fins and limbs, head region morphology, skull, skeletal visceral arches and labial cartilages, middle ear and ear ossicles, visceral clefts and gills, subdivisions of body cavity, vascular, respiratory, excretory, and peripheral nervous systems of vertebrates from fish to the higher mammals. 754 pictures. 69 page biographical study by C. C. Hardy. Bibliography of 1186 references. "For many a day this will certainly be the standard textbook," Journal of Anatomy. Index. Two volumes total 906pp. 5⅜ x 8. 2 volume set S449-50 Paperbound **$5.00**

FINGER PRINTS, PALMS AND SOLES: AN INTRODUCTION TO DERMATOGLYPHICS, Harold Cummins and Charles Midlo. One of the most fascinating of sciences receives careful, thorough treatment. Primitive knowledge of dermatoglyphics; early investigators; fundamental patterns and pattern types; technical methods of classification, identification. Detailed, unique descriptions of uses: identification of twins; paternity cases; racial variation; genetic process; relation of prints to body measurement, criminality and character, blood groups, handedness. New chapter adds information on identification in action, with accounts of criminal cases in which prints played major role. 2nd enlarged edition. 149 figures. 49 tables. 361-item bibliography. Index. xii + 319pp. 5⅝ x 8⅜. T778 Paperbound **$1.95**

Psychology

YOGA: A SCIENTIFIC EVALUATION, Kovoor T. Behanan. A complete reprinting of the book that for the first time gave Western readers a sane, scientific explanation and analysis of yoga. The author draws on controlled laboratory experiments and personal records of a year as a disciple of a yoga, to investigate yoga psychology, concepts of knowledge, physiology, "supernatural" phenomena, and the ability to tap the deepest human powers. In this study under the auspices of Yale University Institute of Human Relations, the strictest principles of physiological and psychological inquiry are followed throughout. Foreword by W. A. Miles, Yale University. 17 photographs. Glossary. Index. xx + 270pp. 5⅜ x 8. T505 Paperbound **$1.75**

CONDITIONED REFLEXES: AN INVESTIGATION OF THE PHYSIOLOGICAL ACTIVITIES OF THE CEREBRAL CORTEX, I. P. Pavlov. Full, authorized translation of Pavlov's own survey of his work in experimental psychology reviews entire course of experiments, summarizes conclusions, outlines psychological system based on famous "conditioned reflex" concept. Details of technical means used in experiments, observations on formation of conditioned reflexes, function of cerebral hemispheres, results of damage, nature of sleep, typology of nervous system, significance of experiments for human psychology. Trans. by Dr. G. V. Anrep, Cambridge Univ. 235-item bibliography. 18 figures. 445pp. 5⅜ x 8. S614 Paperbound **$2.25**

EXPLANATION OF HUMAN BEHAVIOUR, F. V. Smith. A major intermediate-level introduction to and criticism of 8 complete systems of the psychology of human behavior, with unusual emphasis on theory of investigation and methodology. Part I is an illuminating analysis of the problems involved in the explanation of observed phenomena, and the differing viewpoints on the nature of causality. Parts II and III are a closely detailed survey of the systems of McDougall, Gordon Allport, Lewin, the Gestalt group, Freud, Watson, Hull, and Tolman. Biographical notes. Bibliography of over 800 items. 2 Indexes. 38 figures. xii + 460pp. 5½ x 8¾.
T253 Clothbound **$6.00**

SEX IN PSYCHO-ANALYSIS (formerly CONTRIBUTIONS TO PSYCHO-ANALYSIS), S. Ferenczi. Written by an associate of Freud, this volume presents countless insights on such topics as impotence, transference, analysis and children, dreams, symbols, obscene words, masturbation and male homosexuality, paranoia and psycho-analysis, the sense of reality, hypnotism and therapy, and many others. Also includes full text of THE DEVELOPMENT OF PSYCHO-ANALYSIS by Ferenczi and Otto Rank. Two books bound as one. Total of 406pp. 5⅜ x 8.
T324 Paperbound **$1.85**

BEYOND PSYCHOLOGY, Otto Rank. One of Rank's most mature contributions, focussing on the irrational basis of human behavior as a basic fact of our lives. The psychoanalytic techniques of myth analysis trace to their source the ultimates of human existence: fear of death, personality, the social organization, the need for love and creativity, etc. Dr. Rank finds them stemming from a common irrational source, man's fear of final destruction. A seminal work in modern psychology, this work sheds light on areas ranging from the concept of immortal soul to the sources of state power. 291pp. 5⅜ x 8. T485 Paperbound **$1.75**

ILLUSIONS AND DELUSIONS OF THE SUPERNATURAL AND THE OCCULT, D. H. Rawcliffe. Holds up to rational examination hundreds of persistent delusions including crystal gazing, automatic writing, table turning, mediumistic trances, mental healing, stigmata, lycanthropy, live burial, the Indian Rope Trick, spiritualism, dowsing, telepathy, clairvoyance, ghosts, ESP, etc. The author explains and exposes the mental and physical deceptions involved, making this not only an exposé of supernatural phenomena, but a valuable exposition of characteristic types of abnormal psychology. Originally titled "The Psychology of the Occult." 14 illustrations. Index. 551pp. 5⅜ x 8. T503 Paperbound **$2.00**

THE PRINCIPLES OF PSYCHOLOGY, William James. The full long-course, unabridged, of one of the great classics of Western literature and science. Wonderfully lucid descriptions of human mental activity, the stream of thought, consciousness, time perception, memory, imagination, emotions, reason, abnormal phenomena, and similar topics. Original contributions are integrated with the work of such men as Berkeley, Binet, Mills, Darwin, Hume, Kant, Royce, Schopenhauer, Spinoza, Locke, Descartes, Galton, Wundt, Lotze, Herbart, Fechner, and scores of others. All contrasting interpretations of mental phenomena are examined in detail — introspective analysis, philosophical interpretation, and experimental research. "A classic," JOURNAL OF CONSULTING PSYCHOLOGY. "The main lines are as valid as ever," PSYCHOANALYTICAL QUARTERLY. "Standard reading . . . a classic of interpretation," PSYCHIATRIC QUARTERLY. 94 illustrations. 1408pp. 2 volumes. 5⅜ x 8. Vol. 1, T381 Paperbound **$2.50**
Vol. 2, T382 Paperbound **$2.50**

THE DYNAMICS OF THERAPY IN A CONTROLLED RELATIONSHIP, Jessie Taft. One of the most important works in literature of child psychology, out of print for 25 years. Outstanding disciple of Rank describes all aspects of relationship or Rankian therapy through concise, simple elucidation of theory underlying her actual contacts with two seven-year olds. Therapists, social caseworkers, psychologists, counselors, and laymen who work with children will all find this important work an invaluable summation of method, theory of child psychology. xix + 296pp. 5⅜ x 8. T325 Paperbound **$1.75**

Puzzles, Mathematical Recreations

SYMBOLIC LOGIC and THE GAME OF LOGIC, Lewis Carroll. "Symbolic Logic" is not concerned with modern symbolic logic, but is instead a collection of over 380 problems posed with charm and imagination, using the syllogism, and a fascinating diagrammatic method of drawing conclusions. In "The Game of Logic" Carroll's whimsical imagination devises a logical game played with 2 diagrams and counters (included) to manipulate hundreds of tricky syllogisms. The final section, "Hit or Miss" is a lagniappe of 101 additional puzzles in the delightful Carroll manner. Until this reprint edition, both of these books were rarities costing up to $15 each. Symbolic Logic: Index. xxxi + 199pp. The Game of Logic: 96pp. 2 vols. bound as one. 5⅜ x 8. T492 Paperbound **$1.50**

PILLOW PROBLEMS and A TANGLED TALE, Lewis Carroll. One of the rarest of all Carroll's works, "Pillow Problems" contains 72 original math puzzles, all typically ingenious. Particularly fascinating are Carroll's answers which remain exactly as he thought them out, reflecting his actual mental process. The problems in "A Tangled Tale" are in story form, originally appearing as a monthly magazine serial. Carroll not only gives the solutions, but uses answers sent in by readers to discuss wrong approaches and misleading paths, and grades them for insight. Both of these books were rarities until this edition, "Pillow Problems" costing up to $25, and "A Tangled Tale" $15. Pillow Problems: Preface and Introduction by Lewis Carroll. xx + 109pp. A Tangled Tale: 6 illustrations. 152pp. Two vols. bound as one. 5⅜ x 8. T493 Paperbound **$1.50**

AMUSEMENTS IN MATHEMATICS, Henry Ernest Dudeney. The foremost British originator of mathematical puzzles is always intriguing, witty, and paradoxical in this classic, one of the largest collections of mathematical amusements. More than 430 puzzles, problems, and paradoxes. Mazes and games, problems on number manipulation, unicursal and other route problems, puzzles on measuring, weighing, packing, age, kinship, chessboards, joiners', crossing river, plane figure dissection, and many others. Solutions. More than 450 illustrations. vii + 258pp. 5⅜ x 8. T473 Paperbound **$1.25**

THE CANTERBURY PUZZLES, Henry Dudeney. Chaucer's pilgrims set one another problems in story form. Also Adventures of the Puzzle Club, the Strange Escape of the King's Jester, the Monks of Riddlewell, the Squire's Christmas Puzzle Party, and others. All puzzles are original, based on dissecting plane figures, arithmetic, algebra, elementary calculus and other branches of mathematics, and purely logical ingenuity. "The limit of ingenuity and intricacy," The Observer. Over 110 puzzles. Full Solutions. 150 illustrations. vii + 225pp. 5⅜ x 8. T474 Paperbound **$1.25**

MATHEMATICAL EXCURSIONS, H. A. Merrill. Even if you hardly remember your high school math, you'll enjoy the 90 stimulating problems contained in this book and you will come to understand a great many mathematical principles with surprisingly little effort. Many useful shortcuts and diversions not generally known are included: division by inspection, Russian peasant multiplication, memory systems for pi, building odd and even magic squares, square roots by geometry, dyadic systems, and many more. Solutions to difficult problems. 50 illustrations. 145pp. 5⅜ x 8. T350 Paperbound **$1.00**

MAGIC SQUARES AND CUBES, W. S. Andrews. Only book-length treatment in English, a thorough non-technical description and analysis. Here are nasik, overlapping, pandiagonal, serrated squares; magic circles, cubes, spheres, rhombuses. Try your hand at 4-dimensional magical figures! Much unusual folklore and tradition included. High school algebra is sufficient. 754 diagrams and illustrations. viii + 419pp. 5⅜ x 8. T658 Paperbound **$1.85**

CALIBAN'S PROBLEM BOOK: MATHEMATICAL, INFERENTIAL AND CRYPTOGRAPHIC PUZZLES, H. Phillips (Caliban), S. T. Shovelton, G. S. Marshall. 105 ingenious problems by the greatest living creator of puzzles based on logic and inference. Rigorous, modern, piquant; reflecting their author's unusual personality, these intermediate and advanced puzzles all involve the ability to reason clearly through complex situations; some call for mathematical knowledge, ranging from algebra to number theory. Solutions. xi + 180pp. 5⅜ x 8. T736 Paperbound **$1.25**

MATHEMATICAL PUZZLES FOR BEGINNERS AND ENTHUSIASTS, G. Mott-Smith. 188 mathematical puzzles based on algebra, dissection of plane figures, permutations, and probability, that will test and improve your powers of inference and interpretation. The Odic Force, The Spider's Cousin, Ellipse Drawing, theory and strategy of card and board games like tit-tat-toe, go moku, salvo, and many others. 100 pages of detailed mathematical explanations. Appendix of primes, square roots, etc. 135 illustrations. 2nd revised edition. 248pp. 5⅜ x 8. T198 Paperbound **$1.00**

MATHEMAGIC, MAGIC PUZZLES, AND GAMES WITH NUMBERS, R. V. Heath. More than 60 new puzzles and stunts based on the properties of numbers. Easy techniques for multiplying large numbers mentally, revealing hidden numbers magically, finding the date of any day in any year, and dozens more. Over 30 pages devoted to magic squares, triangles, cubes, circles, etc. Edited by J. S. Meyer. 76 illustrations. 128pp. 5⅜ x 8. T110 Paperbound **$1.00**

MATHEMATICAL RECREATIONS, M. Kraitchik. One of the most thorough compilations of unusual mathematical problems for beginners and advanced mathematicians. Historical problems from Greek, Medieval, Arabic, Hindu sources. 50 pages devoted to pastimes derived from figurate numbers, Mersenne numbers, Fermat numbers, primes and probability. 40 pages of magic, Euler, Latin, panmagic squares. 25 new positional and permutational games of permanent value: fairy chess, latruncles, reversi, jinx, ruma, lasca, tricolor, tetrachrome, etc. Complete rigorous solutions. Revised second edition. 181 illustrations. 333pp. 5⅜ x 8.
T163 Paperbound **$1.75**

MATHEMATICAL PUZZLES OF SAM LOYD, selected and edited by M. Gardner. Choice puzzles by the greatest American puzzle creator and innovator. Selected from his famous collection, "Cyclopedia of Puzzles," they retain the unique style and historical flavor of the originals. There are posers based on arithmetic, algebra, probability, game theory, route tracing, topology, counter, sliding block, operations research, geometrical dissection. Includes the famous "14-15" puzzle which was a national craze, and his "Horse of a Different Color" which sold millions of copies. 117 of his most ingenious puzzles in all, 120 line drawings and diagrams. Solutions. Selected references. xx + 167pp. 5⅜ x 8. T498 Paperbound **$1.00**

MATHEMATICAL PUZZLES OF SAM LOYD, Vol. II, selected and edited by Martin Gardner. The outstanding 2nd selection from the great American innovator's "Cyclopedia of Puzzles": speed and distance problems, clock problems, plane and solid geometry, calculus problems, etc. Analytical table of contents that groups the puzzles according to the type of mathematics necessary to solve them. 166 puzzles, 150 original line drawings and diagrams. Selected references. xiv + 177pp. 5⅜ x 8. T709 Paperbound **$1.00**

ARITHMETICAL EXCURSIONS: AN ENRICHMENT OF ELEMENTARY MATHEMATICS, H. Bowers and J. Bowers. A lively and lighthearted collection of facts and entertainments for anyone who enjoys manipulating numbers or solving arithmetical puzzles: methods of arithmetic never taught in school, little-known facts about the most simple numbers, and clear explanations of more sophisticated topics; mysteries and folklore of numbers, the "Hin-dog-abic" number system, etc. First publication. Index. 529 numbered problems and diversions, all with answers. Bibliography. 60 figures. xiv + 320pp. 5⅜ x 8. T770 Paperbound **$1.65**

CRYPTANALYSIS, H. F. Gaines. Formerly entitled ELEMENTARY CRYPTANALYSIS, this introductory-intermediate level text is the best book in print on cryptograms and their solution. It covers all major techniques of the past, and contains much that is not generally known except to experts. Full details about concealment, substitution, and transposition ciphers; periodic mixed alphabets, multafid, Kasiski and Vigenere methods, Ohaver patterns, Playfair, and scores of other topics. 6 language letter and word frequency appendix. 167 problems, now furnished with solutions. Index. 173 figures. vi + 230pp. 5⅜ x 8.
T97 Paperbound **$1.95**

CRYPTOGRAPHY, L. D. Smith. An excellent introductory work on ciphers and their solution, the history of secret writing, and actual methods and problems in such techniques as transposition and substitution. Appendices describe the enciphering of Japanese, the Baconian biliteral cipher, and contain frequency tables and a bibliography for further study. Over 150 problems with solutions. 160pp. 5⅜ x 8. T247 Paperbound **$1.00**

PUZZLE QUIZ AND STUNT FUN, J. Meyer. The solution to party doldrums. 238 challenging puzzles, stunts and tricks. Mathematical puzzles like The Clever Carpenter, Atom Bomb; mysteries and deductions like The Bridge of Sighs, The Nine Pearls, Dog Logic; observation puzzles like Cigarette Smokers, Telephone Dial; over 200 others including magic squares, tongue twisters, puns, anagrams, and many others. All problems solved fully. 250pp. 5⅜ x 8.
T337 Paperbound **$1.00**

101 PUZZLES IN THOUGHT AND LOGIC, C. R. Wylie, Jr. Brand new problems you need no special knowledge to solve! Take the kinks out of your mental "muscles" and enjoy solving murder problems, the detection of lying fishermen, the logical identification of color by a blindman, and dozens more. Introduction with simplified explanation of general scientific method and puzzle solving. 128pp. 5⅜ x 8. T367 Paperbound **$1.00**

MY BEST PROBLEMS IN MATHEMATICS, Hubert Phillips ("Caliban"). Only elementary mathematics needed to solve these 100 witty, catchy problems by a master problem creator. Problems on the odds in cards and dice, problems in geometry, algebra, permutations, even problems that require no math at all—just a logical mind, clear thinking. Solutions completely worked out. If you enjoy mysteries, alerting your perceptive powers and exercising your detective's eye, you'll find these cryptic puzzles a challenging delight. Original 1961 publication. 100 puzzles, solutions. x + 107pp. 5⅝ x 8. T91 Paperbound **$1.00**

MY BEST PUZZLES IN LOGIC AND REASONING, Hubert Phillips ("Caliban"). A new collection of 100 inferential and logical puzzles chosen from the best that have appeared in England, available for first time in U.S. By the most endlessly resourceful puzzle creator now living. All data presented are both necessary and sufficient to allow a single unambiguous answer. No special knowledge is required for problems ranging from relatively simple to completely original one-of-a-kinds. Guaranteed to please beginners and experts of all ages. Original publication. 100 puzzles, full solutions. x + 107pp. 5⅜ x 8. T119 Paperbound **$1.00**

THE BOOK OF MODERN PUZZLES, G. L. Kaufman. A completely new series of puzzles as fascinating as crossword and deduction puzzles but based upon different principles and techniques. Simple 2-minute teasers, word labyrinths, design and pattern puzzles, logic and observation puzzles — over 150 braincrackers. Answers to all problems. 116 illustrations. 192pp. 5⅜ x 8.
T143 Paperbound **$1.00**

NEW WORD PUZZLES, G. L. Kaufman. 100 ENTIRELY NEW puzzles based on words and their combinations that will delight crossword puzzle, Scrabble and Jotto fans. Chess words, based on the moves of the chess king; design-onyms, symmetrical designs made of synonyms; rhymed double-crostics; syllable sentences; addle letter anagrams; alphagrams; linkograms; and many others all brand new. Full solutions. Space to work problems. 196 figures. vi + 122pp. 5⅜ x 8. T344 Paperbound **$1.00**

MAZES AND LABYRINTHS: A BOOK OF PUZZLES, W. Shepherd. Mazes, formerly associated with mystery and ritual, are still among the most intriguing of intellectual puzzles. This is a novel and different collection of 50 amusements that embody the principle of the maze: mazes in the classical tradition; 3-dimensional, ribbon, and Möbius-strip mazes; hidden messages; spatial arrangements; etc.—almost all built on amusing story situations. 84 illustrations. Essay on maze psychology. Solutions. xv + 122pp. 5⅜ x 8. T731 Paperbound **$1.00**

MAGIC TRICKS & CARD TRICKS, W. Jonson. Two books bound as one. 52 tricks with cards, 37 tricks with coins, bills, eggs, smoke, ribbons, slates, etc. Details on presentation, misdirection, and routining will help you master such famous tricks as the Changing Card, Card in the Pocket, Four Aces, Coin Through the Hand, Bill in the Egg, Afghan Bands, and over 75 others. If you follow the lucid exposition and key diagrams carefully, you will finish these two books with an astonishing mastery of magic. 106 figures. 224pp. 5⅜ x 8. T909 Paperbound **$1.00**

PANORAMA OF MAGIC, Milbourne Christopher. A profusely illustrated history of stage magic, a unique selection of prints and engravings from the author's private collection of magic memorabilia, the largest of its kind. Apparatus, stage settings and costumes; ingenious ads distributed by the performers and satiric broadsides passed around in the streets ridiculing pompous showmen; programs; decorative souvenirs. The lively text, by one of America's foremost professional magicians, is full of anecdotes about almost legendary wizards: Dede, the Egyptian; Philadelphia, the wonder-worker; Robert-Houdin, "the father of modern magic;" Harry Houdini; scores more. Altogether a pleasure package for anyone interested in magic, stage setting and design, ethnology, psychology, or simply in unusual people. A Dover original. 295 illustrations; 8 in full color. Index. viii + 216pp. 8⅜ x 11¼.
T774 Paperbound **$2.25**

HOUDINI ON MAGIC, Harry Houdini. One of the greatest magicians of modern times explains his most prized secrets. How locks are picked, with illustrated picks and skeleton keys; how a girl is sawed into twins; how to walk through a brick wall — Houdini's explanations of 44 stage tricks with many diagrams. Also included is a fascinating discussion of great magicians of the past and the story of his fight against fraudulent mediums and spiritualists. Edited by W.B. Gibson and M.N. Young. Bibliography. 155 figures, photos. xv + 280pp. 5⅜ x 8.
T384 Paperbound **$1.25**

MATHEMATICS, MAGIC AND MYSTERY, Martin Gardner. Why do card tricks work? How do magicians perform astonishing mathematical feats? How is stage mind-reading possible? This is the first book length study explaining the application of probability, set theory, theory of numbers, topology, etc., to achieve many startling tricks. Non-technical, accurate, detailed! 115 sections discuss tricks with cards, dice, coins, knots, geometrical vanishing illusions, how a Curry square "demonstrates" that the sum of the parts may be greater than the whole, and dozens of others. No sleight of hand necessary! 135 illustrations. xii + 174pp. 5⅜ x 8.
T335 Paperbound **$1.00**

EASY-TO-DO ENTERTAINMENTS AND DIVERSIONS WITH COINS, CARDS, STRING, PAPER AND MATCHES, R. M. Abraham. Over 300 tricks, games and puzzles will provide young readers with absorbing fun. Sections on card games; paper-folding; tricks with coins, matches and pieces of string; games for the agile; toy-making from common household objects; mathematical recreations; and 50 miscellaneous pastimes. Anyone in charge of groups of youngsters, including hard-pressed parents, and in need of suggestions on how to keep children sensibly amused and quietly content will find this book indispensable. Clear, simple text, copious number of delightful line drawings and illustrative diagrams. Originally titled "Winter Nights Entertainments." Introduction by Lord Baden Powell. 329 illustrations. v + 186pp. 5⅜ x 8½. T921 Paperbound **$1.00**

STRING FIGURES AND HOW TO MAKE THEM, Caroline Furness Jayne. 107 string figures plus variations selected from the best primitive and modern examples developed by Navajo, Apache, pygmies of Africa, Eskimo, in Europe, Australia, China, etc. The most readily understandable, easy-to-follow book in English on perennially popular recreation. Crystal-clear exposition; step-by-step diagrams. Everyone from kindergarten children to adults looking for unusual diversion will be endlessly amused. Index. Bibliography. Introduction by A. C. Haddon. 17 full-page plates. 960 illustrations. xxiii + 401pp. 5⅜ x 8½.
T152 Paperbound **$2.00**

Fiction

FLATLAND, E. A. Abbott. A science-fiction classic of life in a 2-dimensional world that is also a first-rate introduction to such aspects of modern science as relativity and hyperspace. Political, moral, satirical, and humorous overtones have made FLATLAND fascinating reading for thousands. 7th edition. New introduction by Banesh Hoffmann. 16 illustrations. 128pp. 5⅜ x 8. T1 Paperbound **$1.00**

THE WONDERFUL WIZARD OF OZ, L. F. Baum. Only edition in print with all the original W. W. Denslow illustrations in full color—as much a part of "The Wizard" as Tenniel's drawings are of "Alice in Wonderland." "The Wizard" is still America's best-loved fairy tale, in which, as the author expresses it, "The wonderment and joy are retained and the heartaches and nightmares left out." Now today's young readers can enjoy every word and wonderful picture of the original book. New introduction by Martin Gardner. A Baum bibliography. 23 full-page color plates. viii + 268pp. 5⅜ x 8. T691 Paperbound **$1.45**

THE MARVELOUS LAND OF OZ, L. F. Baum. This is the equally enchanting sequel to the "Wizard," continuing the adventures of the Scarecrow and the Tin Woodman. The hero this time is a little boy named Tip, and all the delightful Oz magic is still present. This is the Oz book with the Animated Saw-Horse, the Woggle-Bug, and Jack Pumpkinhead. All the original John R. Neill illustrations, 10 in full color. 287 pp. 5⅜ x 8. T692 Paperbound **$1.45**

FIVE GREAT DOG NOVELS, edited by Blanche Cirker. The complete original texts of five classic dog novels that have delighted and thrilled millions of children and adults throughout the world with their stories of loyalty, adventure, and courage. Full texts of Jack London's "The Call of the Wild"; John Brown's "Rab and His Friends"; Alfred Ollivant's "Bob, Son of Battle"; Marshall Saunders's "Beautiful Joe"; and Ouida's "A Dog of Flanders." 21 Illustrations from the original editions. 495pp. 5⅜ x 8. T777 Paperbound **$1.50**

TO THE SUN? and OFF ON A COMET!, Jules Verne. Complete texts of two of the most imaginative flights into fancy in world literature display the high adventure that have kept Verne's novels read for nearly a century. Only unabridged edition of the best translation, by Edward Roth. Large, easily readable type. 50 illustrations selected from first editions. 462pp. 5⅜ x 8. T634 Paperbound **$1.75**

FROM THE EARTH TO THE MOON and ALL AROUND THE MOON, Jules Verne. Complete editions of 2 of Verne's most successful novels, in finest Edward Roth translations, now available after many years out of print. Verne's visions of submarines, airplanes, television, rockets, interplanetary travel; of scientific and not-so-scientific beliefs; of peculiarities of Americans; all delight and engross us today as much as when they first appeared. Large, easily readable type. 42 illus. from first French edition. 476pp. 5⅜ x 8. T633 Paperbound **$1.75**

THE CRUISE OF THE CACHALOT, Frank T. Bullen. Out of the experiences of many years on the high-seas, First Mate Bullen created this novel of adventure aboard an American whaler, shipping out of New Bedford, Mass., when American whaling was at the height of its splendor. Originally published in 1899, the story of the round-the-world cruise of the "Cachalot" in pursuit of the sperm whale has thrilled generations of readers. A maritime classic that will fascinate anyone interested in reading about the sea or looking for a solid old-fashioned yarn, while the vivid recreation of a brief but important chapter of Americana and the British author's often biting commentary on nineteenth-century Yankee mores offer insights into the colorful era of America's coming of age. 8 plates. xiii + 271pp. 5⅜ x 8½. T774 Paperbound **$1.00**

28 SCIENCE FICTION STORIES OF H. G. WELLS. Two full unabridged novels, MEN LIKE GODS and STAR BEGOTTEN, plus 26 short stories by the master science-fiction writer of all time! Stories of space, time, invention, exploration, future adventure—an indispensable part of the library of everyone interested in science and adventure. PARTIAL CONTENTS: Men Like Gods, The Country of the Blind, In the Abyss, The Crystal Egg, The Man Who Could Work Miracles, A Story of the Days to Come, The Valley of Spiders, and 21 more! 928pp. 5⅜ x 8. T265 Clothbound **$3.95**

DAVID HARUM, E. N. Westcott. This novel of one of the most lovable, humorous characters in American literature is a prime example of regional humor. It continues to delight people who like their humor dry, their characters quaint, and their plots ingenuous. First book edition to contain complete novel plus chapter found after author's death. Illustrations from first illustrated edition. 192pp. 5⅜ x 8. T580 Paperbound **$1.15**

GESTA ROMANORUM, trans. by Charles Swan, ed. by Wynnard Hooper. 181 tales of Greeks, Romans, Britons, Biblical characters, comprise one of greatest medieval story collections, source of plots for writers including Shakespeare, Chaucer, Gower, etc. Imaginative tales of wars, incest, thwarted love, magic, fantasy, allegory, humor, tell about kings, prostitutes, philosophers, fair damsels, knights, Noah, pirates, all walks, stations of life. Introduction. Notes. 500pp. 5⅜ x 8. T535 Paperbound **$1.85**

CATALOGUE OF DOVER BOOKS

3 ADVENTURE NOVELS by H. Rider Haggard. Complete texts of "She," "King Solomon's Mines," "Allan Quatermain." Qualities of discovery, desire for immortality, search for the primitive, for what is unadorned by civilization, have kept these novels of African adventure excitingly alive to readers from R. L. Stevenson to George Orwell. 636pp. 5⅜ x 8.
T584 Paperbound **$2.00**

THE CASTING AWAY OF MRS. LECKS AND MRS. ALESHINE, F. R. Stockton. A charming light novel by Frank Stockton, one of America's finest humorists (and author of "The Lady, or the Tiger?"). This book has made millions of Americans laugh at the reflection of themselves in two middle-aged American women involved in some of the strangest adventures on record. You will laugh, too, as they endure shipwreck, desert island, and blizzard with maddening tranquillity. Also contains complete text of "The Dusantes," sequel to "The Casting Away." 49 original illustrations by F. D. Steele. vii + 142pp. 5⅜ x 8. T743 Paperbound **$1.00**

THREE PROPHETIC NOVELS OF H. G. WELLS. Complete texts of 3 timeless science fiction novels by the greatest master of the art, with remarkable prophecies of technological and social changes that are really taking place!—"When the Sleeper Wakes" (first printing in 50 years), "A Story of the Days to Come," and "The Time Machine" (only truly complete text available). Introduction by E. F. Bleiler. "The absolute best of imaginative fiction," N. Y. Times. 335pp. 5⅜ x 8. T605 Paperbound **$1.45**

SEVEN SCIENCE FICTION NOVELS, H. G. Wells. Full unabridged texts of 7 science-fiction novels of the master. Ranging from biology, physics, chemistry, astronomy, to sociology and other studies, Mr. Wells extrapolates whole worlds of strange and intriguing character. "One will have to go far to match this for entertainment, excitement, and sheer pleasure . . ." NEW YORK TIMES. Contents: The Time Machine, The Island of Dr. Moreau, The First Men in the Moon, The Invisible Man, The War of the Worlds, The Food of the Gods, In The Days of the Comet. 1015pp. 5⅜ x 8. T264 Clothbound **$4.50**

THE PRISONER OF ZENDA and RUPERT OF HENTZAU, Anthony Hope. The first edition to contain the complete story of the English diplomat who becomes King for a Day in the ancient aristocratic Kingdom of Ruritania. Long a favorite of devotees of high adventure, romance, grand intigue. Intelligent thrills presented with verve and elegant excitement. Unabridged reprints. Two volumes bound as one. 14 illustrations by Charles Dana Gibson. 420pp. 5⅜ x 8.
T69 Paperbound **$1.35**

TWO LITTLE SAVAGES, Ernest Thompson Seton. A lively narrative of the adventures of two real boys who decide to go Indian, combined with a storehouse of survival information: how to make a fire without matches, use an axe expertly, smudge mosquitoes, distinguish animal tracks, make mocassins, bows and arrows, learn the stars, etc. A classic of nature and boyhood, certain to awaken nature-interest in any youngster—or oldster. Highly recommended to Scouts, hunters, campers, bird-watchers or even city-dwellers who like to learn about the ways of nature. 293 illustrations by the author. x + 286pp. 5⅜ x 8½.
T985 Paperbound **$1.50**

THREE MARTIAN NOVELS, Edgar Rice Burroughs. Complete unabridged reprinting, in one volume, of Thuvia, Maid of Mars; Chessmen of Mars; The Master Mind of Mars. Hours of science-fiction adventure by a modern master storyteller. Reset in large clear type for easy reading. 16 illustrations by J. Allen St. John, vi + 490 pp. 5⅜ x 8½. T39 Paperbound **$1.75**

THE LAND THAT TIME FORGOT, and THE MOON MAID, Edgar Rice Burroughs. Two of Burroughs's rarest novels, considered by most authorities to be his best work. The first is adventure on a lost island where evolution is an individual matter and rapid, rather than slow and in terms of species; the second is the story of the first exploration of the Moon, the weird cultures that inhabit its interior, the conquest of the Earth by the Moon, and the millennia of struggle between the invaders and the earthmen. Packed full of thrills, thought-provoking. 5 illustrations by J. Allan St. John. 5⅜ x 8½. T358 Paperbound **$2.00**
T1020 Clothbound **$3.75**

PIRATES OF VENUS, LOST ON VENUS, Edgar Rice Burroughs. These are the first two novels describing the adventures of Carson Napier on mysterious Venus. Thrilling adventures and exciting science-fiction situations among the towering jungles, monster-filled seas, and fantastic cities of the Second Planet. Complete and unabridged. Illustrations from original periodical publications. Illustrations by Matania. vi + 340pp. 5⅜ x 8½.
T1053 Paperbound **$1.75**

A PRINCESS OF MARS, A FIGHTING MAN OF MARS, Edgar Rice Burroughs. Two fantastic novels of Mars. "A Princess of Mars" explains how John Carter first came to Mars, and his adventures among the dying civilizations. "A Fighting Man of Mars", an independent novel set in the same adventurous environment, provides hours of thrills among lost cities and monsters. Illustrated by J. Allan St. John. 5⅜ x 8½. T1055 Paperbound **$1.75**

Language Books and Records

GERMAN: HOW TO SPEAK AND WRITE IT. AN INFORMAL CONVERSATIONAL METHOD FOR SELF STUDY, Joseph Rosenberg. Eminently useful for self study because of concentration on elementary stages of learning. Also provides teachers with remarkable variety of aids: 28 full- and double-page sketches with pertinent items numbered and identified in German and English; German proverbs, jokes; grammar, idiom studies; extensive practice exercises. The most interesting introduction to German available, full of amusing illustrations, photographs of cities and landmarks in German-speaking cities, cultural information subtly woven into conversational material. Includes summary of grammar, guide to letter writing, study guide to German literature by Dr. Richard Friedenthal. Index. 400 illustrations. 384pp. 5⅜ x 8½.
T271 Paperbound **$2.00**

FRENCH: HOW TO SPEAK AND WRITE IT. AN INFORMAL CONVERSATIONAL METHOD FOR SELF STUDY, Joseph Lemaitre. Even the absolute beginner can acquire a solid foundation for further study from this delightful elementary course. Photographs, sketches and drawings, sparkling colloquial conversations on a wide variety of topics (including French culture and custom), French sayings and quips, are some of aids used to demonstrate rather than merely describe the language. Thorough yet surprisingly entertaining approach, excellent for teaching and for self study. Comprehensive analysis of pronunciation, practice exercises and appendices of verb tables, additional vocabulary, other useful material. Index. Appendix. 400 illustrations. 416pp. 5⅜ x 8½. T268 Paperbound **$2.00**

A PHRASE AND SENTENCE DICTIONARY OF SPOKEN CHINESE: ENGLISH-CHINESE, CHINESE-ENGLISH. Dictionary of modern Mandarin based not on isolated words but on phrases, sentences that can be used immediately in speaking, translating. 25,000 idiomatic sentences (with English equivalents) chosen for semantic frequency and idiomatic use—probably largest collection ever assembled for Western use. Introductory analyses of pronunciation, syntactical structure discusses phonetics, dialect and regional variation, speech units. Indexed under 10,000 key words from both English to Chinese, Chinese to English. Printed in easily-followed, modern phonetic transcription with clear indications of tone. Characters provided under Chinese entries and indexed. Appendix covers weights and measures, kinship terms. Republication of TM 30-933 (1955), prepared for U.S. Government by nationally-known linguists. ix + 848pp. 6½ x 9¼. T175 Clothbound **$7.50**

AN ENGLISH-FRENCH-GERMAN-SPANISH WORD FREQUENCY DICTIONARY, H. S. Eaton. An indispensable language study aid, this is a semantic frequency list of the 6000 most frequently used words in 4 languages—24,000 words in all. The lists, based on concepts rather than words alone, and containing all modern, exact, and idiomatic vocabulary, are arranged side by side to form a unique 4-language dictionary. A simple key indicates the importance of the individual words within each language. Over 200 pages of separate indexes for each language enable you to locate individual words at a glance. Will help language teachers and students, authors of textbooks, grammars, and language tests to compare concepts in the various languages and to concentrate on basic vocabulary, avoiding uncommon and obsolete words. 2 Appendixes. xxi + 441pp. 6½ x 9¼. T738 Paperbound **$2.45**

NEW RUSSIAN-ENGLISH AND ENGLISH-RUSSIAN DICTIONARY, M. A. O'Brien. Over 70,000 entries in the new orthography! Many idiomatic uses and colloquialisms which form the basis of actual speech. Irregular verbs, perfective and imperfective aspects, regular and irregular sound changes, and other features. One of the few dictionaries where accent changes within the conjugation of verbs and the declension of nouns are fully indicated. "One of the best," Prof. E. J. Simmons, Cornell. First names, geographical terms, bibliography, etc. 738pp. 4½ x 6¼. T208 Paperbound **$2.00**

96 MOST USEFUL PHRASES FOR TOURISTS AND STUDENTS in English, French, Spanish, German, Italian. A handy folder you'll want to carry with you. How to say "Excuse me," "How much is it?", "Write it down, please," etc., in four foreign languages. Copies limited, no more than 1 to a customer. **FREE**

Say It language phrase books

These handy phrase books (128 to 196 pages each) make grammatical drills unnecessary for an elementary knowledge of a spoken foreign language. Covering most matters of travel and everyday life each volume contains:

Over 1000 phrases and sentences in immediately useful forms — foreign language plus English.

Modern usage designed for Americans. Specific phrases like, "Give me small change," and "Please call a taxi."

Simplified phonetic transcription you will be able to read at sight.

The only completely indexed phrase books on the market.

Covers scores of important situations: — Greetings, restaurants, sightseeing, useful expressions, etc.

These books are prepared by native linguists who are professors at Columbia, N.Y.U., Fordham and other great universities. Use them independently or with any other book or record course. They provide a supplementary living element that most other courses lack. Individual volumes in:

Russian 75¢ **Italian 75¢** **Spanish 75¢** **German 75¢**
Hebrew 75¢ **Danish 75¢** **Japanese 75¢** **Swedish 75¢**
Dutch 75¢ **Esperanto 75¢** **Modern Greek 75¢** **Portuguese 75¢**
Norwegian 75¢ **Polish 75¢** **French 75¢** **Yiddish 75¢**
Turkish 75¢ **English for German-speaking people 75¢**
English for Italian-speaking people 75¢ **English for Spanish-speaking people 75¢**

Large clear type. 128-196 pages each. 3½ x 5¼. Sturdy paper binding.

Listen and Learn language records

LISTEN & LEARN is the only language record course designed especially to meet your travel and everyday needs. It is available in separate sets for FRENCH, SPANISH, GERMAN, JAPANESE, RUSSIAN, MODERN GREEK, PORTUGUESE, ITALIAN and HEBREW, and each set contains three 33⅓ rpm long-playing records—1½ hours of recorded speech by eminent native speakers who are professors at Columbia, New York University, Queens College.

Check the following special features found only in LISTEN & LEARN:

- **Dual-language recording. 812 selected phrases and sentences,** over 3200 words, spoken first in English, then in their foreign language equivalents. A suitable pause follows each foreign phrase, allowing you time to repeat the expression. You learn by unconscious assimilation.
- **128 to 206-page manual** contains everything on the records, plus a simple phonetic pronunciation guide.
- **Indexed for convenience. The only set on the market** that is completely indexed. No more puzzling over where to find the phrase you need. Just look in the rear of the manual.
- **Practical.** No time wasted on material you can find in any grammar. LISTEN & LEARN covers central core material with phrase approach. Ideal for the person with limited learning time.
- **Living, modern expressions,** not found in other courses. Hygienic products, modern equipment, shopping—expressions used every day, like "nylon" and "air-conditioned."
- **Limited objective.** Everything you learn, no matter where you stop, is immediately useful. You have to finish other courses, wade through grammar and vocabulary drill, before they help you.
- **High-fidelity recording.** LISTEN & LEARN records equal in clarity and surface-silence any record on the market costing up to $6.

"Excellent . . . the spoken records . . . impress me as being among the very best on the market," **Prof. Mario Pei,** Dept. of Romance Languages, Columbia University. "Inexpensive and well-done . . . it would make an ideal present," CHICAGO SUNDAY TRIBUNE. "More genuinely helpful than anything of its kind which I have previously encountered," **Sidney Clark,** well-known author of "ALL THE BEST" travel books.

UNCONDITIONAL GUARANTEE. Try LISTEN & LEARN, then return it within 10 days for full refund if you are not satisfied.

Each set contains three twelve-inch 33⅓ records, manual, and album.

SPANISH	the set **$5.95**	GERMAN	the set **$5.95**
FRENCH	the set **$5.95**	ITALIAN	the set **$5.95**
RUSSIAN	the set **$5.95**	JAPANESE	the set **$5.95**
PORTUGUESE	the set **$5.95**	MODERN GREEK	the set **$5.95**
MODERN HEBREW	the set **$5.95**		

Trubner Colloquial Manuals

These unusual books are members of the famous Trubner series of colloquial manuals. They have been written to provide adults with a sound colloquial knowledge of a foreign language, and are suited for either class use or self-study. Each book is a complete course in itself, with progressive, easy to follow lessons. Phonetics, grammar, and syntax are covered, while hundreds of phrases and idioms, reading texts, exercises, and vocabulary are included. These books are unusual in being neither skimpy nor overdetailed in grammatical matters, and in presenting up-to-date, colloquial, and practical phrase material. Bilingual presentation is stressed, to make thorough self-study easier for the reader.

COLLOQUIAL HINDUSTANI, A. H. Harley, formerly Nizam's Reader in Urdu, U. of London. 30 pages on phonetics and scripts (devanagari & Arabic-Persian) are followed by 29 lessons, including material on English and Arabic-Persian influences. Key to all exercises. Vocabulary. 5 x 7½. 147pp. Clothbound **$1.75**

COLLOQUIAL PERSIAN, L. P. Elwell-Sutton. Best introduction to modern Persian, with 90 page grammatical section followed by conversations, 35-page vocabulary. 139pp. Clothbound **$1.75**

COLLOQUIAL ARABIC, DeLacy O'Leary. Foremost Islamic scholar covers language of Egypt, Syria, Palestine, & Northern Arabia. Extremely clear coverage of complex Arabic verbs & noun plurals; also cultural aspects of language. Vocabulary. xviii + 192pp. 5 x 7½. Clothbound **$2.50**

COLLOQUIAL GERMAN, P. F. Doring. Intensive thorough coverage of grammar in easily-followed form. Excellent for brush-up, with hundreds of colloquial phrases. 34 pages of bilingual texts. 224pp. 5 x 7½. Clothbound **$1.75**

COLLOQUIAL SPANISH, W. R. Patterson. Castilian grammar and colloquial language, loaded with bilingual phrases and colloquialisms. Excellent for review or self-study. 164pp. 5 x 7½. Clothbound **$1.75**

COLLOQUIAL FRENCH, W. R. Patterson. 16th revision of this extremely popular manual. Grammar explained with model clarity, and hundreds of useful expressions and phrases; exercises, reading texts, etc. Appendixes of new and useful words and phrases. 223pp. 5 x 7½. Clothbound **$1.75**

COLLOQUIAL CZECH, J. Schwarz, former headmaster of Lingua Institute, Prague. Full easily followed coverage of grammar, hundreds of immediately useable phrases, texts. Perhaps the best Czech grammar in print. "An absolutely successful textbook," JOURNAL OF CZECHO-SLOVAK FORCES IN GREAT BRITAIN. 252pp. 5 x 7½. Clothbound **$3.00**

COLLOQUIAL RUMANIAN, G. Nandris, Professor of University of London. Extremely thorough coverage of phonetics, grammar, syntax; also included 70-page reader, and 70-page vocabulary. Probably the best grammar for this increasingly important language. 340pp. 5 x 7½. Clothbound **$2.50**

COLLOQUIAL ITALIAN, A. L. Hayward. Excellent self-study course in grammar, vocabulary, idioms, and reading. Easy progressive lessons will give a good working knowledge of Italian in the shortest possible time. 5 x 7½. Clothbound **$1.75**

COLLOQUIAL TURKISH, Yusuf Mardin. Very clear, thorough introduction to leading cultural and economic language of Near East. Begins with pronunciation and statement of vowel harmony, then 36 lessons present grammar, graded vocabulary, useful phrases, dialogues, reading, exercises. Key to exercises at rear. Turkish-English vocabulary. All in Roman alphabet. x + 288pp. 4¾ x 7¼. Clothbound **$4.00**

DUTCH-ENGLISH AND ENGLISH-DUTCH DICTIONARY, F. G. Renier. For travel, literary, scientific or business Dutch, you will find this the most convenient, practical and comprehensive dictionary on the market. More than 60,000 entries, shades of meaning, colloquialisms, idioms, compounds and technical terms. Dutch and English strong and irregular verbs. This is the only dictionary in its size and price range that indicates the gender of nouns. New orthography. xvii + 571pp. 5½ x 6¼. T224 Clothbound **$2.75**

LEARN DUTCH, F. G. Renier. This book is the most satisfactory and most easily used grammar of modern Dutch. The student is gradually led from simple lessons in pronunciation, through translation from and into Dutch, and finally to a mastery of spoken and written Dutch. Grammatical principles are clearly explained while a useful, practical vocabulary is introduced in easy exercises and readings. It is used and recommended by the Fulbright Committee in the Netherlands. Phonetic appendices. Over 1200 exercises; Dutch-English, English-Dutch vocabularies. 181pp. 4¼ x 7¼. T441 Clothbound **$2.25**

Literature, History of Literature

ARISTOTLE'S THEORY OF POETRY AND THE FINE ARTS, edited by S. H. Butcher. The celebrated Butcher translation of this great classic faced, page by page, with the complete Greek text. A 300 page introduction discussing Aristotle's ideas and their influence in the history of thought and literature, and covering art and nature, imitation as an aesthetic form, poetic truth, art and morality, tragedy, comedy, and similar topics. Modern Aristotelian criticism discussed by John Gassner. lxxvi + 421pp. 5⅜ x 8. T42 Paperbound **$2.00**

INTRODUCTIONS TO ENGLISH LITERATURE, edited by B. Dobrée. Goes far beyond ordinary histories, ranging from the 7th century up to 1914 (to the 1940's in some cases.) The first half of each volume is a specific detailed study of historical and economic background of the period and a general survey of poetry and prose, including trends of thought, influences, etc. The second and larger half is devoted to a detailed study of more than 5000 poets, novelists, dramatists; also economists, historians, biographers, religious writers, philosophers, travellers, and scientists of literary stature, with dates, lists of major works and their dates, keypoint critical bibliography, and evaluating comments. The most compendious bibliographic and literary aid within its price range.

Vol. I. THE BEGINNINGS OF ENGLISH LITERATURE TO SKELTON, (1509), W. L. Renwick, H. Orton. 450pp. 5⅛ x 7⅞. T75 Clothbound **$4.50**

Vol. II. THE ENGLISH RENAISSANCE, 1510-1688, V. de Sola Pinto. 381pp. 5⅛ x 7⅞. T76 Clothbound **$4.50**

Vol. III. AUGUSTANS AND ROMANTICS, 1689-1830, H. Dyson, J. Butt. 320pp. 5⅛ x 7⅞. T77 Clothbound **$4.50**

Vol. IV. THE VICTORIANS AND AFTER, 1830-1940's, E. Batho, B. Dobrée. 360pp. 5⅛ x 7⅞. T78 Clothbound **$4.50**

EPIC AND ROMANCE, W. P. Ker. Written by one of the foremost authorities on medieval literature, this is the standard survey of medieval epic and romance. It covers Teutonic epics, Icelandic sagas, Beowulf, French chansons de geste, the Roman de Troie, and many other important works of literature. It is an excellent account for a body of literature whose beauty and value has only recently come to be recognized. Index. xxiv + 398pp. 5⅜ x 8. T355 Paperbound **$1.95**

THE POPULAR BALLAD, F. B. Gummere. Most useful factual introduction; fund of descriptive material; quotes, cites over 260 ballads. Examines, from folkloristic view, structure; choral, ritual elements; meter, diction, fusion; effects of tradition, editors; almost every other aspect of border, riddle, kinship, sea, ribald, supernatural, etc., ballads. Bibliography. 2 indexes. 374pp. 5⅜ x 8. T548 Paperbound **$1.65**

MASTERS OF THE DRAMA, John Gassner. The most comprehensive history of the drama in print, covering drama in every important tradition from the Greeks to the Near East, China, Japan, Medieval Europe, England, Russia, Italy, Spain, Germany, and dozens of other drama producing nations. This unsurpassed reading and reference work encompasses more than 800 dramatists and over 2000 plays, with biographical material, plot summaries, theatre history, etc. "Has no competitors in its field," THEATRE ARTS. "Best of its kind in English," NEW REPUBLIC. Exhaustive 35 page bibliography. 77 photographs and drawings. Deluxe edition with reinforced cloth binding, headbands, stained top. xxii + 890pp. 5⅜ x 8. T100 Clothbound **$6.95**

THE DEVELOPMENT OF DRAMATIC ART, D. C. Stuart. The basic work on the growth of Western drama from primitive beginnings to Eugene O'Neill, covering over 2500 years. Not a mere listing or survey, but a thorough analysis of changes, origins of style, and influences in each period; dramatic conventions, social pressures, choice of material, plot devices, stock situations, etc.; secular and religious works of all nations and epochs. "Generous and thoroughly documented researches," Outlook. "Solid studies of influences and playwrights and periods," London Times. Index. Bibliography. xi + 679pp. 5⅜ x 8. T693 Paperbound **$2.75**

A SOURCE BOOK IN THEATRICAL HISTORY (SOURCES OF THEATRICAL HISTORY), A. M. Nagler. Over 2000 years of actors, directors, designers, critics, and spectators speak for themselves in this potpourri of writings selected from the great and formative periods of western drama. On-the-spot descriptions of masks, costumes, makeup, rehearsals, special effects, acting methods, backstage squabbles, theatres, etc. Contemporary glimpses of Molière rehearsing his company, an exhortation to a Roman audience to buy refreshments and keep quiet, Goethe's rules for actors, Belasco telling of $6500 he spent building a river, Restoration actors being told to avoid "lewd, obscene, or indecent postures," and much more. Each selection has an introduction by Prof. Nagler. This extraordinary, lively collection is ideal as a source of otherwise difficult to obtain material, as well as a fine book for browsing. Over 80 illustrations. 10 diagrams. xxiii + 611pp. 5⅜ x 8. T515 Paperbound **$2.75**

WORLD DRAMA, B. H. Clark. The dramatic creativity of a score of ages and eras — all in two handy compact volumes. Over 1/3 of this material is unavailable in any other current edition! 46 plays from Ancient Greece, Rome, Medieval Europe, France, Germany, Italy, England, Russia, Scandinavia, India, China, Japan, etc. — including classic authors like Aeschylus, Sophocles, Euripides, Aristophanes, Plautus, Marlowe, Jonson, Farquhar, Goldsmith, Cervantes, Molière, Dumas, Goethe, Schiller, Ibsen, and many others. This creative collection avoids hackneyed material and includes only completely first-rate works which are relatively little known or difficult to obtain. "The most comprehensive collection of important plays from all literature available in English," SAT. REV. OF LITERATURE. Introduction. Reading lists. 2 volumes. 1364pp. 5⅜ x 8. Vol. 1, T57 Paperbound **$2.25**
Vol. 2, T59 Paperbound **$2.25**

MASTERPIECES OF THE RUSSIAN DRAMA, edited with introduction by G. R. Noyes. This only comprehensive anthology of Russian drama ever published in English offers complete texts, in 1st-rate modern translations, of 12 plays covering 200 years. Vol. 1: "The Young Hopeful," Fonvisin; "Wit Works Woe," Griboyedov; "The Inspector General," Gogol; "A Month in the Country," Turgenev; "The Poor Bride," Ostrovsky; "A Bitter Fate," Pisemsky. Vol. 2: "The Death of Ivan the Terrible," Alexey Tolstoy "The Power of Darkness," Lev Tolstoy; "The Lower Depths," Gorky; "The Cherry Orchard," Chekhov; "Professor Storitsyn," Andreyev; "Mystery Bouffe," Mayakovsky. Bibliography. Total of 902pp. 5⅜ x 8.
Vol. 1 T647 Paperbound **$2.00**
Vol. 2 T648 Paperbound **$2.00**

EUGENE O'NEILL: THE MAN AND HIS PLAYS, B. H. Clark. Introduction to O'Neill's life and work. Clark analyzes each play from the early THE WEB to the recently produced MOON FOR THE MISBEGOTTEN and THE ICEMAN COMETH revealing the environmental and dramatic influences necessary for a complete understanding of these important works. Bibliography. Appendices. Index. ix + 182pp. 5⅜ x 8. T379 Paperbound **$1.25**

THE HEART OF THOREAU'S JOURNALS, edited by O. Shepard. The best general selection from Thoreau's voluminous (and rare) journals. This intimate record of thoughts and observations reveals the full Thoreau and his intellectual development more accurately than any of his published works: self-conflict between the scientific observer and the poet, reflections on transcendental philosophy, involvement in the tragedies of neighbors and national causes, etc. New preface, notes, introductions. xii + 228pp. 5⅜ x 8. T741 Paperbound **$1.45**

H. D. THOREAU: A WRITER'S JOURNAL, edited by L. Stapleton. A unique new selection from the Journals concentrating on Thoreau's growth as a conscious literary artist, the ideals and purposes of his art. Most of the material has never before appeared outside of the complete 14-volume edition. Contains vital insights on Thoreau's projected book on Concord, thoughts on the nature of men and government, indignation with slavery, sources of inspiration, goals in life. Index. xxxiii + 234pp. 5⅜ x 8. T678 Paperbound **$1.55**

THE HEART OF EMERSON'S JOURNALS, edited by **Bliss Perry.** Best of these revealing Journals, originally 10 volumes, presented in a one volume edition. Talks with Channing, Hawthorne, Thoreau, and Bronson Alcott; impressions of Webster, Everett, John Brown, and Lincoln; records of moments of sudden understanding, vision, and solitary ecstasy. "The essays do not reveal the power of Emerson's mind . . . as do these hasty and informal writings," N.Y. Times. Preface by Bliss Perry. Index. xiii + 357pp. 5⅜ x 8. T477 Paperbound **$1.85**

FOUNDERS OF THE MIDDLE AGES, E. K. Rand. This is the best non-technical discussion of the transformation of Latin pagan culture into medieval civilization. Covering such figures as Tertullian, Gregory, Jerome, Boethius, Augustine, the Neoplatonists, and many other literary men, educators, classicists, and humanists, this book is a storehouse of information presented clearly and simply for the intelligent non-specialist. "Thoughtful, beautifully written," AMERICAN HISTORICAL REVIEW. "Extraordinarily accurate," Richard McKeon, THE NATION. ix + 365pp. 5⅜ x 8. T369 Paperbound **$1.85**

PLAY-MAKING: A MANUAL OF CRAFTSMANSHIP, William Archer. With an extensive, new introduction by John Gassner, Yale Univ. The permanently essential requirements of solid play construction are set down in clear, practical language: theme, exposition, foreshadowing, tension, obligatory scene, peripety, dialogue, character, psychology, other topics. This book has been one of the most influential elements in the modern theatre, and almost everything said on the subject since is contained explicitly or implicitly within its covers. Bibliography. Index. xlii + 277pp. 5⅜ x 8. T651 Paperbound **$1.75**

HAMBURG DRAMATURGY, G. E. Lessing. One of the most brilliant of German playwrights of the eighteenth-century age of criticism analyzes the complex of theory and tradition that constitutes the world of theater. These 104 essays on aesthetic theory helped demolish the regime of French classicism, opening the door to psychological and social realism, romanticism. Subjects include the original functions of tragedy; drama as the rational world; the meaning of pity and fear, pity and fear as means for purgation and other Aristotelian concepts; genius and creative force; interdependence of poet's language and actor's interpretation; truth and authenticity; etc. A basic and enlightening study for anyone interested in aesthetics and ideas, from the philosopher to the theatergoer. Introduction by Prof. Victor Lange. xxii + 265pp. 4½ x 6⅜. T32 Paperbound **$1.45**

History, Political Science

THE POLITICAL THOUGHT OF PLATO AND ARISTOTLE, E. Barker. One of the clearest and most accurate expositions of the corpus of Greek political thought. This standard source contains exhaustive analyses of the "Republic" and other Platonic dialogues and Aristotle's "Politics" and "Ethics," and discusses the origin of these ideas in Greece, contributions of other Greek theorists, and modifications of Greek ideas by thinkers from Aquinas to Hegel. "Must" reading for anyone interested in the history of Western thought. Index. Chronological Table of Events. 2 Appendixes. xxiv + 560pp. 5⅜ x 8. T521 Paperbound **$1.85**

THE IDEA OF PROGRESS, J. B. Bury. Practically unknown before the Reformation, the idea of progress has since become one of the central concepts of western civilization. Prof. Bury analyzes its evolution in the thought of Greece, Rome, the Middle Ages, the Renaissance, to its flowering in all branches of science, religion, philosophy, industry, art, and literature, during and following the 16th century. Introduction by Charles Beard. Index. xl + 357pp. 5⅜ x 8. T40 Paperbound **$1.95**

THE ANCIENT GREEK HISTORIANS, J. B. Bury. This well known, easily read work covers the entire field of classical historians from the early writers to Herodotus, Thucydides, Xenophon, through Poseidonius and such Romans as Tacitus, Cato, Caesar, Livy. Scores of writers are studied biographically, in style, sources, accuracy, structure, historical concepts, and influences. Recent discoveries such as the Oxyrhinchus papyri are referred to, as well as such great scholars as Nissen, Gomperz, Cornford, etc. "Totally unblemished by pedantry." Outlook. "The best account in English," Dutcher, A Guide to Historical Lit. Bibliography, Index. x + 281pp. 5⅜ x 8. T397 Paperbound **$1.50**

HISTORY OF THE LATER ROMAN EMPIRE, J. B. Bury. This standard work by the leading Byzantine scholar of our time discusses the later Roman and early Byzantine empires from 395 A.D. through the death of Justinian in 565, in their political, social, cultural, theological, and military aspects. Contemporary documents are quoted in full, making this the most complete reconstruction of the period and a fit successor to Gibbon's "Decline and Fall." "Most unlikely that it will ever be superseded," Glanville Downey, Dumbarton Oaks Research Lib. Geneological tables. 5 maps. Bibliography. Index. 2 volumes total of 965pp. 5⅜ x 8. T398, 399 Two volume set, Paperbound **$4.00**

A HISTORY OF ANCIENT GEOGRAPHY, E. H. Bunbury. Standard study, in English, of ancient geography; never equalled for scope, detail. First full account of history of geography from Greeks' first world picture based on mariners, through Ptolemy. Discusses every important map, discovery, figure, travel expedition, war, conjecture, narrative, bearing on subject. Chapters on Homeric geography, Herodotus, Alexander expedition, Strabo, Pliny, Ptolemy, would stand alone as exhaustive monographs. Includes minor geographers, men not usually regarded in this context: Hecataeus, Pytheas, Hipparchus, Artemidorus, Marinus of Tyre, etc. Uses information gleaned from military campaigns such as Punic Wars, Hannibal's passage of Alps, campaigns of Lucullus, Pompey, Caesar's wars, the Trojan War. New introduction by W. H. Stahl, Brooklyn College. Bibliography. Index. 20 maps. 1426pp. 5⅜ x 8. T570-1, clothbound, 2-volume set **$12.50**

POLITICAL PARTIES, Robert Michels. Classic of social science, reference point for all later work, deals with nature of leadership in social organization on government and trade union levels. Probing tendency of oligarchy to replace democracy, it studies need for leadership, desire for organization, psychological motivations, vested interests, hero worship, reaction of leaders to power, press relations, many other aspects. Trans. by E. & C. Paul. Introduction. 447pp. 5⅜ x 8. T569 Paperbound **$2.00**

A HISTORY OF HISTORICAL WRITING, Harry Elmer Barnes. Virtually the only adequate survey of the whole course of historical writing in a single volume. Surveys developments from the beginnings of historiographies in the ancient Near East and the Classical World, up through the Cold War. Covers major historians in detail, shows interrelationship with cultural background, makes clear individual contributions, evaluates and estimates importance; also enormously rich upon minor authors and thinkers who are usually passed over. Packed with scholarship and learning, clear, easily written. Indispensable to every student of history. Revised and enlarged up to 1961. Index and bibliography. xv + 442pp. 5⅜ x 8½. T104 Paperbound **$2.25**

Teach Yourself

These British books are the most effective series of home study books on the market! With no outside help they will teach you as much as is necessary to have a good background in each subject, in many cases offering as much material as a similar high school or college course. They are carefully planned, written by foremost British educators, and amply provided with test questions and problems for you to check your progress; the mathematics books are especially rich in examples and problems. Do not confuse them with skimpy outlines or ordinary school texts or vague generalized popularizations; each book is complete in itself, full without being overdetailed, and designed to give you an easily-acquired branch of knowledge.

TEACH YOURSELF ALGEBRA, P. Abbott. The equivalent of a thorough high school course, up through logarithms. 52 illus. 307pp. 4¼ x 7. T680 Clothbound **$2.00**

TEACH YOURSELF GEOMETRY, P. Abbott. Plane and solid geometry, covering about a year of plane and six months of solid. 268 illus. 344pp. 4½ x 7. T681 Clothbound **$2.00**

TEACH YOURSELF TRIGONOMETRY, P. Abbott. Background of algebra and geometry will enable you to get equivalent of elementary college course. Tables. 102 illus. 204pp. 4½ x 7. T682 Clothbound **$2.00**

TEACH YOURSELF THE CALCULUS, P. Abbott. With algebra and trigonometry you will be able to acquire a good working knowledge of elementary integral calculus and differential calculus. Excellent supplement to any course textbook. 380pp. 4¼ x 7. T683 Clothbound **$2.00**

TEACH YOURSELF THE SLIDE RULE, B. Snodgrass. Basic principles clearly explained, with many applications in engineering, business, general figuring, will enable you to pick up very useful skill. 10 illus. 207pp. 4¼ x 7. T684 Clothbound **$2.00**

TEACH YOURSELF MECHANICS, P. Abbott. Equivalent of part course on elementary college level, with lever, parallelogram of force, friction, laws of motion, gases, etc. Fine introduction before more advanced course. 163 illus. 271pp. 4½ x 7. T685 Clothbound **$2.00**

TEACH YOURSELF ELECTRICITY, C. W. Wilman. Current, resistance, voltage, Ohm's law, circuits, generators, motors, transformers, etc. Non-mathematical as much as possible. 115 illus. 184pp. 4¼ x 7. T230 Clothbound **$2.00**

TEACH YOURSELF HEAT ENGINES E. DeVille. Steam and internal combustion engines; non-mathematical introduction for student, for layman wishing background, refresher for advanced student. 76 illus. 217pp. 4¼ x 7. T237 Clothbound **$2.00**

TEACH YOURSELF TO PLAY THE PIANO, King Palmer. Companion and supplement to lessons or self study. Handy reference, too. Nature of instrument, elementary musical theory, technique of playing, interpretation, etc. 60 illus. 144pp. 4¼ x 7. T959 Clothbound **$2.00**

TEACH YOURSELF HERALDRY AND GENEALOGY, L. G. Pine. Modern work, avoiding romantic and overpopular misconceptions. Editor of new Burke presents detailed information and commentary down to present. Best general survey. 50 illus. glossary; 129pp. 4¼ x 7. T962 Clothbound **$2.00**

TEACH YOURSELF HANDWRITING, John L. Dumpleton. Basic Chancery cursive style is popular and easy to learn. Many diagrams. 114 illus. 192pp. 4¼ x 7. T960 Clothbound **$2.00**

TEACH YOURSELF CARD GAMES FOR TWO, Kenneth Konstam. Many first-rate games, including old favorites like cribbage and gin and canasta as well as new lesser-known games. Extremely interesting for cards enthusiast. 60 illus. 150pp. 4¼ x 7. T963 Clothbound **$2.00**

TEACH YOURSELF GUIDEBOOK TO THE DRAMA, Luis Vargas. Clear, rapid survey of changing fashions and forms from Aeschylus to Tennessee Williams, in all major European traditions. Plot summaries, critical comments, etc. Equivalent of a college drama course; fine cultural background 224pp. 4¼ x 7. T961 Clothbound **$2.00**

TEACH YOURSELF THE ORGAN, Francis Routh. Excellent compendium of background material for everyone interested in organ music, whether as listener or player. 27 musical illus. 158pp. 4¼ x 7. T977 Clothbound **$2.00**

TEACH YOURSELF TO STUDY SCULPTURE, William Gaunt. Noted British cultural historian surveys culture from Greeks, primitive world, to moderns. Equivalent of college survey course. 23 figures, 40 photos. 158pp. 4¼ x 7. T976 Clothbound **$2.00**

Philosophy, Religion

GUIDE TO PHILOSOPHY, C. E. M. Joad. A modern classic which examines many crucial problems which man has pondered through the ages: Does free will exist? Is there plan in the universe? How do we know and validate our knowledge? Such opposed solutions as subjective idealism and realism, chance and teleology, vitalism and logical positivism, are evaluated and the contributions of the great philosophers from the Greeks to moderns like Russell, Whitehead, and others, are considered in the context of each problem. "The finest introduction," BOSTON TRANSCRIPT. Index. Classified bibliography. 592pp. 5⅜ x 8.
T297 Paperbound **$2.00**

HISTORY OF ANCIENT PHILOSOPHY, W. Windelband. One of the clearest, most accurate comprehensive surveys of Greek and Roman philosophy. Discusses ancient philosophy in general, intellectual life in Greece in the 7th and 6th centuries B.C., Thales, Anaximander, Anaximenes, Heraclitus, the Eleatics, Empedocles, Anaxagoras, Leucippus, the Pythagoreans, the Sophists, Socrates, Democritus (20 pages), Plato (50 pages), Aristotle (70 pages), the Peripatetics, Stoics, Epicureans, Sceptics, Neo-platonists, Christian Apologists, etc. 2nd German edition translated by H. E. Cushman. xv + 393pp. 5⅜ x 8. T357 Paperbound **$1.85**

ILLUSTRATIONS OF THE HISTORY OF MEDIEVAL THOUGHT AND LEARNING, R. L. Poole. Basic analysis of the thought and lives of the leading philosophers and ecclesiastics from the 8th to the 14th century—Abailard, Ockham, Wycliffe, Marsiglio of Padua, and many other great thinkers who carried the torch of Western culture and learning through the "Dark Ages": political, religious, and metaphysical views. Long a standard work for scholars and one of the best introductions to medieval thought for beginners. Index. 10 Appendices. xiii + 327pp. 5⅜ x 8. T674 Paperbound **$1.85**

PHILOSOPHY AND CIVILIZATION IN THE MIDDLE AGES, M. de Wulf. This semi-popular survey covers aspects of medieval intellectual life such as religion, philosophy, science, the arts, etc. It also covers feudalism vs. Catholicism, rise of the universities, mendicant orders, monastic centers, and similar topics. Unabridged. Bibliography. Index. viii + 320pp. 5⅜ x 8.
T284 Paperbound **$1.75**

AN INTRODUCTION TO SCHOLASTIC PHILOSOPHY, Prof. M. de Wulf. Formerly entitled SCHOLASTICISM OLD AND NEW, this volume examines the central scholastic tradition from St. Anselm, Albertus Magnus, Thomas Aquinas, up to Suarez in the 17th century. The relation of scholasticism to ancient and medieval philosophy and science in general is clear and easily followed. The second part of the book considers the modern revival of scholasticism, the Louvain position, relations with Kantianism and Positivism. Unabridged. xvi + 271pp. 5⅜ x 8.
T296 Clothbound **$3.50**
T283 Paperbound **$1.75**

A HISTORY OF MODERN PHILOSOPHY, H. Höffding. An exceptionally clear and detailed coverage of western philosophy from the Renaissance to the end of the 19th century. Major and minor men such as Pomponazzi, Bodin, Boehme, Telesius, Bruno, Copernicus, da Vinci, Kepler, Galileo, Bacon, Descartes, Hobbes, Spinoza, Leibniz, Wolff, Locke, Newton, Berkeley, Hume, Erasmus, Montesquieu, Voltaire, Diderot, Rousseau, Lessing, Kant, Herder, Fichte, Schelling, Hegel, Schopenhauer, Comte, Mill, Darwin, Spencer, Hartmann, Lange, and many others, are discussed in terms of theory of knowledge, logic, cosmology, and psychology. Index. 2 volumes, total of 1159pp. 5⅜ x 8. T117 Vol. 1, Paperbound **$2.00**
T118 Vol. 2, Paperbound **$2.00**

ARISTOTLE, A. E. Taylor. A brilliant, searching non-technical account of Aristotle and his thought written by a foremost Platonist. It covers the life and works of Aristotle; classification of the sciences; logic; first philosophy; matter and form; causes; motion and eternity; God; physics; metaphysics; and similar topics. Bibliography. New Index compiled for this edition. 128pp. 5⅜ x 8. T280 Paperbound **$1.00**

THE SYSTEM OF THOMAS AQUINAS, M. de Wulf. Leading Neo-Thomist, one of founders of University of Louvain, gives concise exposition to central doctrines of Aquinas, as a means toward determining his value to modern philosophy, religion. Formerly "Medieval Philosophy Illustrated from the System of Thomas Aquinas." Trans. by E. Messenger. Introduction. 151pp. 5⅜ x 8. T568 Paperbound **$1.25**

LEIBNIZ, H. W. Carr. Most stimulating middle-level coverage of basic philosophical thought of Leibniz. Easily understood discussion, analysis of major works: "Theodicy," "Principles of Nature and Grace," "Monadology"; Leibniz's influence; intellectual growth; correspondence; disputes with Bayle, Malebranche, Newton; importance of his thought today, with reinterpretation in modern terminology. "Power and mastery," London Times. Bibliography. Index. 226pp. 5⅜ x 8. T624 Paperbound **$1.35**

AN ESSAY CONCERNING HUMAN UNDERSTANDING, John Locke. Edited by A. C. Fraser. Unabridged reprinting of definitive edition; only complete edition of "Essay" in print. Marginal analyses of almost every paragraph; hundreds of footnotes; authoritative 140-page biographical, critical, historical prolegomena. Indexes. 1170pp. 5⅜ x 8.
T530 Vol. 1 (Books 1, 2) Paperbound **$2.25**
T531 Vol. 2 (Books 3, 4) Paperbound **$2.25**
2 volume set **$4.50**

THE PHILOSOPHY OF HISTORY, G. W. F. Hegel. One of the great classics of western thought which reveals Hegel's basic principle: that history is not chance but a rational process, the realization of the Spirit of Freedom. Ranges from the oriental cultures of subjective thought to the classical subjective cultures, to the modern absolute synthesis where spiritual and secular may be reconciled. Translation and introduction by J. Sibree. Introduction by C. Hegel. Special introduction for this edition by Prof. Carl Friedrich. xxxix + 447pp. 5⅜ x 8.
T112 Paperbound **$1.85**

THE PHILOSOPHY OF HEGEL, W. T. Stace. The first detailed analysis of Hegel's thought in English, this is especially valuable since so many of Hegel's works are out of print. Dr. Stace examines Hegel's debt to Greek idealists and the 18th century and then proceeds to a careful description and analysis of Hegel's first principles, categories, reason, dialectic method, his logic, philosophy of nature and spirit, etc. Index. Special 14 x 20 chart of Hegelian system. x + 526pp. 5⅜ x 8. T254 Paperbound **$2.25**

THE WILL TO BELIEVE and HUMAN IMMORTALITY, W. James. Two complete books bound as one. THE WILL TO BELIEVE discusses the interrelations of belief, will, and intellect in man; chance vs. determinism, free will vs. determinism, free will vs. fate, pluralism vs. monism; the philosophies of Hegel and Spencer, and more. HUMAN IMMORTALITY examines the question of survival after death and develops an unusual and powerful argument for immortality. Two prefaces. Index. Total of 429pp. 5⅜ x 8. T291 Paperbound **$1.75**

THE WORLD AND THE INDIVIDUAL, Josiah Royce. Only major effort by an American philosopher to interpret nature of things in systematic, comprehensive manner. Royce's formulation of an absolute voluntarism remains one of the original and profound solutions to the problems involved. Part One, Four Historical Conceptions of Being, inquires into first principles, true meaning and place of individuality. Part Two, Nature, Man, and the Moral Order, is application of first principles to problems concerning religion, evil, moral order. Introduction by J. E. Smith, Yale Univ. Index. 1070pp. 5⅜ x 8.
T561 Vol. 1 Paperbound **$2.25**
T562 Vol. 2 Paperbound **$2.25**
Two volume set **$4.50**

THE PHILOSOPHICAL WRITINGS OF PEIRCE, edited by J. Buchler. This book (formerly THE PHILOSOPHY OF PEIRCE) is a carefully integrated exposition of Peirce's complete system composed of selections from his own work. Symbolic logic, scientific method, theory of signs, pragmatism, epistemology, chance, cosmology, ethics, and many other topics are treated by one of the greatest philosophers of modern times. This is the only inexpensive compilation of his key ideas. xvi + 386pp. 5⅜ x 8. T217 Paperbound **$2.00**

EXPERIENCE AND NATURE, John Dewey. An enlarged, revised edition of the Paul Carus lectures which Dewey delivered in 1925. It covers Dewey's basic formulation of the problem of knowledge, with a full discussion of other systems, and a detailing of his own concepts of the relationship of external world, mind, and knowledge. Starts with a thorough examination of the philosophical method; examines the interrelationship of experience and nature; analyzes experience on basis of empirical naturalism, the formulation of law, role of language and social factors in knowledge; etc. Dewey's treatment of central problems in philosophy is profound but extremely easy to follow. ix + 448pp. 5⅜ x 8.
T471 Paperbound **$1.85**

THE PHILOSOPHICAL WORKS OF DESCARTES. The definitive English edition of all the major philosophical works and letters of René Descartes. All of his revolutionary insights, from his famous "Cogito ergo sum" to his detailed account of contemporary science and his astonishingly fruitful concept that all phenomena of the universe (except mind) could be reduced to clear laws by the use of mathematics. An excellent source for the thought of men like Hobbes, Arnauld, Gassendi, etc., who were Descarte's contemporaries. Translated by E. S. Haldane and G. Ross. Introductory notes. Index. Total of 842pp. 5⅜ x 8.
T71 Vol. 1, Paperbound **$2.00**
T72 Vol. 2, Paperbound **$2.00**

THE CHIEF WORKS OF SPINOZA. An unabridged reprint of the famous Bohn edition containing all of Spinoza's most important works: Vol. I: The Theologico-Political Treatise and the Political Treatise. Vol. II: On The Improvement Of Understanding, The Ethics, Selected Letters. Profound and enduring ideas on God, the universe, pantheism, society, religion, the state, democracy, the mind, emotions, freedom and the nature of man, which influenced Goethe, Hegel, Schelling, Coleridge, Whitehead, and many others. Introduction. 2 volumes. 826pp. 5⅜ x 8.
T249 Vol. I, Paperbound **$1.50**
T250 Vol. II, Paperbound **$1.50**

Orientalia

ORIENTAL RELIGIONS IN ROMAN PAGANISM, F. Cumont. A study of the cultural meeting of east and west in the Early Roman Empire. It covers the most important eastern religions of the time from their first appearance in Rome, 204 B.C., when the Great Mother of the Gods was first brought over from Syria. The ecstatic cults of Syria and Phrygia — Cybele, Attis, Adonis, their orgies and mutilatory rites; the mysteries of Egypt — Serapis, Isis, Osiris, the dualism of Persia, the elevation of cosmic evil to equal stature with the deity, Mithra; worship of Hermes Trismegistus; Ishtar, Astarte; the magic of the ancient Near East, etc. Introduction. 55pp. of notes; extensive bibliography. Index. xxiv + 298pp. 5⅜ x 8.
T321 Paperbound **$1.75**

THE MYSTERIES OF MITHRA, F. Cumont. The definitive coverage of a great ideological struggle between the west and the orient in the first centuries of the Christian era. The origin of Mithraism, a Persian mystery religion, and its association with the Roman army is discussed in detail. Then utilizing fragmentary monuments and texts, in one of the greatest feats of scholarly detection, Dr. Cumont reconstructs the mystery teachings and secret doctrines, the hidden organization and cult of Mithra. Mithraic art is discussed, analyzed, and depicted in 70 illustrations. 239pp. 5⅜ x 8. T323 Paperbound **$1.85**

CHRISTIAN AND ORIENTAL PHILOSOPHY OF ART, A. K. Coomaraswamy. A unique fusion of philosopher, orientalist, art historian, and linguist, the author discusses such matters as: the true function of aesthetics in art, the importance of symbolism, intellectual and philosophic backgrounds, the role of traditional culture in enriching art, common factors in all great art, the nature of medieval art, the nature of folklore, the beauty of mathematics, and similar topics. 2 illustrations. Bibliography. 148pp. 5⅜ x 8. T378 Paperbound **$1.25**

TRANSFORMATION OF NATURE IN ART, A. K. Coomaraswamy. Unabridged reissue of a basic work upon Asiatic religious art and philosophy of religion. The theory of religious art in Asia and Medieval Europe (exemplified by Meister Eckhart) is analyzed and developed. Detailed consideration is given to Indian medieval aesthetic manuals, symbolic language in philosophy, the origin and use of images in India, and many other fascinating and little known topics. Glossaries of Sanskrit and Chinese terms. Bibliography. 41pp. of notes. 245pp. 5⅜ x 8.
T368 Paperbound **$1.75**

BUDDHIST LOGIC, F.Th. Stcherbatsky. A study of an important part of Buddhism usually ignored by other books on the subject: the Mahayana buddhistic logic of the school of Dignaga and his followers. First vol. devoted to history of Indian logic with Central Asian continuations, detailed exposition of Dignaga system, including theory of knowledge, the sensible world (causation, perception, ultimate reality) and mental world (judgment, inference, logical fallacies, the syllogism), reality of external world, and negation (law of contradiction, universals, dialectic). Vol. II contains translation of Dharmakirti's Nyayabindu with Dharmamottara's commentary. Appendices cover translations of Tibetan treatises on logic, Hindu attacks on Buddhist logic, etc. The basic work, one of the products of the great St. Petersburg school of Indian studies. Written clearly and with an awareness of Western philosophy and logic; meant for the Asian specialist and for the general reader with only a minimum of background. Vol. I, xii + 559pp. Vol. II, viii + 468pp. 5⅜ x 8½.
T955 Vol. I Paperbound **$2.35**
T956 Vol. II Paperbound **$2.35**
The set **$4.70**

THE TEXTS OF TAOISM. The first inexpensive edition of the complete James Legge translations of the Tao Te King and the writings of Chinese mystic Chuang Tse. Also contains several shorter treatises: the T'ai Shang Tractate of Actions and Their Retributions; the King Kang King, or Classic of Purity; the Yin Fu King, or Classic of the Harmony of the Seen and Unseen; the Yu Shu King, or Classic of the Pivot of Jade; and the Hsia Yung King, or Classic of the Directory for a Day. While there are other translations of the Tao Te King, this is the only translation of Chuang Tse and much of other material. Extensive introduction discusses differences between Taoism, Buddhism, Confucianism; authenticity and arrangement of Tao Te King and writings of Chuang Tse; the meaning of the Tao and basic tenets of Taoism; historical accounts of Lao-tse and followers; other pertinent matters. Clarifying notes incorporated into text. Originally published as Volumes 39, 40 of SACRED BOOKS OF THE EAST series, this has long been recognized as an indispensible collection. Sinologists, philosophers, historians of religion will of course be interested and anyone with an elementary course in Oriental religion or philosophy will understand and profit from these writings. Index. Appendix analyzing thought of Chuang Tse. Vol. I, xxiii + 396pp. Vol. II, viii + 340pp. 5⅜ x 8½. T990 Vol. I Paperbound **$2.00**
T991 Vol. II Paperbound **$2.00**

CATALOGUE OF DOVER BOOKS

EPOCHS OF CHINESE AND JAPANESE ART, Ernest T. Fenollosa. Although this classic of art history was written before the archeological discovery of Shang and Chou civilizations, it is still in many respects the finest detailed study of Chinese and Japanese art available in English. It is very wide in range, covering sculpture, carving, painting, metal work, ceramics, textiles, graphic arts and other areas, and it considers both religious and secular art, including the Japanese woodcut. Its greatest strength, however, lies in its extremely full, detailed, insight-laden discussion of historical and cultural background, and in its analysis of the religious and philosophical implications of art works. It is also a brilliant stylistic achievement, written with enthusiasm and verve, which can be enjoyed and read with profit by both the Orientalist and the general reader who is interested in art. Index. Glossary of proper names. 242 illustrations. Total of 704 pages. 5⅜ x 8½.

T364-5 Two vol. set, paperbound **$5.00**

THE VEDANTA SUTRAS OF BADARAYANA WITH COMMENTARY BY SANKARACHARYA. The definitive translation of the consummation, foremost interpretation of Upanishads. Originally part of SACRED BOOKS OF THE EAST, this two-volume translation includes exhaustive commentary and exegesis by Sankara; 128-page introduction by translator, Prof. Thibaut, that discusses background, scope and purpose of the sutras, value and importance of Sankara's interpretation; copious footnotes providing further explanations. Every serious student of Indian religion or thought, philosophers, historians of religion should read these clear, accurate translations of documents central to development of important thought systems in the East. Unabridged republication of Volumes 34, 38 of the Sacred Books of the East. Translated by George Thibault. General index, index of quotations and of Sanskrit. Vol. I, cxxv + 448pp. Vol. II, iv + 506pp. 5⅜ x 8½.

T994 Vol. I Paperbound **$2.00**
T995 Vol. II Paperbound **$2.00**

THE UPANISHADS. The Max Müller translation of the twelve classical Upanishads available for the first time in an inexpensive format: Chandogya, Kena, Aitareya aranyaka and upanishad, Kaushitaki, Isa, Katha, Mundaka, Taittiriyaka Brhadaranyaka, Svetarasvatara. Prasna — all of the classical Upanishads of the Vedanta school—and the Maitriyana Upanishad. Originally volumes 1, 15 of SACRED BOOKS OF THE EAST series, this is still the most scholarly translation. Prof. Müller, probably most important Sanskritologist of nineteenth century, provided invaluable introduction that acquaints readers with history of Upanishad translations, age and chronology of texts, etc. and a preface that discusses their value to Western readers. Heavily annotated. Stimulating reading for anyone with even only a basic course background in Oriental philosophy, religion, necessary to all Indologists, philosophers, religious historians. Transliteration and pronunciation guide. Vol. I, ciii + 320pp. Vol. II, liii + 350pp.

T992 Vol. I Paperbound **$2.00**
T993 Vol. II Paperbound **$2.00**
The set **$4.00**